Modern **REFRIGERATION** and **AIR CONDITIONING**

LABORATORY MANUAL

ALTHOUSE/TURNQUIST/BRACCIANO

CONTENTS

Module		Page

South Holland, Illinois
THE GOODHEART-WILLCOX COMPANY, INC.
Publishers

NOTE TO THE STUDENT: The Instructor's Manual, which is to be used with the textbook, MODERN REFRIGERATION AND AIR CONDITIONING, by Althouse, Turnquist, and Bracciano, and published by Goodheart-Willcox, explains the use of a class organization and the use of laboratory tasks.

TASK ASSIGNMENTS: The instructor will give the task assignments, either from a term schedule chart or by making assignments as each task is successfully completed. Each student will also be assigned to a work station which will provide the equipment necessary for doing the task.

1. Study the Reference Paragraphs. Use the text index for additional references.

2. Indicate the answers to the task sheet questions.

3. The symbol _____√_____ indicates a check point. As one arrives at a check point, the work to this point must be checked.

4. In general, the first check point TEST√_____ consists of satisfactorily answering the laboratory task questions. The instructor will possibly ask some additional questions to be sure that one is ready to proceed with the manipulative part of the task.

5. The numbers ahead of the check point, as shown: 1-8 √_____, indicate that the instructor will question the student on the work done on Steps 1 through 8. The instructor may initial the task sheet at each check point to indicate that one has approval to proceed with the task.

6. Carefully follow the task instructions.

7. Examine the work station carefully and determine the tools, instruments, and supplies needed to perform the manipulative part of the task. These may differ some from the list on the task laboratory sheet.

LABORATORY TASKS -- Cont'd.

8. If there is any doubt at any time about an action or step, check with the instructor before it is done.

9. Be alert for safety. Look out for electrical connections, belts, flywheels, fans, and other moving parts. Also, avoid using tools and equipment which are not in good condition.

10. Fill in the "data" on the task sheets when blanks are provided for this purpose.

11. The instructor will approve and grade each task as it is completed.

12. Clean up the work station; clean the tools and instruments and return them to their proper place. Also, return any reusable or unused supplies.

13. Upon completion of a task, proceed to the next assigned task.

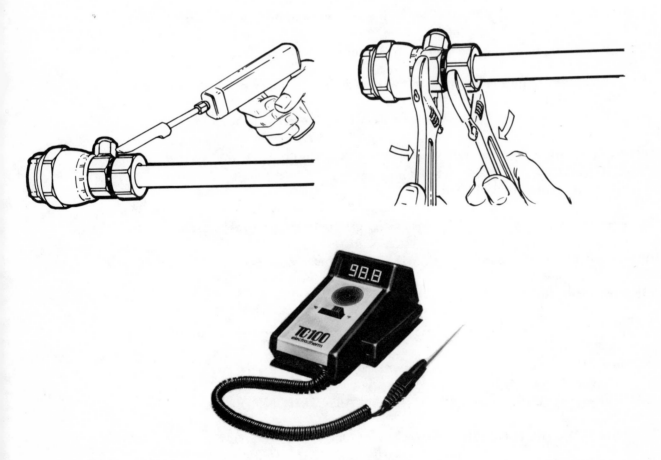

SAFETY RULES WHEN HANDLING REFRIGERANTS

It is recommended that refrigerant cylinders never be filled over 85 percent of their capacity. If overfilled, the liquid expansion may create a hydrostatic pressure which will cause the cylinder to burst.

When a leak in a system is suspected, make certain that the room is thoroughly ventilated before starting to work on the unit. Always check for recommended operating pressures for each refrigerant. Check the refrigerant R-number before charging. Make certain there are no lighted flames near the unit that is suspected of having a leak if Group III refrigerants are used. Always check the I.C.C. cylinder stamp for assurance of a safe cylinder. WEAR GOGGLES AT ALL TIMES WHEN WORKING IN A REFRIGER-ATING MACHINE AREA. THEY WILL PROTECT THE EYES IN CASE OF A SUDDEN LEAK.

Liquid refrigerant on the skin may freeze the skin surface and cause a "frost bite." If this should happen, quickly wash away refrigerant with water. Treat for "frost bite."

If one accidentally gets refrigerant in the eyes and a doctor is not immediately available, in the emergency, wash with mineral oil, as the oil will absorb the refrigerant. Then wash the eyes with a weak boric acid solution. If the refrigerant is ammonia, wash immediately with water.

Some refrigerants, such as R-717 (ammonia), are irritating to eyes, nose and respiratory system. Always purge these refrigerants into a proper purging line and never into the work room.

Always test used compressor oil for acid content with litmus paper before allowing any of it to touch the skin or a severe acid burn may result.

CAUTION: NEVER CUT OR DRILL INTO AN ABSORPTION REFRIGERATION MECHANISM. THE HIGH PRESSURE AMMONIA SOLUTIONS ARE DANGEROUS AND MAY CAUSE BLINDNESS IF THE FLUID GETS INTO THE EYES.

When checking expendable refrigerant systems, always make certain that the safety doors are opened and that the truck body has been vented.

NAME _____ NUMBER ____

MODERN REFRIGERATION AND AIR CONDITIONING
MODULE 1 – BASIC REFRIGERATION LABORATORY TASKS

No.	NAME	TASK TEST GRADE	SIG.	TASK GRADE	SIG.	TASK DATE
1-1	Measure Parts					
1-2	Make Flared Tube Connections					
1-3	Make or Repair Soldered and Brazed Tubing Connection					
1-4	Make or Repair a Swaged Tubing Connection					
1-5	Select Fittings and Make a Complete Tubing Assembly					
1-6	Identify Pipe Fittings					
1-7	Read Gauges and Operate Gauge Manifold					
1-8	Operate Service Valves					
1-9	Install and Test Access Valves and Process Tube Adaptors					
1-10	Identify Assembly Devices, Tools (U.S. Units)					
1-11	Identify Assembly Devices and Tools (Metric Units)					
1-12	Dismantle, Assemble, and Test an External Drive Piston Type Compressor					
1-13	Dismantle, Assemble, and Test an External Drive Rotary Type Compressor					
1-14	Install Belts and Adjust Pulleys and Belts					
1-15	Measure Some Temperatures					
1-16	Test for Leaks					
1-17	Install Gauges on an External Drive Refrigerating System					
1-18	Repair a Leak Using Epoxy Compound					
1-19	Evacuate a System					
1-20	Use a Service Cylinder					

SAFETY IN HANDLING TOOLS AND SUPPLIES

ALWAYS WEAR SAFETY GOGGLES IN THE LABORATORY.

Always pull on a wrench (instead of pushing) to prevent possible injury to the hands if the wrench should slip. It is recommended that a hoist be used in lifting compressors which weigh over 60 lb. (27 kg). Always use leg muscles when lifting objects; never use back muscles. Make certain no oil is spilled on the floor. If it accidentally is spilled, wipe it up immediately.

Avoid putting hands near revolving fans, motor pulleys, or motor belts.

Put guards on powered moving objects such as flywheels, belts, pulleys, fans, etc.

One should never breathe fumes of any kind. Do not neglect the use of a gas mask when working in a refrigerant laden atmosphere. This safety device applies to cleansing bath fumes, soldering fumes, brazing fumes, welding fumes, and the like. It is true that one's body can and will dissipate certain amounts of chemicals and fumes, but some chemicals and fumes accumulate in the body and there may be a delayed effect. GOOD VENTILATION IS OF VITAL IMPORTANCE.

Use only nontoxic materials for cleaning, and always provide adequate ventilation. When cleaning, avoid skin contact and breathing the fumes.

Silver brazing materials sometimes contain cadmium. Fumes from overheated cadmium are very poisonous. Be sure that the work space is well ventilated. If at all possible, use silver brazing alloys which DO NOT contain cadmium.

"Mushroom" heads should be removed from chisels and punches by grinding, as these parts may fly when struck with the hammer and may cause serious injury to some- one. Do not use a screwdriver as a chisel. Always report damaged, worn, or broken tools to the instructor. Only use files with handles, otherwise the tang may injure the hands.

A clean shop is a safe shop. Help keep the shop as clean as possible.

Report any injury, no matter how small, to the instructor.

Oily rags should be stored in a self-closing approved metal container.

MEASURE PARTS

OBJECTIVE: Given industry parts and standard measuring instruments: measure these parts
  to the approved standards in both U.S. conventional and metric units.

REFERENCES: Required – Para. 1-12, 1-64, 2-57 and 2-58.

EQUIPMENT: A box of miscellaneous refrigeration parts for this task.

PREPARATION PROCEDURE:
  1. Study the reference paragraphs, names of parts of the compressor, how to read a rule,
      use a caliper, and how to use and read a micrometer (both U.S. conventional and metric scales).
      TEST√_____
  2. Obtain: Tools – 1 pr. safety goggles.
  3. Obtain: Instruments – 1 1-in. micrometer, 1 2-in. micrometer, 1 6-in. steel rule,
      1 6-ft. steel tape, 1 4-in. inside caliper, 1 25-mm micrometer and 1 150-mm steel rule.
  4. Obtain: Supplies – 1 wiping cloth.

TASK PROCEDURE (WEAR GOGGLES):
  1. Identify the parts by name.
  2. Measure the various parts contained in the box and record the measurements. In general,
      ground and polished parts should be measured with the micrometer. Painted parts may be
      measured with the steel rule or steel tape.   1-2 √_____

CLOSING THE STATION:
  1. Clean the station, clean the equipment, tools and instruments.
  2. Return the tools, instruments and supplies to their proper place.

DATA:

	U.S. conventional	Metric
Piston pin diameters:	_____	_____
Out-of-round:	_____	_____
Valve reed thickness:	_____	_____
Crankshaft bearing main journal, Diameter:	_____	_____
Crankshaft bearing main journal, Out-of-round:	_____	_____
Copper tube OD:	_____	_____
Water pipe: OD of the 1/2 in. (12.7 mm):	_____	_____
Valve plate thickness:	_____	_____
Piston diameter:	_____	
Tapered:	_____	
Belt pulley,		
Outer diameter:	_____	
Cylinder diameter:	_____	
Cylinder, Out-of-round:	_____	

Remarks:

MEASURE PARTS.

Indicate the best answer for each question below by encircling its letter.

1. What is the smallest calibration usually used on steel rules?
    Metric scale rules   English scale rules

Metric		U.S. conventional	
(a)	mm	(a)	Feet and yards.
(b)	m	(b)	Inches only.
(c)	cm	(c)	Inches, 1/2 in., 1/4 in., 1/8 in.
(d)	cm and mm	(d)	1/32 in. or 1/64 in.
(e)	mm, cm, and m	(e)	Calibration of both (c) and (d).

2. What are the calibrations usually used on steel tapes?

Metric		U.S. conventional	
(a)	mm	(a)	Feet and yards.
(b)	m	(b)	Inches and 1/2 in.
(c)	cm	(c)	Inches and 1/4 in.
(d)	cm and mm	(d)	Feet, inches, and 1/16 in.
(e)	mm, cm, and m	(e)	Inches and 1/8 in.

3. What are the smallest divisions on the micrometer thimble?

Metric		U.S. conventional	
(a)	mm	(a)	0.001 in.
(b)	m	(b)	0.1 and 0.001 in.
(c)	cm	(c)	1/8 and 1/64 in.
(d)	0.01 mm	(d)	0.1 and 0.01 in.
(e)	0.01 cm	(e)	1/25 in.

4. The sleeve of a micrometer is divided into 0.1 in. or 1 mm. How many thimble divisions are there between the 0.1 in. or the 1 mm divisions?

Metric		U.S. conventional	
(a)	1	(a)	10
(b)	2	(b)	5
(c)	3	(c)	4
(d)	4	(d)	3
(e)	5	(e)	2

5. The dimensional sleeve on a one inch micrometer is one in. or 25 mm long. How long is the dimensional sleeve on the three inch or 75 mm micrometer?

Metric		U.S. conventional	
(a)	25 mm	(a)	6 in.
(b)	50 mm	(b)	4 in.
(c)	75 mm	(c)	3 in.
(d)	100 mm	(d)	2 in.
(e)	125 mm	(e)	1 in.

MAKE FLARED TUBE CONNECTIONS

OBJECTIVE: Given copper tubing, tools, and fittings: make tube bends and flared connections so the assembly is accurate to 1/4 in. and leakproof at 50 psi pressure.

REFERENCES: Required – Para. 2-1, 2-2, 2-3, 2-6, 2-8, 2-11, 2-12, 2-14 and 2-18.
Supplementary – Para. 2-17.

EQUIPMENT: One work station which has an air compressor complete with a pressure regulator and a flared connection. One work bench with vise.

PREPARATION PROCEDURE:
1. Study carefully Figs. 2-7, 2-9, 2-10, 2-13, 2-14, 2-15, 2-16, and 2-17 in the text.

TEST√ _____

2. Obtain: Tools – 1 tube cutter, 1 flaring tool for single and double flares, 1 8-in. mill file, 1 1/4-in. ext. bending spring, 2 3/4-in. open end wrenches, 2 1-in. open end wrenches, 1 8-in. adj. open end wrench, 1 pr. safety goggles.
3. Obtain: Instruments – 1 6 ft. steel tape.
4. Obtain: Supplies – 1 coil 1/4-in. ACR tubing, 1 coil 1/2-in. ACR tubing, 1 box of assorted 1/4-in. and 1/2-in. tube fittings and flare nuts, 1 bubble liquid suds container, 1 wiping cloth.

TASK PROCEDURE (WEAR GOGGLES):
1. Measure a 5-in. length and a 12-in. length of 1/4 OD tubing. Measure two 8-in. lengths and a 15-in. length of 1/2 OD tubing.
2. Cut the tubing to length. Seal the ends of the coils of tubing from which the pieces are cut in order to keep the coils clean and dry internally.
3. Ream the ends of the cut tubing.
4. Bend 1/4 tubings as follows: 5-in. length, 90 deg.; 12-in. length, 360 deg.
5. Install flare nuts and flare 1/4 tubing.
6. Install flare nuts and single flare one 8-in. length of 1/2 tubing and also the 15-in. length of 1/2 tubing.
7. Bend 8-in. length 90 deg. and 15-in. length 180 deg.   1-7√ _____
8. Install flare nuts and double flare both ends of one 8-in. length of 1/2 tubing.
9. Assemble the tubing into one assembly using unions.
10. Connect assembly to compressed air fitting.
11. Open the compressed air valve slowly and adjust regulator to 50 psi.
12. Test for leaks with bubble liquid. Repair any leaks.
13. Reduce air pressure to 0 psi, remove assembly, cut tubing to remove nuts.

8-13√ _____

CLOSING THE STATION:
Clean up work station and return all materials to tool crib.

DATA:
Tube cutter, Make _____ Capacity _____
Tube flaring tool, Make _____ Tubing Sizes _____ Model _____
1/4 in. ACR tubing, Outside Diameter _____ Inside Diameter _____
1/4 in. flare nut wrench, Size _____ Type of wrench _____
Leak test, Pressure _____ Results _____

Remarks:

MAKE FLARED TUBE CONNECTIONS.

Indicate the best answer for each question below by encircling its letter.

1. What is the meaning of ACR as applied to tubing?
   a. It is cold rolled.
   b. It is suitable for air conditioning and refrigeration applications.
   c. It is intended for air cooled applications only.
   d. It is a certain manufacturer's brand symbol.
   e. It is air cooled rolled.

2. When sawing soft copper tubing, how may the chips be prevented from entering the length of tubing to be immediately used?
   a. Apply air pressure on this length of the tube.
   b. Slant the tube so that the chips will not fall into the length being used.
   c. Pinch the tube.
   d. Stuff rags in the tube.
   e. Use a sawing fixture.

3. What type connections should be made when using soft copper tubing?
   a. Threaded.
   b. Flared or soldered.
   c. Welded.
   d. Use compression fittings.
   e. Swaged.

4. Why are bending springs used?
   a. To provide a better grip on the tube.
   b. To make a uniform curve.
   c. To keep the tube from kinking.
   d. To keep the outside of the tube clean.
   e. To keep the inside of the tube clean.

5. Why should the end of copper tubing to be flared be filed square?
   a. To keep the tubing bright.
   b. To make the flare equal all around.
   c. To make it easy to attach the flaring tool.
   d. To make the flare of proper thickness.
   e. To keep the flare from splitting.

MAKE OR REPAIR SOLDERED AND BRAZED TUBING CONNECTION

OBJECTIVE: Given a soldering-brazing station, copper tubing and fittings: make the assigned joints to a 100 percent leakproof quality.

REFERENCES: Required – Para. 2-20 through 2-24, 2-74 and 14-22. Supplementary – Para. 28-52.

EQUIPMENT: A work bench with vise.

PREPARATION PROCEDURE:
1. Study the reference paragraphs for soldering and silver brazing.
   TEST√ _____
2. Obtain: Tools – 1 air-propane, air-acetylene, or oxy-acetylene torch, 1 6-in. combination pliers, 1 tube cutter, 1 spark lighter, 2 flux brushes, 1 pr. safety goggles.
3. Obtain: Supplies – 1 length 1/4-in. ACR tubing, 1 length 1/2-in. copper tubing, 1 box streamline or sweat (soldered) fittings, 1 length 1/2-in. hard drawn copper tubing, 1 dish soap suds, 1 length silver brazing rod, 1 4-in. square #0 sandpaper or clean steel wool, 1 jar soldering flux, 1 jar silver brazing flux, 1 coil soft solder.

TASK PROCEDURE (WEAR GOGGLES):
1. For the soldering job, prepare an assembly as shown in Fig. 2-29 in the text.
2. Join the pieces by heating the tubing and touching the solder wire to the joint. Allow the heat of the tubing to melt the solder. Do not heat the solder wire with the torch flame.
3. Connect the assembly to the compressed air line, using a flared connection, and test for leaks at 50 psi. Use a soap and water solution. Resolder any joints that leak.

   1-3√ _____

4. Perform the silver brazing job. Select a 1/2-in. hard drawn "T" and three length of 1/2-in. hard drawn tubing. Assemble and silver braze an assembly as shown in Fig. 2-25 in the text.
   4√ _____

CLOSING THE STATION:
   Clean work station and return all materials to tool crib.

DATA:
   SOFT SOLDERING DATA:
   Solder Brand: _____ Alloy _____ Approx. flow temp. _____
   Flux Brand: _____ Approx. composition _____
   Torch Brand: _____ Fuel used _____
         Air _____ Oxygen ____ _____ Tip Size _____
   Leak test results _____
   SILVER BRAZING ALLOY DATA:
   Silver brazing alloy, Brand _____ Alloy _____
         Approx. flow temp. _____ Melt temp. _____
   Flux Brand _____ Approx. composition _____
   Torch, make _____ Fuel used _____ Tip Size _____ Leak test results _____
   _____

Remarks:

MAKE OR REPAIR SOLDERED AND BRAZED TUBING CONNECTION.

Indicate the best answer for each question below by encircling its letter.

1. What is the usual composition of soft solder?
    a. Lead and antimony.
    b. Lead and tin.
    c. Tin and zinc.
    d. Zinc and copper.
    e. Spelter.

2. What is the base of most silver brazing flux?
    a. Vaseline.
    b. Tallow.
    c. Zinc chloride.
    d. Borax.
    e. Sodium chloride.

3. What is the advantage of silver brazing over soft soldering?
    a. Cheaper.
    b. Quicker.
    c. Neater.
    d. Stronger.
    e. Lighter.

4. What is the approximate temperature at which silver brazing alloys flow?
    a. 1000° F.
    b. 1050° F.
    c. 1100° F.
    d. 1145° F.
    e. 1200° F.

5. Why must the flux be removed after soldering and brazing?
    a. It is not.
    b. To help one see the quality of the job.
    c. To prevent corrosion.
    d. To polish the joint.
    e. To make the joint stronger.

Task No. 1-4 Task Grade _____

Name _____

Date _____ Class _____

MAKE OR REPAIR A SWAGED TUBING CONNECTION

OBJECTIVE: Given tubing, swaging tools, a soldering bench or brazing bench: make three different diameter swaged joints and solder or braze to a leakproof quality.

REFERENCES: Required – Para. 2-24 and 2-74.

EQUIPMENT: One soldering or brazing bench complete with source of heat for soldering-brazing.

PREPARATION PROCEDURE:
1. Study the methods used to make swage connections.

TEST√ _____

2. Obtain: Tools – 1 pr. 6-in. pliers, 1 set swaging tools, 1 16-oz. ball peen hammer, 1 spark lighter, 1 tube cutter, 1 safety goggles.
3. Obtain: Supplies – 1 4-in. square #0 clean sandpaper, 1 pad clean steel wool, 1 can clean fresh soldering or brazing flux, 1 coil soft solder or brazing filler metal, 2 short lengths 1/4 OD ACR tubing, 2 short lengths 3/8 OD ACR tubing, 2 short lengths 1/2 OD ACR tubing, 1 bottle soap suds.

TASK PROCEDURE (WEAR GOGGLES):
1. Place the 1/4-in. copper tubing in the flare block with tube end above the flare block a little more than the length of the swage tool shoulder. Tighten flare block on tubing.
2. Insert the 1/4-in. swaging tool in the tubing, hold the flare block and tubing in one hand, and tap the swaging tool with a hammer or tighten swage tool screw.
3. Remove the flare block from the tubing.

1-3√ _____

4. After a suitable 1/4-in. swage joint has been made, make others with the 3/8-in. and 1/2-in. tubing.
5. Solder or braze the joints.

4-5√ _____

6. Test for leaks.

6√ _____

CLOSING THE STATION:
Clean up station. Return all materials to the tool crib.

DATA:
Tubing, OD _____ ID _____

Swaging Tool, Make _____

Sizes of tubing it can swage _____, _____, _____,

_____, _____, _____,

Hammer, Type _____ Size _____

Test results: 1/4-in. _____ 3/8-in. _____ 1/2-in. _____

Remarks:

MAKE OR REPAIR A SWAGED
TUBING CONNECTION.

Indicate the best answer for each question below by encircling its letter.

1. Does swaging make a tubing ID larger or smaller?
    a. No change.
    b. Larger.
    c. Only the OD is larger.
    d. Smaller
    e. Thickens the tubing wall.

2. What is wrong if the tubing splits while it is being swaged?
    a. Tubing is too thin.
    b. Tubing is too soft.
    c. Tubing is too hard.
    d. Swage tool is undersize.
    e. Poor quality tubing.

3. How many joints are soldered when three pieces of tubing are joined with a coupling and a swaged joint?
    a. 2.
    b. 3.
    c. 4.
    d. 5.
    e. 6.

4. How far above the swaging block should the tubing extend?
    a. 1/4 in.
    b. 3/8 in.
    c. 1/4 in. more than OD of tubing.
    d. Length of swaging tool shoulder.
    e. 1/16 in. or more.

5. What OD tubing fits into a swaged 3/8 in. tubing?
    a. 1/4 in.
    b. 5/16 in.
    c. 3/8 in.
    d. 7/16 in.
    e. 1/2 in.

SELECT FITTINGS AND MAKE A COMPLETE TUBING ASSEMBLY

OBJECTIVE: Given tubing, fittings, flaring tools, tube cutter and wrenches: cut, flare, bend, assemble, and test a tubing complex at 50 psi to approved standards.

REFERENCES: Required – Para. 2-1, 2-2, 2-11, 2-12, 2-14, 2-15, 2-18 and 2-74.

EQUIPMENT: A work bench, an air compressor, and an assembly board.

PREPARATION PROCEDURE:
1. Study the reference paragraphs for cutting and flaring tubing. TEST√ _____
2. Obtain: Tools – 1 tube cutter, 1 3/4-in. flare nut wrench, 1 8-in. adj. open end wrench, 1 flaring tool, 1 1/4-in. bending spring, 1 1/2-in. bending spring, 1 1-in. flare nut wrench, 1 pr. safety goggles.
3. Obtain: Instruments – 1 6-ft. steel tape, 1 screw pitch gauge.
4. Obtain: Supplies – 1 coil or length 1/4-in. soft copper tubing, 1 coil or length 1/2-in. soft copper tubing, 1 wiping cloth, 1 bottle soap suds, 4 1/4-in. flare nuts, 4 1/2-in. flare nuts, 1 1/4 MF x 1/2 MF union, 1 1/2 FF flare nut plug, 1 1/4 x 1/4 MF union, 1 1/2 x 1/2 MF union, 1 oil can.

TASK PROCEDURE (WEAR GOGGLES):
1. Insert a 1/8 male pipe x 1/4 male flare elbow with a 1/8-in. male pipe thread into the air compressor outlet, flare and attach a 1/4-in. copper tube to the male flared end of the fitting.
2. Cut tubing and bend as shown below.
3. Install flare nuts and then flare the tubing.
4. Connect the separate pieces together using unions.
    Connect 90 deg. 1/4 to 360 deg. 1/4 to 90 deg. 1/2 to 180 deg. 1/2. 1-4√ _____
5. Connect the 1/4-in. tubing to the air compressor outlet.
6. Test with 50 psi air pressure. Use bubble solution. Repair any leak.
7. Dismantle tubing assembly.   5-7√ _____

CLOSING THE STATION:
    Clean the station and return all materials to tool crib.

DATA:
FITTINGS:

1/4 in. flare nut:	Wrench size _____	Thread size _____
1/2 in. flare nut:	Wrench size _____	Thread size _____
1/2 in. union:	Wrench size _____	Thread size _____
1/4 in. union:	Wrench size _____	Thread size _____
1/4 x 1/2 union:	Wrench size _____	Thread size _____
1/2 in. flare nut plug:	Wrench size _____	Thread size _____

Test for leaks, results _____

Remarks:

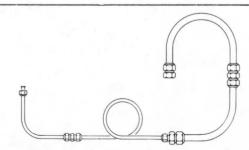

SELECT FITTINGS AND MAKE A COMPLETE TUBING ASSEMBLY.

Indicate the best answer for each question below by encircling its letter.

1. Of what material are tube fittings usually made?
   a. Steel.
   b. Cast iron.
   c. Aluminum.
   d. Copper.
   e. Brass.

2. Which item shown in Figure 2-21 will be required when making any type of flare fitting connection?
   a. A
   b. B
   c. C
   d. D
   e. E

3. What is the common name applied to soldered and silver brazed fittings?
   a. Sweat or streamline.
   b. Flared.
   c. Extruded.
   d. Hard drawn.
   e. Cast.

4. Why is it necessary to use a special flare nut wrench?
   a. These wrenches are larger.
   b. They have longer handles.
   c. They are always offset.
   d. The slot allows them to fit over a tube.
   e. It is not necessary, any box end wrench may be used.

5. What may happen if a flare nut is drawn up too tight?
   a. The wrench may break.
   b. The threads will strip.
   c. The flare will be squeezed out.
   d. The tube will collapse.
   e. The oil will be squeezed out.

IDENTIFY PIPE FITTINGS

OBJECTIVE: Given an assortment of numbered pipe fittings and threaded pipe: identify the kind and size of each fitting and then make an approved piping assembly.

REFERENCES: Required – Para. 2-26, 2-27 and 2-74.

EQUIPMENT: One work bench fitted with pipe vise and compressed air outlet.

PREPARATION PROCEDURE:
1. Study the reference paragraphs and pipe manufacturers' catalogs.

                                                              TEST√_____

2. Obtain: Tools – 1 10-in. pipe wrench, 1 14-in. pipe wrench.
3. Obtain: Instruments – 1 6-in. rule, 1 8-in. outside caliper.
4. Obtain: Supplies – 1 tube pipe sealing compound, 1 kit of pipe fittings and threaded pipe, 1 bottle soap suds.

TASK PROCEDURE:
1. Identify each fitting and measure for size. Record in data section.   1√_____
2. Assemble a square shaped pipe assembly with a 45 deg. angle pipe section in middle. See the illustration below for Task 1-6. Put sealing compound on threads. Corners must be at 90 deg. angles.
3. Pressure test at 50 psi air pressure. Use soap suds.   2-3√_____
4. Dismantle the assembly. Clean the sealing compound from the threads. 4√_____

CLOSING THE STATION:
    Clean the bench, vise, instruments, and tools.
    Return the kit to the tool crib.

DATA:

90 deg. Elbows, Size 1___ 2___ 3___	45 deg. Elbows, Size 1___ 2___ 3___
Street Ells, Size 1___ 2___ 3___	Couplings, Size 1___ 2___ 3___
Reducing Couplings, Size 1___ 2___ 3___	Plugs, Size 1___ 2___ 3___
Tees, Size 1___ 2___ 3___	Unions, Size 1___ 2___ 3___
Nipples, Long, Size 1___ 2___ 3___	Nipples, Short Size 1___ 2___ 3___
Pressure Test: Leaks _____	Repaired _____ No Leaks _____

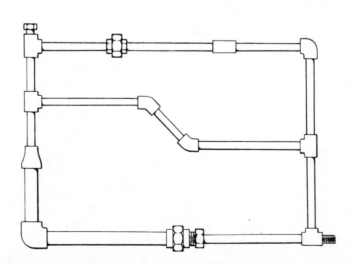

IDENTIFY PIPE FITTINGS.

Indicate the best answer for each question below by encircling its letter.

1. What are the initials for pipe threads?
    a. APT.
    b. NTT.
    c. NPT.
    d. SPT.
    e. NWT.

2. What is the shape of each thread?
    a. Vee.
    b. Square.
    c. U-Shaped.
    d. Buttress.
    e. Round.

3. What tool should be used to recut a burred pipe thread?
    a. File.
    b. Knife.
    c. Wire brush.
    d. Die.
    e. Tap.

4. How do pipe threads seal together?
    a. Gasket.
    b. Cut on a taper.
    c. "O" rings.
    d. They do not.
    e. Each thread is tapered.

5. How many wrenches should be used to install a coupling on a pipe?
    a. One.
    b. Two.
    c. Three.
    d. Pliers are used.
    e. One pliers and one pipe wrench.

Task No. 1-7 Task Grade _____
Name _____
Date _____ Class _____

READ GAUGES AND OPERATE GAUGE MANIFOLD

OBJECTIVE: Given several gauges, a complete gauge manifold, and an air supply: connect the
gauge manifold to the air supply, read the gauges, operate the gauge manifold valves, and
accurately obtain the correct readings.

REFERENCES: Required – Para. 2-52 through 2-56, 2-74, 11-27, 11-28 and 11-82.
Supplementary – Para. 14-7 and 14-109.

EQUIPMENT: One work bench fitted with a compressed air outlet, a vacuum pump and a vise.

PREPARATION PROCEDURE:
1. Study the reference paragraphs.   TEST√ _____
2. Obtain: Tools – 1 valve wrench, 1 3/4 in. wrench, 1 pr. safety goggles.
3. Obtain: Instruments – 1 gauge manifold, 1 kit of gauges.
4. Obtain: Supplies – 3 flexible manifold lines.

TASK PROCEDURE (WEAR GOGGLES):
1. Have the instructor set the gauge dial pointers, then record the readings. Record the
readings in the data section.   1√ _____
2. Install the gauge manifold on the air compressor and vacuum pump:
   a. Connect the air compressor opening to the high-pressure gauge opening of the gauge
      manifold using a 1/4-in. tubing. WEAR GOGGLES! Use the 3/4-in. open end wrench.
   b. Connect the vacuum pump opening to the low-pressure gauge opening of the gauge
      manifold using 1/4-in. tubing.   2√ _____
3. Start air compressor and vacuum pump.
4. Operate manifold valves to:
   a. Middle hose has (1) atmospheric pressure; (2) high pressure; (3) vacuum;
   b. Low-pressure line has pressure.   3-4√ _____
5. Shut off air compressor and vacuum pump.
6. Remove the gauge manifold.   5-6√ _____

CLOSING THE STATION:
Clean the work station and return the tools and supplies to the tool crib.

DATA:
Practice Gauge Dial Readings, 1_____ 2_____ 3_____ 4_____ 5_____
Gauge Manifold:

	Compound Gauge	Pressure Gauge
Lowest reading on dial		
Highest reading on dial		
Kind and size of gauge connection		
Gauge size		

Manifold make _____ Material _____
Low-Pressure Gauge make _____ Dial Size _____
Fitting _____ Max. Pressure _____ Min. Pressure _____
High-Pressure Gauge make _____ Dial Size _____
Fitting _____ Maximum Pressure _____
Low-Pressure Connection Size _____
High-Pressure Connection Size _____
Middle-Pressure Connection Size _____

Remarks:

READ GAUGES AND OPERATE GAUGE MANIFOLD.

Indicate the best answer for each question below by encircling its letter.

1. How many gauges are usually installed in refrigerating systems?
   a.   One pressure gauge.
   b.   Two pressure gauges.
   c.   Three pressure gauges.
   d.   Four pressure gauges.
   e.   Five pressure gauges.

2. How many pressure scales does a compound gauge have?
   a.   One pressure scale.
   b.   Two pressure scales.
   c.   Three pressure scales.
   d.   Four pressure scales.
   e.   Five pressure scales.

3. How are pressures below atmospheric pressure measured?
   a.   In lbs. per sq. inch.
   b.   In inches of mercury.
   c.   In atmospheres.
   d.   In inches of water.
   e.   In lbs. per sq. in. absolute.

4. What is the size of the average gauge fitting connection?
   a.   1/8 in. external pipe threads.
   b.   1/4 in. external pipe threads.
   c.   3/8 in. external National Fine threads.
   d.   1/8 in. external NF threads.
   e.   In. external NF threads.

5. What happens if a pressure higher than the maximum dial reading is imposed on a gauge?
   a.   It will not harm the gauge.
   b.   It will injure the gauge mechanism.
   c.   It is not possible.
   d.   The dial will break.
   e.   The threads will strip.

OPERATIVE SERVICE VALVES

OBJECTIVE: Given a refrigerating system with three service valves: operate the valves to give the specified pressures.

REFERENCES: Required - Para. 2-71, 2-74, 11-27 and 11-82.
   Supplementary - 14-8 and 14-109.

EQUIPMENT: One work bench complete with a refrigeration system having air pressure and air vacuum pump connections.

PREPARATION PROCEDURE:
   1. Study the paragraph references.   TEST√_____
   2. Obtain: Tools - 1 8-in. adj. end wrench, 1 1/4-in. square ratchet wrench,
       1 pr. safety goggles.
   3. Obtain: Supplies - 1 kit of miscellaneous service valves, 2 24-in. lengths of 1/4-in.
       flared tubing .

TASK PROCEDURE (WEAR GOGGLES):
   1. Dismantle the service valves in the kit.
   2. Have the instructor check the dismantled valves.   1-2√_____
   3. Operate the system:
       a. Connect the system to the compressed air and vacuum using 1/4 flared tubing.
       b. Adjust the valves to allow air out the LRSV but with the gauge openings closed.
       c. Adjust the valves to allow air out the LRSV but with the DSV gauge fittings also
           releasing air.
       d. Adjust the valves to allow the gauge fittings to release air but not to allow air
           to go to the LRSV.   3√_____
   4. Isolate the compressor. Position the valves to permit pumping the gas out of the
                                                                   4√_____

CLOSING THE STATION:
   Clean up the station and tools, then return all the materials to the tool crib.

DATA:

	SSV	DSV	LRSV
Valve Stem Diameter			
Valve Stem Wrench Size			
Gauge Opening Threads, Size and Kind			
Refrigerant Opening Threads, Size, Kind			
Packing Nut Threads, Size and Kind			
Packing Nut Wrench Size			
Flange Hole, Center Distance			
Valve, Manufacturer			
Valve, Body Material			
Valve, Stem Material			
Valve, Stem Packing Material			
Condition of Valves			

OPERATE SERVICE VALVES.

Indicate the best answer for each question below by encircling its letter.

1.   Of what materials are most service valve stems made?
   a.   Steel.
   b.   Copper.
   c.   Brass.
   d.   Monel.
   e.   Tool steel.

2.   Of what materials are most service valve bodies made?
   a.   Steel.
   b.   Brass.
   c.   Monel.
   d.   Aluminum.
   e.   Cast iron.

3.   What kind of threads are used in the gauge opening of a service valve?
   a.   Pipe.
   b.   NF.
   c.   NC.
   d.   National extra fine.
   e.   Any kind of thread.

4.   What kind of threads does a packing nut have?
   a.   Internal NP.
   b.   External NP.
   c.   NF.
   d.   Internal NC.
   e.   External NC.

5.   What is the diameter of a 1/4 square end service valve stem?
   a.   1/4 in.
   b.   5/16 in.
   c.   3/8 in.
   d.   3/16 in.
   e.   7/16 in.

INSTALL AND TEST ACCESS VALVES AND PROCESS TUBE ADAPTORS

OBJECTIVE: Given an empty hermetic system, access valves, tube adaptors and tools: connect the access valves and tube adaptor to leakproof quality.

REFERENCES: Required – Para. 11-26 through 11-33 and 11-82.

EQUIPMENT: One no-charge hermetic system or a suitable "mock-up" panel board.

PREPARATION PROCEDURE:
1. Study the paragraph references.   TEST√_____
2. Obtain: Tools – 1 set open end wrenches, 1 set process tube adaptors, 2 8-in. adj. open end wrenches, 1 set valve adaptors, 1 tube cutter, 1 oxy-acetylene outfit, 1 spark lighter, 1 pr. safety goggles, 1 pr. welder goggles, #4 lens.
3. Obtain: Instruments – 1 gauge manifold complete with refrigerant lines.
4. Obtain: Supplies – 1 1/4-tubing piercing valve (clamp on), 1 3/8-in. tubing piercing valve (clamp on), 1 wiping cloth, 1 1/4-in. saddle piercing valve, 1 3/8-in saddle piercing valve, 1 roll silver brazing flux, 1 1 to 2 lb. refrigerant cylinder, 1 practice tube with fittings, 1 roll silver brazing filler metal.

TASK PROCEDURE (WEAR GOGGLES):
1. Install the service valve on the valve adaptor on the system or on a practice adaptor. Select the adaptor, the valve stem adaptor, and the gaskets; install, tighten, and then install the gauge manifold. Operate the system or pressurize the practice tube, check pressures, and test for leaks.

                                                                    1 √_____

2. Install either the 1/4-in. or the 3/8-in. clamp piercing valve. Pierce the tube, install the gauge manifold, check the pressures and check for leaks.
                                                                    2 √_____

3. Silver braze the saddle valve body to a clean straight part of the suction line or a practice tube. Allow to cool, assemble the valve, connect the gauge manifold, operate the system, check the pressure and test for leaks.
                                                                    3√_____

4. Use tube cutter to remove the end of the process tube (be careful of released refrigerant), install process tube adaptor, install gauge manifold, gas pressurize the system or mock-up panel board, test for leaks.   4√_____

CLOSING THE STATION:
        Clean the work station and return all materials to tool crib.

DATA:

Valve Adaptor Kit, Make_____ Clamp-on Valve, Make_____ Size_____
Saddle Valve, Make_____ Size_____
Process Tube Adaptor Kit, Make_____ Size_____

Remarks:

INSTALL AND TEST ACCESS VALVES AND PROCESS TUBE ADAPTORS.

Indicate the best answer for each question below by encircling its letter.

1. Does the service valve attachment have threads on it?
   a. Yes.
   b. No.
   c. On some models.
   d. Only if it is a high pressure unit.
   e. No valve stem is used.

2. What permits the service valve attachment to be swiveled to any position?
   a. Tapered threads.
   b. A swivel nut on the valve attachment.
   c. The attachment fitting has tapered threads.
   d. It cannot be swiveled.
   e. A compressible gasket.

3. How does the piercing needle provide a leak-proof joint when turned all the way in?
   a. It does not.
   b. A synthetic rubber gasket.
   c. The needle seats on the walls of the pierced hole.
   d. A nylon sealant is used.
   e. A 45 deg. flare.

4. How is maximum refrigerant flow obtained through a Schrader or Dill valve core?
   a. Core all the way out.
   b. Core depressed half way.
   c. Core removed.
   d. Core all the way in.
   e. Core depressed even with fitting.

5. How many gaskets does a Schrader or Dill valve core have?
   a. One.
   b. Two.
   c. Three.
   d. Four.
   e. Five.

IDENTIFY ASSEMBLY DEVICES AND TOOLS (U.S. CONVENTIONAL UNITS)

OBJECTIVE: Given an assortment of assembly devices, a compressor, tools and measuring
instruments: identify the assembly devices and dismantle and assemble. A visual inspection
must indicate that the parts are in their correct places; also, a torque wrench test must show
that the parts have been correctly tightened.

REFERENCES: Required – Para. 2-29 through 2-37 and 28-46.
    Supplementary – Para. 2-38 through 2-43, 2-46, 2-47, 2-49, 2-66, 2-67, 2-74 and 28-48.

EQUIPMENT: Work station which provides a work bench, a bench vise, some boxes to receive small
parts, screws, nuts, and bolts, and a small open type reciprocating compressor.

PREPARATION PROCEDURE:
   1. Study the various types of assembly devices, assembly tools and instruments. Study the
       reference paragraphs.   TEST√_____
   2. Obtain: Tools – 1 tool kit which contains an assortment of end wrenches, socket wrenches,
       box end wrenches, and adjustable wrenches necessary to perform this task, 1 torque
       wrench and sockets, 1 8-in. fine mill file.
   3. Obtain: Instruments – 1 1-in. micrometer, 1 6-in. steel rule, 1 4-in. outside caliper,
       1 thread gauge.
   4. Obtain: Supplies – 1 oiler containing refrigerant oil, 1 wiping cloth.

TASK PROCEDURE:
   1. Examine the assembly devices, locate a sample of each assembly device as listed on the
       data sheet below.   1√_____
   2. Use the micrometer, steel rule and the thread gauge to measure the assembly devices and
       record.
   3. Remove the cylinder head, crankcase pan and service valves from the open compressor.
   4. Assemble the compressor and properly tighten the assembly devices and torque to correct
       values.
                                                      2-4√_____
CLOSING THE STATION:
    Clean the work station and return all materials to the tool crib.

DATA:

Cap Screw, Length_____	Diameter_____	Threads_____	Wrench Size_____	Kind_____
Bolt, Length_____	Diameter_____	Threads_____	Wrench Size_____	Kind_____
Nut, Type_____	Diameter_____	Threads_____	Wrench Size_____	Kind_____
Round Head Machine Screw, Length_____	Dia._____	Threads_____	Tool, Kind_____	Size_____
Hexagon Head Machine Screw, Length_____	Dia._____	Threads_____	Tool, Kind_____	Size_____
Plain Washer, Thickness_____	OD_____		ID_____	
Lock Washer, Thickness_____	OD_____		ID_____	
Allen Set Screw, Length_____	Dia._____	Threads_____	Wrench, Kind_____	Size_____

Remarks:

IDENTIFY ASSEMBLY DEVICES AND TOOLS (U.S. CONVENTIONAL UNITS).

Indicate the best answer for each question below by encircling its letter.

1. What is the usual purpose of nylon inserts in cap screws and nuts used on refrigeration machinery?
    a. To make it run quieter.
    b. To hold oil.
    c. To avoid static electricity.
    d. To lock the nut or screw in place.
    e. To eliminate vibration.

2. Why is it necessary to use a torque wrench when assembling compressor parts?
    a. It gives greater leverage.
    b. To avoid breaking the screw or bolt.
    c. To eliminate the use of lock washers.
    d. To squeeze out the oil.
    e. To eliminate distortion.

3. National Coarse threads are usually used in which of the following refrigerating applications?
    a. Tapped holes in cast iron.
    b. Tapped holes in steel.
    c. Bolts and nuts in highly stressed applications.
    d. Fittings requiring close adjustment.
    e. Threads on thin walled pipe.

4. What diameter tap drill should be used to drill a hole to be tapped for a 3/8 - 16 cap screw?
    a. 3/8 in.
    b. R.
    c. Q.
    d. O.
    e. 17/64 in.

5. Why is it necessary to use number and letter drills when drilling for various diameter tapped holes?
    a. To make tapping easier.
    b. For use in thin metal.
    c. To give maximum threads.
    d. For use in thick metal.
    e. For use in blind holes.

IDENTIFY ASSEMBLY DEVICES AND TOOLS (METRIC UNITS)

OBJECTIVE: Given assembly devices, tools, and a compressor: identify the assembly devices, the tools, and then dismantle and assemble the compressor. A visual inspection must indicate that the parts are in the correct places. Also, a torque wrench test must show that parts have been correctly tightened.

REFERENCES: Required – Para. 1-12, 2-6, 2-19, 2-31, 2-58, 2-67 and 2-74.
        Supplementary – Para. 1-64.

EQUIPMENT: One work bench with bench vises. Some boxes to receive small parts. A small metric size compressor.

PREPARATION PROCEDURE:
    1. Study the paragraph references.   TEST√ _____
    2. Obtain: Tools – 1 set metric open wrenches, 1 set metric socket wrenches.
    3. Obtain: Instruments – 1 metric rule, 1 0–25 mm micrometer.
    4. Obtain: Supplies – 1 wiping cloth, 1 set of metric assemble devices.

TASK PROCEDURE:
    1. Identify type and size of each metric assembly device in the kit.
    2. Identify kind and size of metric tool to be used with each assembly device.
                                                1-2√ _____

    3. Dismantle the metric dimensional compressor.
                                                3√ _____

    4. Assemble the metric dimensional compressor.
                                                4√ _____

CLOSING THE STATION:
        Clean the work station, compressor, tools, and instruments, and return the tools, instruments and the kit to the tool crib.

DATA:

Cap Screw, Length _____	Diameter _____	Threads _____	Wrench Size _____	Kind _____
Bolt, Length _____	Diameter _____	Threads _____	Wrench Size _____	Kind _____
Nut, Type _____	Diameter _____	Threads _____	Wrench Size _____	Kind _____
Round Head Machine Screw, Length _____	Dia. _____	Threads _____	Tool, Kind _____	Size _____
Hexagon Head Machine Screw, Length _____	Dia. _____	Threads _____	Tool, Kind _____	Size _____
Plain Washer, Thickness _____		OD _____	ID _____	
Lock Washer, Thickness _____		OD _____	ID _____	
Allen Set Screw, Length _____	Dia. _____	Threads _____	Wrench, Kind _____	Size _____

Remarks:

IDENTIFY ASSEMBLY DEVICES AND TOOLS (METRIC UNITS).

Indicate the best answer for each question below by encircling its letter.

1. In what metric units is a cap screw diameter measured?
   a. Torr.
   b. Centimetres.
   c. Metres.
   d. Millimetres.
   e. Millimetres of Hg.

2. What is the metric wrench size for an eight mm cap screw?
   a. 12 mm.
   b. 10 mm.
   c. 8 mm.
   d. 6 mm.
   e. 4 mm.

3. How are metric threads measured?
   a. Threads per mm.
   b. Threads per cm.
   c. Cm per thread.
   d. Mm per thread.
   e. Depth of thread.

4. How many different screw thread specifications may be used on a 10 mm bolt?
   a. 1
   b. 2
   c. 3
   d. 4
   e. 5

5. Where is a twelve point metric socket wrench used?
   a. On small cap screws.
   b. On 12-sided bolt heads.
   c. On 4-sided bolt heads.
   d. On large bolts only.
   e. On all bolt heads.

DISMANTLE, ASSEMBLE AND TEST AN EXTERNAL DRIVE PISTON TYPE COMPRESSOR

OBJECTIVE: Given an external drive piston type compressor and the necessary tools: dismantle, assemble and test the compressor to specified pumping ability.

REFERENCES: Required – Para. 4-24, 4-27 through 4-36 and 4-61.
Supplementary – Para. 11-69, 11-82, 14-36 through 14-42, and 14-109.

EQUIPMENT: Work station which provides a bench with 4-in. machinist vise, trays to receive small parts, screws, nuts, and bolts, and an open type small commercial refrigeration compressor and compressor test stand.

PREPARATION PROCEDURE:
1. Study the details of construction of an open type compressor in the paragraph references.
TEST√ _____
2. Obtain: Tools – 1 tool kit containing an assortment of end wrenches, socket wrenches, box wrenches, and adj. wrenches necessary to perform the task, 1 torque wrench and sockets, 1 flywheel pulley, 1 pr. safety goggles.
3. Obtain: Instruments – 1 1-in. micrometer, 1 1 to 2-in. micrometer, 1 compound gauge, 1 high-pressure gauge, 1 speed counter, 1 1 to 2-in. inside micrometer, 1 6-in steel rule, 1 thread gauge.
4. Obtain: Supplies – 1 wiping cloth, 1 oil can with refrigerant oil.

TASK PROCEDURE (WEAR GOGGLES).
1. Remove the flywheel and record data.
2. Remove the cylinder head and record data.
3. Remove the valve plate and record.
4. Remove the crankcase and record.
5. Remove one connecting rod and record.   1-5√ _____
6. Assemble the compressor, tighten and torque all assembly devices.
7. Put oil in the compressor and mount the compressor on test stand.
8. Test the compressor for vacuum and pressure.   6-8√ _____

CLOSING THE STATION:
Clean station and return materials to tool crib.

DATA:

Compressor, Make _____ Type _____ Capacity _____ Refrigerant _____
Flywheel, dia. _____ Fastening Device _____ Wrench Size _____ Threads _____
Cylinder Head Cap Screws, No. _____ Length _____ Dia. _____ Threads _____ Wrench Size _____
Gasket Material, Top Gasket _____ Bottom Gasket _____
Valve Plate Material _____ Intake Valve Material _____ Exhaust Valve Material _____
Crankcase Cap Screws, No. _____ Length _____ Dia. _____ Threads _____ Wrench Size _____
Seal Cap Screws, No. _____ Length _____ Dia. _____ Threads _____ Wrench Size _____
Connecting Rod Cap Screws, No. _____ Length _____ Dia. _____ Threads _____ Wrench Size _____

Remarks:

DISMANTLE, ASSEMBLE AND TEST AN EXTERNAL DRIVE PISTON TYPE COMPRESSOR.

Indicate the best answer for each question below by encircling its letter.

1. What material is usually used for compressor cylinders?
    a. Aluminum.
    b. Copper.
    c. Cast iron.
    d. Steel.
    e. Brass.

2. How many inches of vacuum should a good compressor be capable of creating?
    a. 36 in.
    b. 28 in.
    c. 24 in.
    d. 15 in.
    e. 10 in.

3. Which type of piston crankshaft arrangement does not use a connecting rod?
    a. Scotch yoke.
    b. Eccentric.
    c. Conventional.
    d. Hotchkiss.
    e. "Vee" type.

4. Which type of compressor has the cylinders parallel to the crankshaft?
    a. Swash plate.
    b. Eccentric.
    c. Conventional.
    d. Scotch yoke.
    e. Hotchkiss.

5. Where are compressor valves usually located on open type compressors?
    a. In the cylinder head.
    b. In a valve plate.
    c. In the piston head.
    d. In the tubing.
    e. No valves are needed.

DISMANTLE, ASSEMBLE AND TEST AN EXTERNAL
DRIVE ROTARY TYPE COMPRESSOR

OBJECTIVE: Given an external drive rotary compressor and the necessary tools: dismantle, reassemble, and then pressure and vacuum test to required accuracy. (A minimum of 13-in. of vacuum must be achieved.)

REFERENCES: Required - Para. 4-41, 4-42, 4-43, 4-44 and 4-61.
    Supplementary - Para. 11-70 and 11-71.

EQUIPMENT: Work station which provides a work bench with 4-in. machinist vise; test stand; trays to receive small parts; and a rotary type refrigeration compressor.

PREPARATION PROCEDURE:
1.   Study the construction and operation of a rotary type compressor in the reference paragraphs.

                              TEST√_____

2.   Obtain: Tools - 1 tool kit consisting of an assortment of end wrenches, socket wrenches, box wrenches, and adj. wrenches necessary to perform task; 1 torque wrench and sockets, 1 pr. safety goggles.
3.   Obtain: Instruments - 1 1-in. micrometer, 1 6-in. steel rule, 1 thread gauge, 1 compound gauge.
4.   Obtain: Supplies - 1 wiping cloth, 1 oil can with refrigerant oil.

TASK PROCEDURE (WEAR GOGGLES):
1.   Dismantle the compressor and record the data requested below.
2.   Assemble the compressor. Use the torque wrench to draw up the cap screws to the torque indicated. The torque specifications are to be provided by the instructor. Oil all surfaces including the cylinder and valves. Turn the compressor shaft by hand to be sure it turns freely.
3.   Run compressor on test stand; determine pressure and vacuum.

                              1-3√_____

CLOSING THE STATION:
    Clean the station and return materials to tool crib.

DATA:

Compressor, Make_____ Model_____ Capacity_____
End Plate Cap Screws, No._____ Length_____ Dia._____ Threads_____ Wrench Size_____
Crankshaft Eccentric, Diameter_____ Length_____
Roller, ID_____ OD_____ Length_____
Housing, ID_____ Length_____

Remarks:

DISMANTLE, ASSEMBLE AND TEST AN EXTERNAL DRIVE ROTARY TYPE COMPRESSOR.

Indicate the best answer for each question below by encircling its letter.

1. Why is a check valve needed in the suction line of a rotary compressor?
   a. To control the compressor outlet pressure.
   b. To keep a positive pressure in the compressor at all times.
   c. To keep pressure from backing up in the suction line.
   d. To remove the oil from the low side.
   e. To keep oil from going into the high side.

2. What is special about crankshaft seal construction used on rotary compressors?
   a. Nothing.
   b. Must operate without friction.
   c. Must operate under high pressures.
   d. Must operate under high temperatures.
   e. Must operate under a light vacuum.

3. The length of the intake opening on a rotary compressor is approximately:
   a. 45 deg. of crankshaft travel.
   b. 60 deg. of crankshaft travel.
   c. 90 deg. of crankshaft travel.
   d. 120 deg. of crankshaft travel.
   e. 270 deg. of crankshaft travel.

4. The volumetric efficiency of a rotary compressor is usually quite good because:
   a. There is no intake valve to open.
   b. There is a large clearance volume.
   c. The compressor speed is very low.
   d. A positive action exhaust valve is used.
   e. All compressor surfaces are sealed with heavy oil.

5. What should be the length of the vanes in a rotary compressor?
   a. Slightly shorter than the rotor or roller.
   b. Slightly longer than the rotor or roller.
   c. Considerably shorter than the rotor or roller.
   d. Considerably longer than the rotor or roller.
   e. Exactly the same length as the rotor or roller.

INSTALL BELTS AND ADJUST PULLEYS AND BELTS

OBJECTIVE: Given an external (open) drive compressor and the necessary tools: dismantle, assemble, adjust and test the assembly to specifications.

REFERENCES: Required – Para. 4-24, 4-35, 4-49, 7-4, 7-43 and 7-44.
     Supplementary – Para. 14-35, 14-42, 14-89 and 14-109.

EQUIPMENT: A small commercial system which uses a belt-driven open type motor .

PREPARATION PROCEDURE:
1. Study the recommended procedures and specifications for installing a belt.
               TEST√_____
2. Obtain: Tools – 1 set Allen set screw wrenches, 1 8-in. adj. open end wrench, 1 set open end wrenches, 1 set socket wrenches, 1 flywheel puller, 1 pulley puller, 1 pr. safety goggles.
3. Obtain: Instruments – 1 belt length gauge, 1 belt tension gauge.
4. Obtain: Supplies – 1 wiping cloth, 1 oiler (SAE 30).

TASK PROCEDURE (WEAR GOGGLES):
1. Loosen the belt adjustment of the single belt installation, remove the belt, the pulley, and the flywheel.
2. Inspect the belt. Inspect shafts, pulleys and flywheel. Install the flywheel and pulley. Install the belt. Adjust the pulley for alignment. Finally, adjust for correct belt tension.
3. Operate and check belt tension.
               1-3√_____

CLOSING THE STATION:
    Clean up the station and return the materials to the tool crib.

DATA:

Single Belt Flywheel, Dia._____ Groove Width_____ Shaft Dia._____ Fastening Device_____
Single Belt Pulley, Dia._____ Groove Width_____ Shaft Dia._____ Fastening Device_____
Belt Width_____ Length_____ Condition_____
Pulleys in Line, Yes____ No____ Pulley Shafts Parallel, Yes_____ No_____
Belt Tension_____

Remarks:

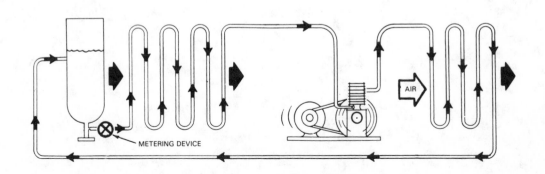

INSTALL BELTS AND ADJUST PULLEYS AND BELTS.

Indicate the best answer for each question below by encircling its letter.

1. What is the width of an A belt?
    a. 1/4 in.
    b. 3/8 in.
    c. 1/2 in.
    d. 5/8 in.
    e. 3/4 in.

2. What is the most common way to measure the length of a belt?
    a. Inside length.
    b. The length around the complete distance outside of the belt.
    c. The inside length times two.
    d. The length 1/2 of its depth.
    e. The length 2/3 of its depth.

3. In what direction should a belt rotate?
    a. Clockwise.
    b. Counterclockwise.
    c. With the pull on the top section of the belt.
    d. With the pull on the bottom section of the belt.
    e. In any direction.

4. Why should the shafts be parallel?
    a. To keep the pulley from loosening.
    b. To keep proper tension.
    c. To keep the belt from coming loose.
    d. To reduce vibration.
    e. To reduce bearing and belt wear.

5. What is one way to check for correct belt tension?
    a. There is no evidence of slipping.
    b. There is no glazing of belt wearing surfaces.
    c. The belt does not flap as it revolves.
    d. The belt will move 1/2 in. out-of-line with a ten lb. force.
    e. The belt will move 1/2 in. out-of-line with a 150 lb. force.

MEASURE SOME TEMPERATURES

OBJECTIVE: Given several different thermometers, a 32° F bath, a 212° F bath: check the
accuracies of the thermometers.

REFERENCES: Required - Para. 1-7, 1-8, 1-9, 1-11, 1-64, 2-51 and 2-74.
Supplementary - Para. 27-1, 28-2 and 28-16.

EQUIPMENT: Work station which provides a drain (sink), a hot plate, and a container for water
or refrigerant.

PREPARATION PROCEDURE:
1.   Study thermometer scales and temperature conversion factors and tables.

TEST√_____

2.   Obtain: Tools - 1 wide-necked thermos bottle, 1 tablespoon, 1 qt. aluminum open-topped
can, 1 small beaker, 1 pr. safety goggles.
3.   Obtain: Instruments - 1 glass-stemmed thermometer calibrated in degrees F, 1 glass-stemmed
thermometer calibrated in degrees C, 1 dial thermometer, 1 recording thermometer.
4.   Obtain: Supplies - 1 carton crushed ice, 1 pkg. rock salt (fine), 1 pkg. paper toweling,
1 1-lb. cylinder R-12, 1 hot plate.

TASK PROCEDURE (WEAR GOGGLES):
1.   Fill the thermos bottle with crushed ice and water. Stir.
2.   Insert the two thermometers. Note and record the temperature.
3.   Pour out the water. Add 2 tablespoons full of rock salt. Add some water and stir for at
least 3 minutes.
4.   Insert the two thermometers. Note and record the temperature.   1-4√_____
5.   Fill the one-quart aluminum can about 3/4 full with warm water and place it on the
hot plate.
6.   Install the two thermometers in the can. Heat to boiling. Record the temperatures.
7.   Add two tablespoons full of rock salt to the boiling water; BE CAREFUL, IT MAY BOIL
OVER.
8.   Repeat Steps 1 and 2 above, using only some liquid R-12, instead of ice and water.

5-8√_____

CLOSING THE STATION:
Clean up the station and return materials to the tool crib.

DATA:

	Stem Thermometer				Dial Thermometer				Rec. Thermometer		
	°F	°C	°R	K	°F	°C	°R	K	°F	°R	K
Ice water mixture											
Ice salt mixture											
Boiling salt water											
R-12											

Remarks.

MEASURE SOME TEMPERATURES.

Indicate the best answer for each question below by encircling its letter.

1. What is the temperature Fahrenheit at which ice melts?
    a. 0° F.
    b. 39° F.
    c. 40° F.
    d. 32° F.
    e. 68° F.

2. What is the temperature Celsius at which ice melts?
    a. 0° C.
    b. 32° C.
    c. 20° C.
    d. -32° C.
    e. 100° C.

3. What is the temperature Fahrenheit at which water boils?
    a. 68° F.
    b. 100° F.
    c. 180° F.
    d. 212° F.
    e. 240° F.

4. Which of the following list of Fahrenheit temperatures indicates the temperature of absolute 0 Fahrenheit?
    a. 0° F.
    b. -273°F.
    c. -100°F.
    d. 0° Rankin.
    e. 0 Kelvin.

5. What mechanism other than fluid expansion is commonly used for temperature measurement?
    a. A bimetal strip.
    b. Expansion and contraction of ice.
    c. Expansion and contraction of air.
    d. A vacuum.
    e. Ice-salt mixture.

TEST FOR LEAKS

OBJECTIVE: Given a leaking refrigerating system, several leak detecting devices: locate all of the leaks to approved standards.

REFERENCES: Required – Para. 11-38 through 11-43, 11-82, 14-9 and 14-109.

EQUIPMENT: An operating refrigerating machine which has known leaks.

PREPARATION PROCEDURE:
1. Study the system and also the leak detecting devices as per instrument list below. Study the reference paragraphs.

    TEST√_____

2. Obtain: Tools – 1 set service valve wrenches, 1 pr. safety goggles.
3. Obtain: Instruments – 1 oxy-acetylene outfit complete with halide torch adaptor, 1 alcohol-fired halide torch, 1 electronic leak detector, 1 gauge manifold complete with refrigerant lines.
4. Obtain: Supplies – 1 sulphur dioxide spray can, 1 soap or synthetic suds dispenser, 1 color trace, 1 wiping cloth, 1 bottle ammonia, 1 12-in. length of 1/4 tubing with flare nuts and flare plugs.

TASK PROCEDURE (WEAR GOGGLES):
1. Install gauge manifold on refrigerating system and operate the system.
2. Test on several joints with: (1) Soap or synthetic suds, (2) Both oxy-acetylene and alcohol-fired halide torch leak detectors, (3) Electronic leak detector.
3. Loosen gauge manifold refrigeration line at high side connection very slowly until electronic tester indicates leak.
4. Apply the halide leak detectors; if no leak is found, loosen a fitting very slowly until flame color change indicates a leak.
5. Apply the suds test; if no leak is found, slowly loosen joint until suds bubbles indicate a leak.   1-5 √_____
6. Shut down system.
7. Put a drop of color leak trace liquid in a connecting tubing. Connect one end of tube to high side pressure. Plug the other end. Pressurize; slowly open plugged end of tube until color dye appears. Remove.
8. Use sulphur dioxide spray can on open ammonia bottle. Slightly loosen bottle stopper; apply sulphur dioxide spray, until a fog appears.   6-8 √_____

CLOSING THE STATION:
   Clean the station and return the materials to the tool crib.

DATA:
Electronic Leak Detector, Make_____ Model _____
Oxy-acetylene Halide Leak Detector, Make_____ Suds Unit, Make _____
Alcohol Halide Leak Detector, Make _____
Sulphur Dioxide Spray Can, Make_____ Dye Trace Make _____

Remarks:

TEST FOR LEAKS.

Indicate the best answer for each question below by encircling its letter.

1. Which refrigerant can be tested for leaks by using a halide leak detector?
   a. R-12.
   b. R-717.
   c. R-744.
   d. R-763.
   e. Air.

2. What color of the halide torch flame indicates a leak?
   a. Red.
   b. Blue.
   c. Yellow.
   d. Green.
   e. Colorless.

3. How does an electronic leak detector indicate a refrigerant leak?
   a. A flame color change.
   b. A meter reading, light or bell.
   c. A color change in tube.
   d. A color trace.
   e. Bubbles.

4. How does the leaking refrigerant reach the halide flame?
   a. It is mixed with the fuel.
   b. It is drawn through a sniffer tube.
   c. A pump is used.
   d. An aspirator is used.
   e. The refrigerant is in the air around the flame shield.

5. Why must the alcohol fuel be very clean?
   a. To obtain a good flame color.
   b. To enable the fuel to go through the small passage.
   c. To prevent corrosion.
   d. To build up enough pressure to keep the flame burning.
   e. To keep the alcohol from exploding.

INSTALL GAUGES ON AN EXTERNAL DRIVE REFRIGERATING SYSTEM

OBJECTIVE: Given an external drive system complete with service valves, and the necessary tools: install gauge manifold to obtain accurate readings.

REFERENCES: Required – Para. 2-71, 2-74, 11-27, 11-28, 11-82, 14-7, 14-8, 14-33, 14-34 and 14-109. Supplementary – Para. 14-42.

EQUIPMENT: An operating small external drive type refrigerating system charged with R-12, and a box of typical service valves.

PREPARATION PROCEDURE:
1. Study the various types of gauges and the construction of service valves by which gauges may be installed in a refrigerating system.   Study the reference paragraphs.
                                                                        TEST√ _____
2. Obtain: Tools – 1 8-in. adj. open end wrench, 1 pr. safety goggles, 1 1/4-in. valve stem wrench.
3. Obtain: Instruments – 1 gauge manifold complete with three flexible lines .
4. Obtain: Supplies – 1 wiping cloth, 1 oiler with refrigerant oil.

TASK PROCEDURE (WEAR GOGGLES):
1. Install the gauge manifold lines to the compressor SSV and the DSV.
2. Purge the gauge manifold and lines.
3. Operate the system to be sure that the operation is normal. Record the pressures.
                                                                        1-3 √ _____
4. Operate the compressor and adjust the valves to a position and pressure suitable for removing the compressor.   4√ _____
5. Close the liquid receiver service valve (LRSV) and operate the compressor and adjust the LRSV to a position suitable for removing the refrigerant control. Record the pressures.
6. Record the pressures at the time the system was ready for removing the compressor.
                                                                        5-6 √ _____
7. Record the conditions at the time that the system was ready for removing the automatic expansion valve.
8. Return the valves to normal operating settings. Operate a few minutes. Remove the gauge manifold.   7-8 √ _____

CLOSING THE STATION:
    Clean the station and return the materials to the tool crib.

DATA:
Tabulate the procedure for removing the gauge manifold:

1	3	5
2	4	6

Compound Gauge Make: _____ Scale Calibrations _____
Pressure Gauge Make: _____ Scale Calibrations _____
Gauge Fitting: Threads Type_____ Size _____

Remarks:

INSTALL GAUGES ON AN EXTERNAL DRIVE REFRIGERATING SYSTEM.

Indicate the best answer for each question below by encircling its letter.

1. How should a gauge opening plug be threaded into a hot service valve body?
   a. Loosely.
   b. Very tightly.
   c. Until all threads are in the body.
   d. Snugly.
   e. Up to a 30 foot pound torque.

2. What kind of threads are used in the gauge opening of a service valve?
   a. Pipe.
   b. NF.
   c. NC.
   d. National extra fine.
   e. Any kind of thread.

3. What happens when a two-way service valve stem is turned all the way out?
   a. It will come out.
   b. It closes the gauge opening.
   c. It closes the refrigerant line.
   d. It is front seated.
   e. Nothing.

4. How may a "frozen" valve stem be loosened?
   a. By using a larger wrench.
   b. By hammering on it.
   c. By heating the valve body.
   d. By using a pipe wrench.
   e. By using oil.

5. When should the service valve packing nut be loosened?
   a. Only if the valve stem turns with difficulty.
   b. Whenever the valve is used.
   c. Only to replace the packing.
   d. When the packing leaks.
   e. When the valve stem breaks.

REPAIR A LEAK USING EPOXY COMPOUNDS

OBJECTIVE: Given a leaking aluminum evaporator and an epoxy repair kit: repair the leak and test, and obtain a leakproof repair.

REFERENCES: Required – Para. 2-28 and 2-74.
Supplementary – Para. 11-62 and 11-82.

EQUIPMENT: Work station which provides a pressurized device, such as an evaporator or tube, which has a leak.

PREPARATION PROCEDURE:
1.   Study the step-by-step procedure for making an epoxy leak repair.

TEST√_____
2.   Obtain: Tools – 1 8-in. adj. wrench, 1 3/4-in. flare nut wrench, 1 1-in. flare nut wrench, 1 8-in. fine mill file, 1 pr. safety goggles.
3.   Obtain: Instruments – 1 0-150 psi gauge.
4.   Obtain: Supplies – 1 epoxy repair kit, 1 soap solution container, 1 brush for applying soap solution, 1 4-in. x 4-in. #0 sandpaper.

TASK PROCEDURE (WEAR GOGGLES):
1.   Pressurize the part in which the leak is suspected. Apply soap solution, and locate and mark the leak.
2.   Remove the part from the system, clean the surface surrounding the leak.

1-2 √_____
3.   Mix the epoxy compound according to the directions on the containers. Apply immediately to the surface to be repaired.
4.   It will require approximately 24 hours for the epoxy to completely harden to a condition for testing.
5.   After suitable hardening time, use 100 psi air pressure to test for leaks. Use soap solution.

3-5 √_____
6.   If there is still a leak, the task will have to be repeated.

CLOSING THE STATION:
Clean the station and return all materials to the tool crib.

DATA:

Epoxy Name: _____
Recommended Hardening Time: _____
Recommended Setting Time: _____

Remarks:

REPAIR A LEAK USING EPOXY COMPOUNDS.

Indicate the best answer for each question below by encircling its letter.

1. What is the most important requirement which applies to the preparation for making an epoxy repair?
   a. Well ventilated space.
   b. Proper surface for mixing.
   c. Space must be at the correct temperature.
   d. Humidity of space must be controlled.
   e. The part must be carefully cleaned.

2. What should be the pressure inside the part being repaired with epoxy compounds?
   a. It may be at normal operating pressure.
   b. It should be under a vacuum.
   c. It must be at atmospheric pressure.
   d. The pressure must be increased as the epoxy sets.
   e. The pressure does not matter.

3. What is the most desirable characteristic of an epoxy repair process?
   a. Very cheap.
   b. Takes very little time.
   c. Can be placed in service immediately.
   d. It is chemically inert.
   e. No preparatory cleaning required.

4. What is the recommended procedure for cleaning a surface preparatory to making an epoxy repair?
   a. Burn off joint with torch flame.
   b. Sand and clean with acetone.
   c. Clean with gasoline.
   d. Clean with steel wool and shellac.
   e. Clean with pumice and alcohol.

5. How is a large hole repaired using an epoxy compound?
   a. The same way.
   b. A large hole should be welded.
   c. Use a patch of metal.
   d. Use a screw plug.
   e. Arc spot the hole.

EVACUATE A SYSTEM

OBJECTIVE: Given a refrigerating system, and the necessary tools: evacuate the system of air and moisture to approved standards.

REFERENCES: Required – Para. 2-73, 2-74, 11-75, 11-76 and 11-82.
  Supplementary – Para. 1-22, 1-64, 14-10 and 14-109.

EQUIPMENT: A portable high vacuum pump similar to the vacuum pump shown in Figs. 11-106 and 11-107. Also, an operating refrigerating system which has been opened and is in need of being evacuated.

PREPARATION PROCEDURE:
1. Study the installation and service operations which require the use of a vacuum pump.
                                                                  TEST√ _____
2. Obtain: Tools – 1 8-in. adj. open end wrench, 1 service valve ratchet wrench, 1 3/4-in. flare nut wrench, 1 1-in. flare nut wrench, 1 pr. safety goggles.
3. Obtain: Instruments – 1 gauge manifold complete with refrigerant lines, 1 electronic high vacuum gauge.
4. Obtain: Supplies – 1 can refrigerant oil, 1 wiping cloth, 1 R-12 service cylinder and refrigerant.

TASK PROCEDURE (WEAR GOGGLES):
1. Inspect the vacuum pump oil. If dirty (dark color), replace the oil.
2. Install the gauge manifold.
3. Operate the refrigerator compressor with the discharge service valve closed and the gauge manifold set for purging, as shown in Figs. 11-104 or 14-23.
4. Shut off the refrigerant flow at the liquid receiver service valve. Operate the compressor to create a high vacuum. Exhaust to the atmosphere.
5. Connect the high vacuum pump to the center gauge manifold opening.
6. Operate the high vacuum pump and draw as high a vacuum as possible. Record.
                                                                  1-6 √ _____
7. Close the manifold valve and disconnect the gauge manifold. Open the service valve and return the system to normal operation.

CLOSING THE STATION:
  Clean the station and return the materials to the tool crib.

DATA:

Low-Side Pressure at Start _____
High-Side Pressure at Start _____
Refrigerant Control, Type _____
High Vacuum Pump, Make _____
Vacuum Obtained with High Vacuum Pump _____

Remarks:

EVACUATE A SYSTEM.

Indicate the best answer for each question below by encircling its letter.

1. Assuming that a compressor is in good condition, what limits the degree of vacuum that it will develop?
   a. Speed of compressor.
   b. Kind of refrigerant used.
   c. The temperature of the room.
   d. The amount of oil in the compressor.
   e. The clearance volume of the compressor.

2. What service operations may best be performed with the aid of a high vacuum pump?
   a. Setting a motor control.
   b. Checking the amount of refrigerant in a system.
   c. Checking the amount of oil in a system.
   d. Dehydration of a system.
   e. Setting the thermostatic expansion valve.

3. What instrument is often combined with the high vacuum pump as an assembly?
   a. A high vacuum gauge.
   b. A drier.
   c. A gauge manifold.
   d. A filter.
   e. An acid indicator.

4. What is a good vacuum, measured in millimetres of mercury column?
   a. 5-10
   b. 25-35
   c. 40-50
   d. 55-65
   e. 70-80

5. What is the micron equivalent of 1 in. of vacuum?

   a. 500
   b. 2,000
   c. 2,500
   d. 20,000
   e. 25,400

Task No. 1-20 Task Grade _____
Name _____
Date _____ Class _____

USE A SERVICE CYLINDER

OBJECTIVE: Given a refrigerating system, and the necessary tools: charge the system and then discharge one lb. of refrigerant.

REFERENCES: Required – Para. 11-26 through 11-30, 11-82, 14-11, 14-12, 14-30, and 14-109.

EQUIPMENT: A small commercial open type refrigerating system partially charged with R-12.

PREPARATION PROCEDURE:
1. Study the refrigerant cylinder and system assigned. Study the reference paragraphs.
   TEST √_____

2. Obtain: Tools – 1 ratchet valve stem wrench, 1 set open end wrenches, 1 set sockets and handles, 1 8-in. adj. open end wrench, 1 pr. safety goggles.
3. Obtain: Instruments – 1 gauge manifold, complete with refrigerant lines, 1 weighing scale, 1 leak detector, 1 charging cylinder.
4. Obtain: Supplies – 1 wiping cloth.

TASK PROCEDURE (WEAR GOGGLES):
1. Install the gauge manifold in the system.
2. Connect the cylinder, test for leaks, and charge 1 lb. R-12 into the system low side.
3. Remove the refrigerant cylinder.
   1-3 √_____
4. Connect the service cylinder to the system and test for leaks.
5. Remove up to 1 lb. of refrigerant from the system and store it in the service cylinder. Use a weighing scale.
6. Remove the service cylinder and gauge manifold.
   4-6 √_____
7. Shut down the system.

CLOSING THE STATION:
   Clean up the station and return the materials to the tool crib.

DATA:

System, Make _____ _____ Model _____ Type _____
Service Cylinder, Make _____ Model _____ Cylinder Capacity _____
Amount Charged into System _____
Amount Removed from System _____

Remarks:

USE A SERVICE CYLINDER.

Indicate the best answer for each question below by encircling its letter.

1. Why must one be careful of the amount of refrigerant put into a cylinder?
    a. Always allow for the expansion of the gas.
    b. Always allow for expansion of the cylinder.
    c. Always allow for expansion of possible moisture.
    d. If full of liquid, the cylinder will burst.
    e. Refrigerant is expensive.

2. What will liquid refrigerant do to the eyes and skin?
    a. Burn the eyes and skin.
    b. Freeze the eyes and skin.
    c. Irritate the eyes and skin.
    d. Nothing.
    e. Lubricate the eyes.

3. Why should the low side pressure be kept within reasonable limits when charging refrigerant into the low side?
    a. To keep from overworking the compressor.
    b. To prevent liquid pumping.
    c. To speed up the operation.
    d. To prevent freezing the cylinder.
    e. To prevent rupturing the cylinder.

4. Why does heating the cylinder with hot water speed up the charging operation?
    a. Warm gas pumps better.
    b. The liquid evaporates faster.
    c. It removes the oil from the refrigerant.
    d. It keeps the charging line clean.
    e. It warms the compressor.

5. Why must the head pressure be controlled?
    a. To maintain the proper condensing pressure.
    b. To prevent injury to the system.
    c. To speed up the operation.
    d. To stop leaks.
    e. To save refrigerant.

MODERN REFRIGERATION AND AIR CONDITIONING
MODULE 2 - BASIC ELECTRICAL LABORATORY TASKS

No.	NAME	TASK TEST GRADE	SIG.	TASK GRADE	SIG.	TASK DATE
2-1	Electrical Connections					
2-2	Use a Voltmeter, Ammeter and Ohmmeter					
2-3	Trace a 24V Electrical Circuit					
2-4	Trace a 120V Electrical Circuit					
2-5	Dismantle and Assemble a Single-Phase Motor					
2-6	Check and Adjust a Thermostat					
2-7	Check a Current Relay					
2-8	Check a Potential Relay					
2-9	Check a Thermal Relay					
2-10	Check a Solid State Relay					
2-11	Check a Solenoid Valve					
2-12	Test an Open Type Capacitor Start Electric Motor					
2-13	Test a Capacitor Start Hermetic Motor					
2-14	Test and Operate a Capacitor Start-Capacitor Run Hermetic Motor.					
2-15	Replace a Relay and Overload Protector					
2-16	Replace a Condenser Fan Motor					
2-17	Replace an Evaporator Fan Motor					
2-18	**Check All Electrical Components of a 120V Refrigerating System**					
2-19	Check a 120V System with a 24V Control Circuit					
2-20	Trace the Circuits and Draw the Wiring Diagram for a Commercial Refrigerating System					

SOME SAFETY RULES WHEN HANDLING ELECTRICAL CIRCUITS

ALWAYS DISCONNECT THE ELECTRICAL POWER AND MAKE SURE NO ONE CAN TURN IT ON WHILE THE ELECTRICAL PARTS OF A REFRIGERATOR OR AIR CONDITIONING SYSTEM ARE BEING REMOVED, REPAIRED, REPLACED, ETC.

All of us can see or hear what electricity can do, such as light, power, heat, communications. But, it is hard to be alert against the dangers of electricity, because this energy is hidden in the wires (conductors). What causes electrical energy to hurt and even kill people is that the body or parts of the body can become an electrical conductor. When this happens, all too often the electricity will burn part of the body and/or cause muscle spasms, injure the nervous system, stop the heart from beating, etc.

A circuit that can give one a shock should never be used. When anyone feels the shock, it is too late!

One cannot be too careful. Electrical shock can be avoided if just a few safety measures are remembered and practiced.

Test the system with a voltmeter to make sure it has no potential. (Power off: no charged capacitor in the circuit.)

Insulate the body as much as possible; use tools with insulated handles, be sure the material one is standing on is an insulator (wood, concrete, etc.) and that this material is dry. If a damp situation cannot be avoided, wear rubber gloves and rubber boots.

Voltages above 24V can cause current (amperes) to flow through parts of the body. Remember, most circuits are at least 120V and 15 amperes. Only 0.025 of an ampere (25 milliamperes) across the heart can kill.

Lock the switches open to prevent someone from closing them during installation or service operations. The switch should also be tagged to warn other people. Or, remove the fuses and put them in a pocket or tool kit. Put a note on the switch and fuse box to warn people not to close this circuit.

Always short a capacitor with a resistor before touching its terminals. If it is charged, it may discharge 200 to 500 volts into one's body.

If a person has been subjected to electrical shock, make the person lie down and then keep them warm. If unconscious, artifical resuscitation is necessary. Always call a physician if someone has suffered severe electrical shock.

Replace worn electric wires or those which have brittle insulation. (To test: Poor insulation will crack when the wire is bent into a tight loop.)

Use only screwdrivers with completely insulated handles (wood or plastic). Use only wrenches and pliers with insulated handles. This habit is double insurance against electrical shocks.

Always use instruments to check a circuit to see if it is electrically charged before handling wires, terminal, or parts.

Always solder or crimp solid metal terminals on the ends of stranded wire. Avoid using stranded wire ends to attach the wire to the terminals.

Electrically ground all metal parts of a refrigeration system to eliminate any danger of receiving a shock if the circuit should become grounded to the frame of a cabinet or a part of the mechanism.

Always use the correct size fuse in a circuit. An oversize fuse may allow fires and burned-out equipment.

ELECTRICAL CONNECTIONS

OBJECTIVE: Given a refrigeration electrical circuit, wire, terminals and the necessary tools: replace the wires in a satisfactory manner.

REFERENCES: Required - Para. 6-20, 6-76 through 6-80, 7-30, 8-37 and 8-43.

EQUIPMENT: A complete operating domestic refrigerator of automatic defrost or of no-frost design; or a mock-up panel board.

PREPARATION PROCEDURE:
1. Study the reference paragraphs.   TEST√ _____
2. Obtain: Tools - 1 terminal replacement pliers, 1 set reg. screwdrivers, 1 set Phillips screwdrivers, 1 8-in. electrician's pliers, 1 6-in. slim nose pliers, 1 soldering gun.
3. Obtain: Instruments - 1 0 to 100,000 ohmmeter, 1 test light, 1 0-25 a-c ammeter, 1 0-300 a-c voltmeter.
4. Obtain: Supplies - 1 roll #14 insulated stranded wire, 1 roll #14 insulated solid wire, 1 roll 50-50 solder, 1 can solder flux, 1 roll plastic tape, 1 box grommet terminals, 1 box wire terminals (variety), 1 wiping cloth.

TASK PROCEDURE:
1. Make practice connections with both stranded wire and solid wire. Remove just enough insulation to mount the terminal. Do not nick the wire or wire strands.
                                                            1 √ _____
2. Replace all the wiring on the refrigerator or practice board, or rewire the system assigned.
3. Test all the wiring for continuity with the test light.
4. Test all the terminals, connections, and wiring with the ohmmeter.
                                                            2-4 √ _____

CLOSING THE STATION:
    Clean the work station and return the material to the tool crib.

DATA:

Stranded Wire, Size _____ Insulation, Kind _____ Thickness _____
Solid Wire, Size _____ Insulation, Kind _____ Thickness _____
Solid Wire Terminal Screw Size _____ Type _____
Soldered Terminal, Wire Size _____ Terminal Type _____
Test Light Results, Terminals _____ Wires _____
Ohmmeter Results, Terminals _____ Wires _____

Remarks:

ELECTRICAL CONNECTIONS.

Indicate the best answer for each question below by encircling its letter.

1. How should a solid wire be wrapped around a terminal screw?
   a. Opposite the direction the screw turns as it is tightened.
   b. The same direction the screw is turned as it is tightened.
   c. It should be wrapped twice around the screw.
   d. It should be kept straight.
   e. A terminal should be used.

2. Which of the following is the largest conductor?
   a. No. 8
   b. No. 10
   c. No. 12
   d. No. 14
   e. No. 16

3. What should be heated when soldering a terminal to a stranded wire?
   a. The wire only.
   b. The terminal only.
   c. The solder only.
   d. The flux and solder only.
   e. The wire and terminal only.

4. How should stranded wire be connected to a screw terminal?
   a. Wrap wire clockwise around screw.
   b. Wrap wire counter-clockwise around screw.
   c. Solder the wire, then wrap around the screw.
   d. Fasten a terminal to wire end.
   e. Separate the strands of wire and wrap around screw in both directions.

5. What should be the resistance across a clean tight terminal?
   a. 0 ohms.
   b. 50 ohms.
   c. 5,000 ohms.
   d. 50,000 ohms.
   e. 100,000 ohms.

USE A VOLTMETER, AMMETER, AND OHMMETER

OBJECTIVE: Given a complete operating refrigerating system, and the necessary tools: electrically check the electrical circuits for satisfactory operation.

REFERENCES: Required – Para. 6-11, 6-14, 6-20, 6-79, 6-80, 8-1, 8-28, 8-43, 10-15, 10-45, 11-8, 11-21 and 11-82. Supplementary – Para. 7-45 and 7-50.

EQUIPMENT: An operating domestic refrigerator which provides a frozen food compartment and an automatic ice maker.

PREPARATION PROCEDURE:
1. Study the reference paragraphs for the circuits and controls used on a modern domestic refrigerator which has a frozen foods compartment and an automatic ice maker. TEST√_____
2. Obtain: Tools – 1 6-in. regular screwdriver, 1 2-in. blade putty knife, 1 6-in. Phillip's head screwdriver, 1 pr. safety goggles.
3. Obtain: Instruments – 2 glass-stemmed thermometers calibrated in degrees F, 1 test light, 1 electrical combination voltmeter, ammeter, and ohmmeter (multimeter).
4. Obtain: Supplies – 1 wiping cloth.

TASK PROCEDURE (WEAR GOGGLES):
1. Remove the motor compartment door and necessary trim in order to expose the wiring.
2. Starting with the power supply plug, study and then sketch the wiring diagram for the refrigerator. Show the separate circuits as follows:
    a. The motor control thermostat and motor compressor circuit.
    b. The defrost, or, if "no-frost" system, show the fan circuits.
    c. The cabinet light circuits.
    d. The ice maker circuits.
    e. The condenser fan circuit.   1-2√_____
3. Check and record the closed circuit voltage and amperage of each circuit.
4. Check the resistance of each circuit (POWER OFF!).
5. Operate the refrigerator and record the following temperatures:
    a. The temp. inside food storage compartment_____°F.
    b. The temp. inside freezer compartment_____°F.
6. Replace all covers and doors and leave the refrigerator in operation.
7. Have wiring diagram checked and approved by the instructor.   3-7√_____

CLOSING THE STATION:

   Clean the work station and return all materials to the tool crib.

DATA:
Refrigerator, Make_____Model_____Type_____Size_____
Relay, Make_____Model_____Type_____
Motor-Compressor, Make_____Model_____Safety Devices_____
Evaporator Fan-Motor, Make_____Model_____
Condenser Fan-Motor, Make_____Model_____
Automatic Ice Cube Maker, Make_____Model_____
EER Rating _____

	Voltage	Amperage	Resistance
Motor Compressor Circuit			
Condenser Fan Circuit			
Evaporator Fan Circuit			
Defrost Circuit			
Ice Maker Circuit			
Cabinet Light Circuit			

	Voltmeter	Ammeter	Ohmmeter
Maximum Reading			
Smallest Division on Scale			

USE A VOLTMETER, AMMETER, AND OHMMETER.

Indicate the best answer for each question below by encircling its letter.

1. What controls the cabinet temperature in most household refrigerators?
   a. A thermostatic expansion valve.
   b. A capillary tube.
   c. A thermostat in the frozen foods compartment.
   d. A thermostat in the perishable foods compartment.
   e. The amount of ice in the automatic ice maker.

2. If a refrigerator does not operate (run), what is the first circuit which should be checked?
   a. The wall outlet.
   b. The thermostat motor control.
   c. The cabinet light circuit.
   d. The motor relay.
   e. The electrical defrost circuit.

3. What circuits are usually broken when the refrigerator door is opened?
   a. All.
   b. Light only.
   c. Light and motor.
   d. Fans and lights.
   e. Fans only.

4. How is a voltmeter connected to a circuit?
   a. Parallel.
   b. Series.
   c. Only across switches.
   d. Only across motors.
   e. Only across resistances.

5. Why is an ohmmeter used only with the power off?
   a. Accuracy.
   b. To reduce inductance.
   c. To reduce resistance.
   d. Power will ruin ohmmeter.
   e. It makes no difference.

TRACE A 24V ELECTRICAL CIRCUIT

OBJECTIVE: Given a 24V circuit and a test light and/or ohmmeter: check the components and wiring of the circuit.

REFERENCES: Required – Para. 6-79, 6-80, 7-44, 7-50, 8-1 and 8-43.
Supplementary – Para. 6-11, 6-14, 6-20, 8-28, 20-14, 20-19, 20-41, 20-55, 24-5, 24-16, 24-23, 24-43 and 24-53.

EQUIPMENT: A heating or cooling system with a stepdown transformer and a low voltage control system.

PREPARATION PROCEDURE:
1. Study the system and the paragraph references.   TEST√_____
2. Obtain: Tools – 1 4-in. regular screwdriver. 1 6-in. slim nose pliers.
3. Obtain: Instruments – 1 electrical multimeter (volts, amps, ohms), 1 test light.
4. Obtain: Supplies – 1 wiping cloth, 1 square fine sandpaper.

TASK PROCEDURE:
1. With power off, check the continuity of the 24V circuit using an ohmmeter or test light.
2. With power on, check voltage and amperage of:
    a. Circuit.   d. Solenoid or relay.
    b. Transformer output.   e. Limit control.
    c. Thermostat.
3. Clean terminals and/or replace terminals if faults are found.
4. Replace components if faulty.   1-4√_____
5. Make circuit operational and leave in operating condition.   5√_____

CLOSING THE STATION:
Clean up station and return materials to the tool crib.

DATA:	Continuity (Power off)	Amperage	Voltage
Circuit			
Transformer			
Thermostat			
Relay			
Solenoid			
Limit Switch			

Transformer, Make _____ Capacity _____ VA _____
Thermostat, Make _____ Maximum Setting _____ Minimum Setting _____
Relay, Make _____ Rating, Watts _____ Voltage _____
Solenoid, Make _____ Rating _____
Limit Switch, Make _____ Maximum Setting _____ Minimum Setting _____

Remarks:

TRACE A 24V ELECTRICAL CIRCUIT.

Indicate the best answer for each question below by encircling its letter.

1. What kind of electricity does the 24V circuit use?
    a. Static.
    b. a-c.
    c. d-c.
    d. Line.
    e. Rectified.

2. Are good connections more important at low voltages?
    a. Yes.
    b. No.
    c. They are the same.
    d. Only soldered connections for low voltages.
    e. Only mechanical connections for low voltages.

3. Is low voltage wiring as well insulated as power wiring?
    a. Yes.
    b. No.
    c. They are the same.
    d. They both must be in steel conduit.
    e. Bare, solid wires are used for low voltage.

4. What is a popular ammeter?
    a. One with needle point leads.
    b. One that is placed in parallel with the load.
    c. One with movable tongs (clamps).
    d. One with a 1000 ampere scale reading.
    e. 0-5 ampere scale meter.

5. What does the relay control?
    a. Thermostat.
    b. A pressurestat.
    c. The normal voltage circuit.
    d. The lighting circuit.
    e. The amount of current.

Task No. 2-4 Task Grade _____
Name _____
Date _____ Class _____

TRACE A 120V ELECTRICAL CIRCUIT

OBJECTIVE: Given a complete refrigerating system, a combination voltmeter, ammeter, and ohmmeter (multimeter), and the necessary tools: check all the electrical wiring and components.

REFERENCES: Required – Para. 6-11, 6-20, 6-79, 6-80, 8-1, 8-8, 8-9, 8-17, 8-28, 8-43, 10-15, 10-45, 11-8 and 11-82. Supplementary – Para. 11-21, 14-85 and 14-109.

EQUIPMENT: An operating refrigerating system.

PREPARATION PROCEDURE:
1. Study the electrical circuits and controls used on a modern refrigerating system. Study the reference paragraphs.   TEST√ _____
2. Obtain: Tools – 1 6-in. regular screwdriver, 1 2-in. blade putty knife, 1 6-in. Phillip's head screwdriver, 1 pr. safety goggles.
3. Obtain: Instruments – 2 glass-stemmed thermometers calibrated in degrees F, 1 test light, 1 combination voltmeter, ammeter, and ohmmeter (multimeter).
4. Obtain: Supplies – 1 wiping cloth.

TASK PROCEDURE (WEAR GOGGLES):
1. Starting with the power supply plug, sketch the wiring diagram for the system. Show the separate circuits as follows: a. The motor control thermostat and motor compressor circuit. b. The defrost system. c. The door switches and light circuits. d. The ice maker circuits. e. The condenser fan circuit. f. The evaporator fan circuit.
                                                                        1 √ _____

2. Operate the system and record the following temperatures:
     a. The evaporator _____ °F.
     b. The condenser _____ °F.
3. Record type of motor control relay used on this refrigerator.
4. Record the voltage and amperage of each circuit.   2-4 √ _____

CLOSING THE STATION:
     Clean the work station and return the material to the tool crib.

DATA:
Refrigerating System, Make_____ Model_____
               Type_____ Size_____
Relay, Make_____ Model_____ Type_____
Motor-Compressor, Make_____ Model_____ Safety Devices_____
Evaporator Fan-Motor, Make_____ Model_____
Condenser Fan-Motor, Make_____ Model_____
Automatic Ice Cube Maker, Make_____ Model_____

	Motor-Compressor	Evaporator Fan	Condenser Fan	Defrost Unit
Amperage				
Voltage				

Remarks:

TRACE A 120V ELECTRICAL CIRCUIT.

Indicate the best answer for each question below by encircling its letter.

1. Refer to Figs. 8-8, 8-10, 8-11, 8-12 and 8-13 in the text. Which one of these differential adjustment settings will provide the most uniform normal temperature?
   a. Fig. 8-8 A.
   b. Fig. 8-10 A-1.
   c. Fig. 8-11 B-1.
   d. Fig. 8-12 A-2.
   e. Fig. 8-13 A-2.

2. Refer to Fig. 8-27 in the text. What is the purpose of the cam on the ice maker mechanism?
   a. It controls the water in the unit.
   b. It controls the heating of the mold.
   c. It controls the amount of ice made.
   d. It controls the freezing time.
   e. It controls the entire operating cycle.

3. What is the condition of the thermostat if the voltage across the terminals is 120V?
   a. The points are closed.
   b. The points are open.
   c. The power is off.
   d. Evaporator is too warm.
   e. Thermostat is broken.

4. What other circuit besides the motor-compressor does the thermostat control?
   a. Lights.
   b. Condenser fan motor.
   c. None.
   d. The ice maker.
   e. Butter conditioner.

5. Is the relay coil always in the circuit?
   a. Yes.
   b. No.
   c. Only thermal relays.
   d. Only current relays.
   e. Only potential relays.

DISMANTLE AND ASSEMBLE A SINGLE-PHASE MOTOR

OBJECTIVE: Given a single-phase motor, and the necessary tools: dismantle the motor, assemble, test it, and return it to satisfactory operating condition.

REFERENCES: Required – Para. 4-49, 6-48, 6-77, 6-80, 7-2 through 7-5, 7-8, 7-9, 7-10, 7-39 through 7-42 and 7-50.
   Supplementary – Para. 7-34, 7-36 and 14-85 through 14-89.

EQUIPMENT: Work station which provides a work bench with vise and trays to receive small parts, screws, nuts and bolts; a fractional horsepower induction motor; a motor test stand.

PREPARATION PROCEDURE:
1.   Study the reference paragraphs and an external drive refrigeration motor.

TEST√_____

2.   Obtain: Tools – 1 6-in. adj. end wrench, 1 1/2 x 5/8-in. box end wrench, 1 6-in. screwdriver, 1 scriber, 1 pr. safety goggles.
3.   Obtain: Instruments – 1 1-in. micrometer, 1 0-300 volt a-c voltmeter, 1 0-25 amp. a-c ammeter, 1 speed indicator.
4.   Obtain: Supplies – 1 wiping cloth, 1 oiler with SAE 30 oil.

TASK PROCEDURE (WEAR GOGGLES):
1.   Inspect the motor carefully before dismantling. Run the motor and record voltage, amperage, and rpm.
2.   Scribe a mark on end bells and stator for alignment. Remove the end bells and inspect the bearings.
3.   Remove the rotor from the stator. Note the starting device mechanism.
4.   Test the stator for circuit continuity and ground.
5.   Test the capacitor.
6.   Assemble the motor.
7.   Mount the motor on the test stand preparatory to making a running test.

1-7√_____

8.   Connect the motor to the power line through a fused switch, and operate the motor.
9.   Mount the motor on the motor test stand. Measure and record the torque, rpm, voltage and current draw.

8-9√_____

CLOSING THE STATION:
   Clean up the station and return all materials to the tool crib.

DATA:

Torque		Current Draw		rpm	
Nameplate Rating: hp		rpm		Current Draw	
Motor, Make		Type		Voltage	
Phase	Capacitor, Size		rpm	End Play	
Before Dismantling, Amperes		Volts		Speed	
After Assembly, Amperes		Volts		Speed	

Remarks:

DISMANTLE AND ASSEMBLE A SINGLE-PHASE MOTOR.

Indicate the best answer for each question below by encircling its letter.

1. What is an open circuit?
   a. Electricity cannot flow.
   b. Insulation is removed.
   c. All wiring is exposed.
   d. Cover is removed.
   e. Wiring is not hermetically sealed.

2. What controls the type of motor selected for an open type refrigerating system?
   a. Type of refrigerant control used.
   b. Type of motor control used.
   c. Speed of the compressor.
   d. Refrigerant used.
   e. Temperature in the refrigerated space.

3. If a certain design of motor does not have the capacity to start under a load, which type of refrigerant control should be used?
   a. Automatic expansion valve.
   b. Low side float.
   c. Capillary tube.
   d. High side float.
   e. Thermostatic expansion valve.

4. Which of the open type motors may use a rotor having a winding?
   a. Capacitor.
   b. Repulsion start induction.
   c. Any single phase motor.
   d. Any motor if a pressure type motor control is used.
   e. Direct current motor only.

5. At what part of the refrigerating cycle is the motor current the highest?
   a. At the instant of starting.
   b. At the time that the condenser pressure is the highest.
   c. At the time that the low side pressure is highest.
   d. At the time that the low side pressure is lowest.
   e. No difference; same at all times.

CHECK AND ADJUST A THERMOSTAT

OBJECTIVE: Given a refrigerating system with a thermostatic motor control and the necessary tools:
remove, check, install and adjust the thermostat to a satisfactory cycle.

REFERENCES: Required – Para. 4-23, 4-61, 8-2 through 8-13, 8-18 through 8-21, 8-43, 12-37,
12-39, 12-40, 12-41 and 12-74.
Supplementary – Para. 24-3 through 24-15 and 24-53.

EQUIPMENT: A domestic unit, a replacement thermostat, and a variable temperature water bath.

PREPARATION PROCEDURE:
1. Study the system and the reference paragraphs.   TEST√_____
2. Obtain: Tools – 1 4-in. screwdriver, 1 6-in. adj. end wrench, 1 pr. safety goggles.
3. Obtain: Instruments – 1 pan for temperature water bath, 1 0-220 °F thermometer,
1 test light, 1 relay tester.
4. Obtain: Supplies – 1 4-in. sq. fine sandpaper, 1 5-lbs. of water ice, 1 2-lbs. fine
rock salt, 1 can cleaning fluid.

TASK PROCEDURE (WEAR GOGGLES):
1. If the system is nonoperational, check it with motor starting relay tester. Determine if
thermostat is faulty through the use of a test light. If it is nonoperational, proceed with
the next step.   1√_____
2. Remove the motor control from the unit, being careful not to damage the power element.
3. Test the control. Determine the cut-in and cut-out temperatures by means of a temperature
bath. (Salt, ice and water may be used for a temperature bath, but a refrigerating
temperature bath is better.)
4. Install the control in a circuit in series with a light. Determine the type of range and
differential adjustments.
5. Repair or replace the control. Adjust the cut-in to 25 °F and the cut-out to 15 °F.
6. Install the control in the unit and operate the system.   2-6√_____

CLOSING THE STATION:
Clean up the station and return all materials to the tool crib.

DATA:
Make of Control_____ Type_____ Serial No. _____
Range Adjustment: Method: Screw_____ Knob_____ Nut_____
Differential Adjustment: Type_____
Method: Screw_____ Knob_____ Nut_____
Capillary Tube, Length: _____ Diameter_____ Bulb Dia._____
Overload Cut-Out: Yes_____ No_____ Rating_____
Original Settings: Cut-In_____ Cut-Out_____
One Turn Range Adj. Changes--Cut-In Temp._____ Degrees
Cut-Out Temp._____ Degrees
One Turn Diff. Adj. Changes-- Cut-in Temp._____ Degrees
Cut-Out Temp._____ Degrees

Remarks:

CHECK AND ADJUST A THERMOSTAT.

Indicate the best answer for each question below by encircling its letter.

1. What is one type of differential control?
    a. Range.
    b. Temperature.
    c. Cut-in only.
    d. Pressure.
    e. Cycling.

2. Where are thermostatic motor control bulbs usually located?
    a. In the brine.
    b. On the top of evaporator.
    c. On the bottom of the evaporator.
    d. On the side of the evaporator.
    e. At the outlet of the evaporator.

3. How may a thermostat be tested and adjusted?
    a. With a brine bath.
    b. With a pressure pump.
    c. With an electric heating coil.
    d. With a vacuum pump.
    e. With air pressure.

4. With what is the thermostatic element charged?
    a. Alcohol and water.
    b. Sulphur dioxide.
    c. Methyl chloride.
    d. R-12
    e. A volatile liquid.

5. Why must the thermostatic bulb be clamped firmly to the evaporator?
    a. To enable good heat transfer.
    b. To stop rattles.
    c. To prevent leaks.
    d. To make a good electrical ground.
    e. To prevent breakage.

CHECK A CURRENT RELAY

OBJECTIVE: Given a hermetic refrigerating system with a current relay and the proper tools and instruments: check the relay for correct operation.

REFERENCES: Required – Para. 7-10, 7-11, 7-15, 7-19, 7-24, 7-50, 8-23, 8-24, 8-28 and 8-43.
Supplementary – Para. 11-19, 11-20, 11-21, 11-82 and 14-90.

EQUIPMENT: An operating hermetic system which has a current relay.

PREPARATION PROCEDURE:
1. Study carefully text Figs. 8-33 through 8-38, and Fig. 8-46.   TEST√ _____
2. Obtain: Tools – 1 4-in. screwdriver, 1 6-in. pr. diagonal pliers, 1 6-in. adj. wrench, 1 8-in. linesman's pliers, 1 electric soldering gun, 1 pr. safety goggles.
3. Obtain: Instruments – 1 electric analyzer with a built-in variable capacitor and a manual switch for closing the starting circuit, 1 electrical combination voltmeter, ammeter, and ohmmeter (multimeter), 1 test lamp.
4. Obtain: Supplies – 1 wiping cloth, 1 4-in. square 00 sandpaper, 1 roll plastic tape.

TASK PROCEDURE (WEAR GOGGLES):
1. Check the complete unit. Start the unit if possible.
2. If the unit will not start, disconnect the motor leads (discharge the capacitor) and connect the test analyzer. If the unit starts satisfactorily with the analyzer, then the trouble is in the external electrical circuit, either in the relay, the capacitor, the thermostat, the wiring, or the overload protector.
3. Check the overload protector with the test lamp or with ohmmeter. If it is operational, continue.   1-3√ _____
4. Disconnect the relay from the circuit and substitute either a good relay or the relay section of the analyzer (consult the analyzer instructions). Leave the old capacitor in the circuit. Be very careful if soldered connections are used. Label each wire removed to aid correct rewiring.
5. The replacement relay must be an exact replica (electrically) of the original. If at all possible use a genuine replacement part.
6. Try to start the unit again. If it starts, the trouble was somewhere in the relay.   4-6√ _____

CLOSING THE STATION:
Clean up the station and return all materials to the tool crib.

DATA:

Hermetic System, Name _____ Model _____ Year _____
            Serial No. _____ Type _____
Refrigerant, Kind _____ Amount _____
Motor, Horsepower _____ Volts _____
      Starting Amperes _____ Running Amperes _____
Overload Protector, Make _____ Capacity _____
Relay, Make _____ Model _____
      Serial No. _____ Type _____

Remarks:

CHECK A CURRENT RELAY.

Indicate the best answer for each question below by encircling its letter.

1. What type of relay does not need electromagnets?
   a. Magnetic type.
   b. Voltage type.
   c. Amperage type.
   d. Hot wire type.
   e. Weight type.

2. What may be wrong if the relay takes too long before the starting circuit is opened?
   a. The capacitor is shorted.
   b. The starting winding is grounded.
   c. The voltage is too high.
   d. The unit is overloaded.
   e. The unit is too cold.

3. What circuit is energized after the motor reaches operating speed?
   a. Both starting and running winding.
   b. Only the running winding.
   c. Only the starting winding.
   d. None of them.
   e. Only the relay circuit.

4. What special precaution must be taken with a weight-type operated relay?
   a. None.
   b. It must be carefully leveled.
   c. It must be kept cool.
   d. It must be over capacity.
   e. It must be noise insulated.

5. Why must relay covers be kept as tight as possible?
   a. It is not necessary.
   b. Dust will cause the points to deteriorate.
   c. To keep the unit cool.
   d. To keep the unit warm.
   e. To minimize relay noise.

CHECK A POTENTIAL RELAY

OBJECTIVE: Given a hermetic refrigerating system with a potential relay and the necessary tools
and instruments: check the relay for correct operation.

REFERENCES: Required – Para. 7-10, 7-11, 7-12, 7-15, 7-48, 7-50, 8-25, 8-28 and 8-43.
Supplementary – Para. 11-19, 11-20, 11-21 and 11-82.

EQUIPMENT: A refrigerating system which has a potential relay.

PREPARATION PROCEDURE:
1.   Study the domestic unit assigned; also, Figs. 8-41, 8-42, and 8-47. TEST √ _____
2.   Obtain: Tools – 1 4-in. screwdriver, 1 6-in. diagonal pliers, 1 pr. safety goggles.
3.   Obtain: Instruments – 1 motor-starting relay tester, 1 electrical combination voltmeter,
ammeter and ohmmeter (multimeter), 1 test light.
4.   Obtain: Supplies – 1 roll of 1/2-in. plastic tape, 1 4-in. square of 00 sandpaper,
1 wiping cloth.

TASK PROCEDURE (WEAR GOGGLES):
1.   Check the complete unit and start it if possible.
2.   If the unit will not start, disconnect the motor leads and connect the test analyzer.
If the unit starts satisfactorily with the analyzer, the problem is in the external
electrical circuit and not in the motor.
3.   Check the external circuit, thermostat, wiring, overload, etc.; if they check out
satisfactorily, continue.
4.   Remove the relay from the circuit and substitute a good relay or use the relay analyzer.
If the relay is bad, replace it.   1-4√ _____
5.   Reassemble the unit using the new relay. Start the unit. If it is now operational, the
trouble was in the relay.   5√ _____

CLOSING THE STATION:
Clean the station and return all materials to the tool crib.

DATA:

Hermetic System, Name _____ Model _____ Year _____
                    Serial Number _____ Type _____
Motor: Starting Amperes _____ Running Amperes _____
Refrigerant: Kind _____ Amount _____
Motor: Horsepower _____ Volts _____
        Starting Amperes _____ Running Amperes _____
Overload Protector _____ Capacity _____
Relay: Make _____ Model _____
       Serial No. _____ Type _____

Remarks:

CHECK A POTENTIAL RELAY.

Indicate the best answer for each question below by encircling its letter.

1. How many basic types of relays are used on hermetic systems?
   a. One.
   b. Two.
   c. Three.
   d. Four.
   e. Five.

2. What is the purpose of the relay?
   a. Permits electricity to flow through the running winding until the motor reaches 2/3 of its speed and then opens the running winding.
   b. Permits electricity to flow through the starting winding until the motor reaches 1/3 of its speed and then opens the starting winding.
   c. To prevent the overheating of the running winding.
   d. To prevent burnout from high temperatures.
   e. To control the box temperature.

3. What is the basis of operation of the potential relay?
   a. An increase in voltage across the relay as the unit approaches and reaches its rated speed.
   b. A decrease in amperage as the unit approaches and reaches its rated speed.
   c. The difference in magnetic impulses.
   d. The potential difference between the two magnetic forces.
   e. The operation of a magnetic coil connected to the solenoid.

4. In what position are the points in a potential relay during the off cycle?
   a. Closed.
   b. Midway.
   c. Open.
   d. This is dependent upon the unit.
   e. There are no points.

5. If an exact potential relay replacement is not available, what may be substituted for it?
   a. Replace with a hot wire relay.
   b. Use one with a higher voltage rating.
   c. Use one with a lower voltage rating.
   d. Replace with a current relay.
   e. Place a solid wire between the terminals.

CHECK A THERMAL RELAY

OBJECTIVE: Given a hermetic refrigerating system with a thermal relay and the necessary tools and instruments: check the thermal relay to approved operational efficiency.

REFERENCES: Required - Para. 7-10, 7-11, 7-19, 8-22, 8-23, 8-26 and 8-43.
      Supplementary - Para. 7-47, 7-48, 7-50, 8-28, 11-19, 11-20, 11-21, 11-82, 14-90 and 14-109.

EQUIPMENT: An operating hermetic system which has a thermal relay.

PREPARATION PROCEDURE:
1. Study carefully text Figs. 8-43 through 8-47.   TEST√ _____
2. Obtain: Tools - 1 4-in. screwdriver, 1 6-in. diagonal plier, 1 6-in. adj. wrench, 1 electric soldering gun, 1 pr. safety goggles.
3. Obtain: Instruments - 1 electrical combination voltmeter, ammeter and ohmmeter (multimeter), 1 test light, 1 relay tester.
4. Obtain: Supplies - 1 wiping cloth, 1 roll of 1/2-in. plastic tape, 1 4-in. sq. of 00 sandpaper.

TASK PROCEDURE (WEAR GOGGLES):

1. Check the complete unit; start the unit if possible.
2. Check the other parts of the circuit; the motor, capacitor, overload cut-out and thermostat; make certain that the proper fuse size has been used in the main circuit.
3. If all above parts check out okay, check the relay tester.
4. Check the system with the analyzer.   1-4√ _____
5. Remove relay from circuit, and substitute a good relay of same capacity.
6. Operate the system.   5-6√ _____

CLOSING THE STATION:
      Clean the station and return all materials to the tool crib.

DATA:

Hermetic System, Name _____ Model _____ Year _____
      Serial Number _____ Type _____
Refrigerant, Kind _____ Amount _____
Motor: Horsepower _____ Volts _____
      Starting Amperes _____ Running Amperes _____
Overload Protector: Make _____ Capacity _____
Relay: Make _____ Model _____
      Serial Number _____ Type _____

Remarks:

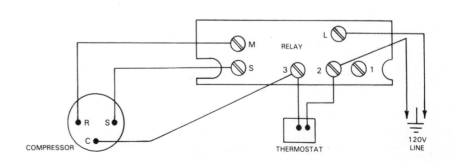

CHECK A THERMAL RELAY.

Indicate the best answer for each question below by encircling its letter.

1. What is the purpose of the relay?
   a. To protect against an overload.
   b. To keep the motor from running too fast.
   c. To disconnect the starting winding at the proper moment.
   d. To take the place of the thermostat.
   e. To disconnect the capacitor when the unit stops.

2. How many sets of points does a hot wire relay have?
   a. One.
   b. Two.
   c. Three.
   d. Four.
   e. Five.

3. What opens the contact points of a hot wire relay?
   a. A weight.
   b. A toggle spring.
   c. Thermal expansion.
   d. A bimetal strip.
   e. Magnetism.

4. Where is the relay usually located?
   a. In the thermostat.
   b. In the motor.
   c. On the condensing unit.
   d. In the capacitor box.
   e. On the evaporator.

5. What will most thermal relays do when the unit is using too much current?
   a. Nothing.
   b. Burn out.
   c. Open the circuit.
   d. Close the starting circuit.
   e. Burn out the capacitor.

CHECK A SOLID STATE RELAY

OBJECTIVE: Given a hermetic refrigerating system with a solid state relay and the necessary
tools and instruments: check the relay.

REFERENCES: Required – Para. 7-10, 7-11, 7-15, 7-50, 8-22, 8-23, 8-27, 8-28 and 8-43.
Supplementary – Para. 7-20, 7-24, 7-48, 11-19, 11-20, 11-21, 11-82, 14-90 and 14-109.

EQUIPMENT: One hermetic refrigerating system with a solid state relay.

PREPARATION PROCEDURE:
1.   Study the references and manufacturer's literature.   TEST √ _____
2.   Obtain: Tools – 1 4-in. regular screwdriver, 1 6-in. diagonal plier, 1 6-in. adj.
     wrench, 1 pr. safety goggles.
3.   Obtain: Instruments – 1 electrical combination voltmeter, ammeter and
     ohmmeter (multimeter), 1 test light.
4.   Obtain: Supplies – 1 wiping cloth, 1 roll plastic tape, 1 4-in. square 00 sandpaper.

TASK PROCEDURE (WEAR GOGGLES):
1.   Check the complete system; start the unit if possible.
2.   If it does not start, check the other parts of the electrical circuit. These include the motor,
     capacitor, overload cut-out, thermostat, etc. Make certain that there is power to the system.
3.   If all these parts are operational, remove the relay.   1-3 √ _____
4.   Test solid state relay ONLY with an ohmmeter.
5.   Replace relay with a new one of the same specifications.
6.   Operate the system.   4-6 √ _____

CLOSING THE STATION:
        Clean the work station and return all the material to the tool crib.

DATA:

Hermetic System, Name _____ Model _____ Year _____
                Serial Number _____ Type _____
Refrigerant, Kind _____ Amount _____
Motor, Horsepower _____ Volts _____
        Starting Amperes _____ Running Amperes _____
Overload Protector, Name _____ Capacity _____
Relay, Name _____ Model _____
        Serial No. _____ Type _____

Remarks:

CHECK A SOLID STATE RELAY.

Indicate the best answer for each question below by encircling its letter.

1. Which type of relay is least sensitive to the ampere rating?
   a. Thermal.
   b. Solid state.
   c. Current.
   d. Potential.
   e. All are the same.

2. Does a solid state relay have any moving parts?
   a. Yes.
   b. No.
   c. Only one.
   d. Two.
   e. Three.

3. Can a solid state relay be substituted for the other relays?
   a. Yes.
   b. No.
   c. Only thermal relay.
   d. Only current relay.
   e. Only potential relay.

4. What solid state devices are built into a solid state relay?
   a. Transistors.
   b. Triacs.
   c. Diodes.
   d. Transistors and triacs.
   e. Transistors, diodes, and triacs.

5. What type single-phase hermetic motor does not use a relay?
   a. Capacitor start-Induction.
   b. Capacitor start-Capacitor run.
   c. Split phase.
   d. Permanent split capacitor.
   e. Polyphase.

CHECK A SOLENOID VALVE

OBJECTIVE: Given a refrigerating system with a solenoid valve and the necessary tools and instruments: check the solenoid valve for satisfactory operation.

REFERENCES: Required - Para. 3-22, 5-19, 5-20, 5-32, 8-31, 8-43, 12-29, 12-51, 12-58, 12-74, 14-95, and 14-109. Supplementary - Para. 14-76.

EQUIPMENT: One refrigerating system with either a solenoid hot gas valve, water valve, bypass valve, or liquid line valve.

PREPARATION PROCEDURE:
1. Study the reference paragraphs and manufacturer's literature.   TEST√_____
2. Obtain: Tools - 1 4-in. regular screwdriver, 1 6-in. slim nose pliers, 1 6-in. adj. wrench, 1 6-in. screwdriver, 1 pr. safety goggles.
3. Obtain: Instruments - 1 electrical combination voltmeter, ammeter and ohmmeter (multimeter), 1 test light.
4. Obtain: Supplies - 1 wiping cloth, 1 roll plastic tape, 1 4-in. square 00 sandpaper.

TASK PROCEDURE (WEAR GOGGLES):
1. Check the complete system; operate the solenoid if possible.
2. If the solenoid does not operate, first check the power-in, the wiring, and the solenoid circuit switch.
3. If the leads and components are operational, remove the solenoid coil.
4. Test the solenoid coil for open circuit, short, and grounds.   1-4√_____
5. If coil is defective, replace with a good coil of the same specifications (size, voltage, watts).
6. Operate the system   5-6√_____

CLOSING THE STATION:
       Clean the work station and return all the material to the tool crib.

DATA:

Refrigerating System, Make_____ Model_____Year_____
                     Serial Number_____ Type_____
Refrigerant, Kind_____ Amount_____
Solenoid, Make_____ Model_____
       Voltage_____ Watts_____
Solenoid Application_____ Line (Water or Refrigerant) Size_____
Motor-Compressor, Horsepower_____ Voltage_____
Starting Amperes_____ Running Amperes_____

Remarks:

CHECK A SOLENOID VALVE.

Indicate the best answer for each question below by encircling its letter.

1. What part of a solenoid moves?
    a. Coil.
    b. Points.
    c. Bimetal.
    d. Core.
    e. Both bimetal and points.

2. What are two popular types of solenoid valves?
    a. One-way and two-way.
    b. Two-way and three-way.
    c. One-way and three-way.
    d. Two-way and four-way.
    e. Three-way and four-way.

3. How many different voltages are popular for solenoids?
    a. 1
    b. 2
    c. 3
    d. 4
    e. 5

4. How does the fluid pressure help operate the solenoid valve?
    a. Helps close the valve.
    b. Has no effect.
    c. Helps open the valve.
    d. Helps open and close the valve.
    e. Is used to operate the points.

5. Why must some solenoid valves be plumbed vertically?
    a. Neater.
    b. Keeps coil cooler.
    c. Required by Electrical Code.
    d. To permit core to move freely.
    e. Solenoid will not operate otherwise.

TEST AN OPEN TYPE CAPACITOR-START ELECTRIC MOTOR

OBJECTIVE: Given an external drive capacitor-start motor and the necessary tools and instruments: dismantle, check, assemble and test.

REFERENCES: Required – Para. 4-49, 6-44, 6-48, 6-80, 7-4, 7-5, 7-8, 7-10, 7-34, 7-35, 7-37, 7-38, 7-42, 7-50 and 14-89.
  Supplementary – Para. 6-76 through 6-79, 7-36, 7-43, 7-44 and 7-45.

EQUIPMENT: One external drive capacitor-start electric motor, one motor testing stand, one bench.

PREPARATION PROCEDURE:
1. Study the reference paragraphs and manufacturer's literature.   TEST√_____
2. Obtain: Tools – 1 set of sockets and handles, 1 set 4-in. screwdrivers, 1 pr. 6-in. slim nose pliers, 1 6-in. adj. end wrench, 1 pulley puller, 1 scriber, 1 pr. safety goggles.
3. Obtain: Instruments – 1 electrical combination voltmeter, ammeter and ohmmeter (multimeter), 1 test light, 1 capacitor tester.
4. Obtain: Supplies – 1 wiping cloth, 1 roll plastic tape, 1 4-in. square 00 sandpaper.

TASK PROCEDURE (WEAR GOGGLES):
1. Remove motor from its base; scribe position before removal; clean motor.
2. Remove pulley from shaft using pulley puller.
3. Test motor for operation, for grounds, for shorts, for open circuits.   1-3√_____
4. Dismantle motor:
   a. Scribe matching marks on end bells and stator.
   b. Remove capacitor (discharge capacitor!).
   c. Remove end bells.
   d. Remove rotor.
5. Clean and test running winding, starting winding, capacitor, and switch for grounds, shorts and open circuits. Test capacitor with capacitor tester.   4-5√_____
6. Repair or replace defective parts.
7. Assemble motor, checking that bearings do not bind; correct if necessary. Oil bearings if required.
8. Mount motor on test stand, connect and test. Obtain current and voltage readings.
                                                                      6-8√_____
9. Install motor on base and check operation.   9√_____

CLOSING THE STATION:
   Clean station and return all materials to tool crib.

DATA:

Motor, Make_____	Model_____	Serial No._____
Voltage_____	Starting Current_____	Running Current_____
Shaft Size_____	Pulley Dia._____	Groove Width_____
Capacitor, Make_____	Voltage_____	Mfd._____
Before Tear-Down Readings, Voltage_____	Amperage_____	Resistance_____
After Assembly Readings, Voltage_____	Amperage_____	Resistance_____

Remarks:

TEST AN OPEN TYPE CAPACITOR-START ELECTRIC MOTOR.

Indicate the best answer for each question below by encircling its letter.

1. On what does the principle of operation of the capacitor type motor depend?
    a. Capacitor boosts voltage.
    b. Capacitor boosts amperage.
    c. Capacitor increases resistance.
    d. Capacitor decreases resistance.
    e. Capacitor operates like another phase in current flow.

2. What should an ohmmeter read when its leads are on the two terminals of a good capacitor?
    a. O.
    b. Infinity.
    c. Between 1000 to 2000 ohms.
    d. Below 500 ohms.
    e. Above 10,000 ohms.

3. Why do some capacitors have a small resistor connected to the two terminals?
    a. To reduce current flow to the capacitor.
    b. To keep the capacitor from overheating.
    c. To slowly discharge the capacitor when circuit is open.
    d. Capacitors do not have resistors.
    e. To help make easier connections.

4. What is a capacitor made of?
    a. Resistors.
    b. Inductance coils.
    c. Aluminum foil and insulation.
    d. Electrodes with a spark gap.
    e. Diodes and a coil.

5. Why does a capacitor overheat?
    a. Voltage too low.
    b. Has an open circuit.
    c. Oversize.
    d. Room too warm.
    e. Too frequent starting of motor.

TEST A CAPACITOR-START HERMETIC MOTOR

OBJECTIVE: Given a hermetic refrigerating system with a capacitor-start motor compressor and the necessary tools and instruments: check the motor compressor for correct operation.

REFERENCES: Required – Para. 4-25, 6-48, 6-74, 6-75, 6-76, 6-79, 6-80, 7-9 through 7-14, 7-16, 7-18, 7-37, 7-38, 7-50, 11-20 and 11-21.
   Supplementary – Para. 11-73 and 11-82.

EQUIPMENT: One hermetic refrigerating system with a capacitor-start induction run motor.

PREPARATION PROCEDURE:
1. Study the reference paragraphs and system service manual.   TEST√_____
2. Obtain: Tools – 1 4-in. screwdriver, 1 6-in. slim nose pliers, 1 pr. safety goggles.
3. Obtain: Instruments – 1 electrical combination voltmeter, ammeter and ohmmeter (multimeter), 1 test light, 1 motor starting cord, 1 capacitor tester.
4. Obtain: Supplies – 1 wiping cloth, 1 roll plastic tape, 1 4-in. square 00 sandpaper.

TASK PROCEDURE (WEAR GOGGLES):
1. Check the complete system and operate if possible.
2. If system will not operate, shut off power and remove the starting relay and overload protector from the motor compressor.
3. Test the motor for open circuit, grounds, and shorts using test light and ohmmeter.
4. Test the capacitor with capacitor tester for open circuit, shorts, grounds and capacity. If faulty, replace with exact duplicate.   1-4√_____
5. Connect motor test cord with good capacitor to motor terminals and start motor compressor.
6. If operational, replace wiring and operate system.

          5-6√_____

CLOSING THE STATION:
   Clean work station and return all material to the tool crib.

DATA:

Hermetic System, Make_____ Model_____ Year_____
          Serial Number_____ Type_____
Refrigerant, Kind_____ Amount_____
Motor, Horsepower_____ Volts_____
          Starting Amperes_____ Running Amperes_____
Overload Protector, Make_____ Capacity_____
Relay, Make_____ Model_____
          Serial No._____ Type_____
Capacitor, Name_____ Model_____
          Volts_____ Mfd._____

Remarks:

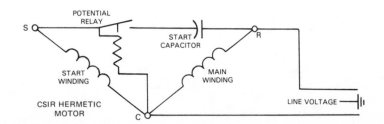

CSIR HERMETIC MOTOR

TEST A CAPACITOR-START HERMETIC MOTOR.

Indicate the best answer for each question below by encircling its letter.

1. Which ohmmeter test of the three motor terminals has the highest resistance?
    a. Start to common.
    b. Run to common.
    c. Start to run.
    d. All are the same.
    e. The resistance is 0 for each test.

2. What is one electrical method to loosen a stuck single-phase hermetic motor compressor?
    a. It cannot be done.
    b. Use low voltage.
    c. Use polyphase power.
    d. Put a capacitor in running winding circuit.
    e. Use a larger capacitor.

3. If one lead of an ohmmeter is on a terminal, where must the other one be to check for grounds?
    a. On one other terminal.
    b. On two other leads.
    c. Neither of the leads on a terminal.
    d. On the hermetic housing.
    e. On the overload protector terminal.

4. What happens when one installs an under-capacity capacitor?
    a. No change.
    b. Motor will overheat.
    c. Motor will run too fast.
    d. Capacitor will overheat.
    e. Motor will run too slowly.

5. What is the best way to test for a shorted winding?
    a. Test light.
    b. Ammeter.
    c. Voltmeter.
    d. Ohmmeter.
    e. Thermometer.

TEST AND OPERATE A CAPACITOR START-CAPACITOR RUN HERMETIC MOTOR

OBJECTIVE: Given a refrigerating system with a hermetic capacitor start-capacitor run motor and the necessary tools and instruments: check for proper operation.

REFERENCES: Required - Para. 4-25, 4-49, 6-74, 6-75, 6-76, 6-79, 6-80, 7-9 through 7-14, 7-19, 7-37, 7-38, 7-50, 11-20, 11-21, 11-73, 11-82, 14-90 and 14-109.
Supplementary - Para. 7-47, 14-92 and 14-93.

EQUIPMENT: A capacitor start-capacitor run hermetic refrigerator motor-compressor system.

PREPARATION PROCEDURE:
1. Study the service manual and reference paragraphs for a capacitor start-capacitor run motor.   TEST√ _____
2. Obtain: Tools - 1 6-in. screwdriver, 1 6-in. adj. open end wrench, 1 pr. safety goggles.
3. Obtain: Instruments - 1 electrical combination voltmeter, ammeter, and ohmmeter (multimeter), 1 capacitor tester, 1 test light.
4. Obtain: Supplies - 1 wiping cloth.

TASK PROCEDURE (WEAR GOGGLES):
1. Check the complete system and operate if possible.
2. If the system will not operate, shut off the power and remove the starting relay, overload relay, starting capacitor, and running capacitor.   Tag any wires removed to insure correct reconnecting.
3. Test the motor winding circuits for continuity, grounds, and open circuits.
4. Test the capacitors. Replace if necessary.   1-4√ _____
5. Test relay and replace relay if necessary.
6. Reconnect the starter relay capacitors and operate the system.   5-6√ _____

CLOSING THE STATION:
Clean the work station and return all materials to the tool crib.

DATA:

Motor Compressor, Make_____ Model_____
Serial Number_____ hp_____ rpm_____
Voltage_____ Phase_____ Hertz_____
Starting Current_____ Running Current_____
Starting Capacitor Model_____ Capacity_____
              Mfd_____ Voltage_____
Running Capacitor Model_____ Capacity_____
              Mfd_____ Voltage_____

Remarks:

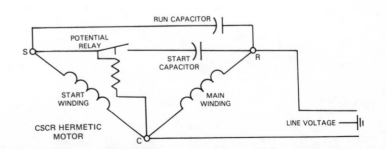

TEST AND OPERATE A CAPACITOR START-CAPACITOR RUN HERMETIC MOTOR.

Indicate the best answer for each question below by encircling its letter.

1. What is another name for capacitor?
    a. Meter.
    b. Stator.
    c. Condenser.
    d. Rotor.
    e. Indicator.

2. How many kinds of capacitors are there?
    a. One.
    b. Two.
    c. Three.
    d. Four.
    e. Five.

3. How is the starting capacitor connected to the starting winding electrically?
    a. In series.
    b. In parallel.
    c. Either way.
    d. Between the starting and running winding.
    e. It is not connected to either the starting or running winding.

4. Why must a capacitor be shorted before it is handled?
    a. It may burn out.
    b. It may give one a shock.
    c. It may break.
    d. It may start running.
    e. It may wear out.

5. What type of capacitor is usually used for continuous operation?
    a. The electrolytic capacitor.
    b. Any type.
    c. Copper graphite.
    d. An oversize capacitor.
    e. A water-cooled capacitor.

REPLACE A RELAY AND OVERLOAD PROTECTOR

OBJECTIVE: Given a hermetic system with a relay, overload protector and the necessary tools and instruments: remove, test and replace the relay and overload protector.

REFERENCES: Required – Para. 6-73, 6-79, 6-80, 7-25, 7-27, 7-28, 7-29, 7-31, 7-37, 7-49, 7-50, 8-22 through 8-28 and 8-43. Supplementary – Para. 7-38.

EQUIPMENT: One hermetic system.

PREPARATION PROCEDURE:
1. Study the unit assigned and reference paragraphs.   TEST✓_____
2. Obtain: Tools – 1 8-in. lineman's pliers, 1 6-in. adj. wrench, 1 soldering gun, 1 4-in. 1/4-in. x 3/32-in. screwdriver, 1 pr. safety goggles.
3. Obtain: Instruments – 1 electrical combination voltmeter, ammeter and ohmmeter (multimeter), 1 electrical analyzer kit complete, 1 test light.
4. Obtain: Supplies – 1 12-in. length of 1/8-in. dia. 50-50 solder, 1 can noncorrosive flux, 1 roll 3/4-in. width plastic tape, 1 4-in. sq. 00 sandpaper.

TASK PROCEDURE (WEAR GOGGLES):
1. Disconnect the motor from the system (short any capacitors to prevent a shock). Mark each wire in reference to its terminal as the wires are disconnected.
2. If an analyzer is used, connect the analyzer leads to the motor terminal leads according to the directions that accompany each analyzer. Test the continuity of each winding. Test for grounds and shorts. If the electrical properties are satisfactory but the unit will not start, try using a larger capacitor, a higher voltage, or a capacitor in the running circuit to reverse the rotation. CAUTION: CAREFULLY FOLLOW THE INSTRUCTIONS IN PARA. 7-49.   1-2✓_____
3. If a test light and/or an ohmmeter is used, check for continuity, shorts and internal winding shorts. Connect a capacitor in the starting circuit and check unit by using a manual relay.
4. If the motor does function, any electrical trouble will be in the external circuit. However, if the overload has been operating too frequently, the current draw and the overheating of the motor should be checked.
5. Reassemble the wiring of the system and operate unit.   3-5✓_____

CLOSING THE STATION:
　　　　Clean the station and return all material to the tool crib.

DATA:
Motor, Make_____ Horsepower_____ Voltage_____ Starting Amperes_____ Running Amperes_____

Terminal Diagram –
　(sketch and label)　　　Starting Winding Terminal

　　　　　　　　　　　　　Running Winding Terminal

　　　　　　　　　　　　　Common Terminal

Test, Continuity, Starting Winding_____ Running Winding_____
　　　Ground,　Starting Winding_____ Running Winding_____
　　　Shorts,　Starting Winding_____ Running Winding_____
Relay, Make_____ Model_____
　　　Condition, Good_____ Replace_____
Overload Protector, Make_____ Model_____
　　　Condition, Good_____ Replace_____

REPLACE A RELAY AND OVERLOAD PROTECTOR

Indicate the best answer for each question below by encircling its letter.

1. What is continuity?
   a. A grounded wire.
   b. A broken wire.
   c. A complete electrical circuit.
   d. An open circuit.
   e. A bare wire.

2. What windings do most hermetic motors have?
   a. A stator and rotor winding.
   b. A stator winding only.
   c. Two stator windings.
   d. Two rotor windings.
   e. One rotor winding.

3. Which is the common lead?
   a. The left side lead.
   b. The right side lead.
   c. The middle terminal.
   d. The terminal with both a running and starting
      winding connection.
   e. The running winding lead.

4. How many terminals do most hermetic motors have?
   a. One.
   b. Two.
   c. Three.
   d. Four.
   e. Five.

5. How may an electrically grounded winding be detected?
   a. One will get a shock.
   b. The unit will not run.
   c. A current will flow from one terminal to another.
   d. A current will flow from a terminal to the housing.
   e. Too much refrigeration.

REPLACE A CONDENSER FAN MOTOR

OBJECTIVE: Given a refrigerating system with a condenser fan motor and the necessary tools and instruments: replace and check a fan motor.

REFERENCES: Required – Para. 4-13, 6-48, 6-80, 7-1 through 7-4, 7-31, 7-32, 7-34, 7-40, 7-41, 7-42, 7-46 and 7-50.
  Supplementary – Para. 7-33 and 7-39.

EQUIPMENT: An operating hermetic refrigerator which has a condenser fan.

PREPARATION PROCEDURE:
1. Study the assigned refrigeration system and the reference paragraphs.   TEST√ _____
2. Obtain: Tools – 1 set terminal pliers and terminals, 1 6-in. slim nose pliers, 1 8-in. electrician's pliers, 1 set small open end wrenches, 1 set small sockets and handles, 1 set spin sockets, 1 soldering gun, 1 set Allen set screw wrenches, 1 6-in. reg. screwdriver, 1 4-in. Phillips screwdriver, 1 pr. safety goggles.
3. Obtain: Instruments – 1 comb. volt-amp-ohmmeter for 120V circuits, 1 test light, 1 capacitor tester, 1 dial indicator.
4. Obtain: Supplies – 1 wiping cloth, 1 container of clean soft solder flux, 1 roll 50-50 solder, 1 roll 1/2-in. plastic tape.

TASK PROCEDURE (WEAR GOGGLES):
1. Operate the system and measure the voltage and current for the fan motor.
2. Shut off the system, disconnect the power source, label the terminal leads and remove the fan and fan motor.
3. Remove the fan from the motor shaft, clean the motor, dismantle the motor if possible.
4. Check the continuity of windings and resistance of windings.
5. Assemble motor, check bearing wear and end play with dial indicator.   1-5√ _____
6. Reinstall the motor and fan in the system. Position of the fan on the shaft and position of the motor in bracket is very important.
7. Make the electrical connections.
8. Operate the system and check for noise and the voltage and amperage readings.
                                                                6-8√ _____

CLOSING THE STATION:
    Clean up the work station and return all the material to the tool crib.

DATA:

System, Make _____ Model _____
    Type _____ Capacity _____
    Starting Amperes _____ Running Amperes _____
Condenser Motor, Voltage _____ Current _____ Type Motor _____
Condenser Motor Winding Resistance _____

Remarks:

REPLACE A CONDENSER FAN MOTOR.

Indicate the best answer for each question below by encircling its letter.

1. How are fans most commonly fastened to the shafts?
   a. Lock washers.
   b. Machine screws.
   c. Flat keys.
   d. Allen set screws.
   e. Cap screws.

2. What may happen if there is too much motor end play?
   a. The motor will not start.
   b. The fan will come loose.
   c. The fan will rub against its housing.
   d. The motor fan will be noisy.
   e. The current load will be too low.

3. What will be the result of a loose or high resistance wiring connection to the fan motor?
   a. A fire.
   b. The motor will not start.
   c. The motor will be noisy.
   d. The motor will not reach its operating speed.
   e. The motor will overheat.

4. What should be done if a fan blade is bent out-of-line?
   a. Straighten it.
   b. Replace it.
   c. Operate it as is.
   d. If possible, bend the other blades to match.
   e. Rebalance by using knife edges.

5. What oil should be used on bronze motor bearings?
   a. SAE 0
   b. SAE 30
   c. SAE 50
   d. SAE 70
   e. SAE 90

REPLACE AN EVAPORATOR FAN MOTOR

OBJECTIVE: Given a refrigerating system with an evaporator fan and the necessary tools and
   instruments: test, repair or replace the fan motor.

REFERENCES: Required – Para. 4-13, 6-48, 6-80, 7-1 through 7-4, 7-31, 7-32, 7-34, 7-40, 7-41,
   7-42, 7-46, 7-50, 10-15, 10-16, 10-45, 11-21, 11-82, 12-20 and 12-74.
   Supplementary – Para. 7-33, 7-39, 10-24, 14-4 and 14-109.

EQUIPMENT: Refrigerating system with a forced convection evaporator.

PREPARATION PROCEDURE:
1. Study the assigned system and the reference paragraphs.   TEST√_____
2. Obtain: Tools – 1 set of allen wrenches, 1 set of socket wrenches, 1 screwdriver,
    1 pr. 6-in. diagonal pliers, 1 pr. safety goggles.
3. Obtain: Instruments – 1 electrical combination voltmeter, ammeter and ohmmeter (multimeter).
4. Obtain: Supplies – 1 wiping cloth, 1 oiler – SAE 30, 1 roll of 1/2-in. electrical tape.

TASK PROCEDURE (WEAR GOGGLES):
1. Check the complete unit and allow it to operate for a few minutes. Determine if the
    evaporator fan motor is operating.
2. Check the fan and motor for noise or overheating.
3. Check all connections to make certain there are no loose connections. Then check
    the motor amperage and voltage.   1-3√_____
4. Shut off power, disconnect all electric wiring, tagging each one as to its terminal.
5. Unbolt motor from base mounting and loosen fan on shaft.
6. Remove fan, clean and test for open circuit, shorts and grounds.
7. Install a new motor of same electrical specifications.
8. Reconnect all wires and operate unit. Make certain fan is rotating in proper direction
    and is in correct position on shaft.   4-8√_____

CLOSING THE STATION:
   Clean the work station and return all the material to the tool crib.

DATA:
System, Motor, Make_____ Horsepower_____ Current_____ Voltage_____
Shaft Size_____ Fan Diameter_____ Type_____
Original Readings: Volts_____ Current_____
Motor Trouble_____
Burned Out_____ Loose Fan_____
Worn Bearings_____ Fan Blade Touching Housing_____
Replacement Readings, Volts_____ Current_____ Noise_____

Remarks:

REPLACE AN EVAPORATOR FAN MOTOR.

Indicate the best answer for each question below by encircling its letter.

1. What is the most difficult internal electrical trouble to locate?
    a. A short.
    b. A ground.
    c. A burned winding.
    d. A broken line.
    e. A lack of continuity.

2. How will loose or dirty connections be indicated?
    a. Too much voltage drop.
    b. Dry bearings.
    c. Too much amperage drop.
    d. A rumbling sound.
    e. Out of balance fan.

3. What size fan motor should be used as a replacement?
    a. 1/10 hp more.
    b. 1/10 hp less.
    c. One size smaller.
    d. The same size.
    e. One size larger.

4. What should be done to the electrical wires when removing a part?
    a. They must be labeled.
    b. Nothing.
    c. Cut them as close to the unit as possible.
    d. Clean them with a dilute acid.
    e. Do not disconnect them.

5. What device is used to direct the air in a combination refrigerator-freezer
    when one fan motor is used with a single evaporator?
    a. Air flow control.
    b. Solenoid valve.
    c. Two-temperature valve.
    d. Two thermostatic expansion valves.
    e. Plate type evaporator.

CHECK ALL ELECTRICAL COMPONENTS OF A 120V REFRIGERATING SYSTEM

OBJECTIVE: Given a refrigerating system and the necessary tools and instruments: check all the wiring and electrical components.

REFERENCES: Required – Para. 4-23, 4-25, 5-19, 5-20, 5-32, 6-8, 6-9, 6-11, 6-14, 6-20, 6-28, 6-29, 6-30, 6-75, 6-76, 6-78, 6-79, 6-80, 7-47, 8-1, 8-2, 8-28, 8-37, 8-38, 8-43, 10-24, 10-45, 11-8, 11-19, 11-21 and 11-82.
Supplementary – Para. 6-67, 7-43, 7-44 and 7-45.

EQUIPMENT: One complete 120V refrigerating system.

PREPARATION PROCEDURE:
1. Study the refrigerating system and the reference paragraphs.   TEST√_____
2. Obtain: Tools – 1 6-in. side cutter pliers, 1 6-in reg. screwdriver.
3. Obtain: Instruments – 1 test light, 1 electrical combination voltmeter, ammeter, and ohmmeter (multimeter), 1 capacitor tester.
4. Obtain: Supplies – 1 wiping cloth, 1 roll plastic tape.

TASK PROCEDURE:
1. Study the electrical circuitry and components system.
2. Make an electrical diagram of the electrical system and record the data. 1-2√_____
3. Operate the system and check the voltage and amperage.
4. Remove the electrical parts except motor-compressor from the system (BE SURE THE POWER IS DISCONNECTED) and tag each line as to its terminal or connection.
5. Check each electric part for resistance, grounds, open circuit, and shorts.
6. Assemble the electrical parts into the electrical system.
7. Operate the system. Use the instruments to check the voltage and current.
                                                                            3-7√_____

CLOSING THE STATION:
Clean the work station and return all material to the tool crib.

DATA:
Compressor Motor, Make_____ Model_____ rpm_____
            Voltage_____ Phase_____ Rated Current, Start_____ Run_____
Starting Capacitor, Make_____ Voltage_____ Mfd_____
Running Capacitor, Make_____ Voltage_____ Mfd_____
Condenser Fan Motor, Make_____ Model_____ rpm_____
            Voltage_____ Phase_____ Rated Watts, Run_____
Evaporator Fan Motor, Make_____ Model_____
            Voltage_____ Phase_____ Rated Watts, Run_____
Motor Control, Make_____ Model_____
            Capacity, Voltage_____ Current_____
Solenoid Valve, Make_____ Model_____ Electrical Rating_____
Voltage Checks, Before_____ After Assembly_____
Current Checks, Before_____ After Assembly_____
Condition of Electrical System_____

Remarks:

CHECK ALL ELECTRICAL COMPONENTS OF A 120V REFRIGERATING SYSTEM.

Indicate the best answer for each question below by encircling its letter.

1. How are the electrical power devices usually electrically connected to each other?
    a. In series.
    b. In parallel.
    c. In series-parallel.
    d. In parallel-series-parallel combinations.
    e. In series-parallel-series combinations.

2. What is the correct reasoning when there is a voltage drop at a terminal?
    a. There is a loose or dirty connection.
    b. The terminal is too large.
    c. The electrical load is too small.
    d. The voltmeter is connected incorrectly.
    e. The terminal is grounded.

3. Why must the wiring size be checked?
    a. It must be strong enough.
    b. It must be able to carry the voltage imposed.
    c. It must be able to carry the starting current.
    d. It must be able to carry the running current.
    e. It should not be too large.

4. Do the motor control points carry all the current when a magnetic starter is used?
    a. Yes.
    b. No.
    c. Only during starting.
    d. Only during running.
    e. Only the motor current.

5. How should a voltmeter be connected into a circuit?
    a. In series.
    b. In parallel.
    c. Its prongs are clamped around the insulated wire.
    d. It is used only at the power source.
    e. It is used with a shunt.

CHECK A 120V SYSTEM WITH A 24V CONTROL CIRCUIT

OBJECTIVE: Given a complete system powered by 120V, controlled by a 24V circuit, and the necessary tools and instruments: check and service both circuits to approved standards.

REFERENCES: Required – Para. 6-1, 6-2, 6-4, 6-5, 6-7, 6-8, 20-41, 20-55, 23-5, 24-3, 24-5, 24-9, 24-13, 24-20, 24-21, 24-23, 24-36 and 24-53.
Supplementary – Para. 12-58 and 23-32.

EQUIPMENT: One refrigerating system, one heating system, or a combination.

PREPARATION PROCEDURE:
1. Study the system and the reference paragraphs.   TEST√_____
2. Obtain: Tools – 1 set socket wrenches, 1 set screwdrivers, 1 set pliers, 1 soldering gun, 1 pr. safety goggles.
3. Obtain: Instruments – 1 combination voltmeter, ammeter and ohmmeter (multimeter), 1 test light, 1 capacitor tester.
4. Obtain: Supplies – 1 wiping cloth, 1 roll tape, 1 roll 50-50 solder, 1 can solder flux.

TASK PROCEDURE (WEAR GOGGLES):
1. Study the 120V and 24V circuits and their parts.
2. Operate the 24V system. (If a furnace, check the procedure for starting fuel flow.)
                                                                     1-2√_____
3. Check the voltage and current.
4. Shut off system.
5. Remove all 24V parts, tagging all lines and terminals.
6. Test each part for grounds, shorts, open circuits (continuity).
7. Install the 24V parts.
8. Operate the system and check the voltage and current.   3-8√_____

CLOSING THE STATION:
Clean the work station and return all the material to the tool crib.

DATA:

Transformer, Make _____ Capacity VA _____
Thermostat, Make _____ Type _____
            Max. Reading _____ Min. Reading _____
Limit Control, Make _____ Type _____
            Settings, On _____ Off _____
Relay Coil, Make _____ Watts _____
Voltage, Before Dismantling _____ After Assembly _____
Current, Before Dismantling _____ After Assembly _____

Remarks:

CHECK A 120V SYSTEM WITH A 24V CONTROL CIRCUIT.

Indicate the best answer for each question below by encircling its letter.

1. What type transformer is used to produce 24 volts?
   a. Delta.
   b. Wye.
   c. Auto transformer.
   d. Stepdown.
   e. Vibrator.

2. How does the 24V circuit operate the 120V circuit?
   a. It does not.
   b. By thermal switch.
   c. By snap switch.
   d. By relay coil.
   e. By timer.

3. How are 120V to 24V transformers rated for capacity?
   a. Watts.
   b. Kilowatts.
   c. Volt amperes.
   d. Voltage.
   e. Milliamperes.

4. Why is a 24V circuit used?
   a. To allow shorter power wires.
   b. 24V circuits have more current.
   c. Bare wires can be used.
   d. Can use same transformer as doorbell circuit.
   e. Thermostat points last longer.

5. In what circuits are the limit controls located?
   a. Separate circuit.
   b. 24V circuit.
   c. 120V circuit.
   d. Both 24V and 120V circuits.
   e. Either the 24V or 120V circuit.

TRACE THE CIRCUITS AND DRAW THE WIRING DIAGRAM
FOR A COMMERCIAL REFRIGERATING SYSTEM

OBJECTIVE: Given a one to three-horsepower commercial refrigerating system for a walk-in cabinet or display case: trace the electrical circuits and draw a wiring diagram.

REFERENCES: Required – Para. 3-10, 3-22, 8-1, 8-2, 8-20, 8-43, 12-29, 12-58, 12-74, 14-85, 14-95 and 14-109.
Supplementary – Para. 12-37 and 12-51.

EQUIPMENT: 1 one to three-horsepower system with a blower evaporator, and a condenser fan.

PREPARATION PROCEDURE:
1.   Study the commercial refrigerating system and the reference paragraphs.

TEST✓_____

2.   Obtain: Tools – 1 pr. terminal pliers, 1 pr. 6-in. side cutting pliers, 1 6-in. reg. screwdriver.
3.   Obtain: Instruments – 1 test light, 1 combination voltmeter, ammeter and ohmmeter (multimeter).
4.   Obtain: Supplies – 1 wiping cloth, 1 5-ft. length No. 12 wire, 1 roll 1/2-in. plastic tape, 1 set of terminals.

TASK PROCEDURE:
1.   Study the electrical circuitry of the system.
2.   Make an electrical diagram of the system and fill out the data sheet.   1-2 ✓_____
3.   Operate the system. Use the instruments to check the voltage and current.

3 ✓_____

CLOSING THE STATION:
Clean the station and return all materials to the tool crib.

DATA:

Compressor Motor, Make_____ Model_____ rpm_____
    Voltage_____ Phase_____ Rated Current, Start_____ Run_____
Starting Capacitor, Make_____ Voltage_____ Mfd_____
Running Capacitor, Make_____ Voltage_____ Mfd_____
Evaporator Blower Motor, Make_____ Model_____ rpm_____
    Voltage_____ Phase_____ Rated Current_____
Condenser Fan Motor, Make_____ Model_____ rpm_____
    Voltage_____ Phase_____ Rated Current_____
Motor Control, Make_____ Model_____ Capacity, Voltage_____ Current_____
Relay, Make_____ Model_____ Rating_____
Overload Protectors, Make_____ Model_____ Rating_____
Voltage Checks_____ Percent Current Checks_____
Condition_____

Remarks:

TRACE THE CIRCUITS AND DRAW THE WIRING DIAGRAM
FOR A COMMERCIAL REFRIGERATING SYSTEM.

Indicate the best answer for each question below by encircling its letter.

1. Can the induction ammeter prongs be placed around both wires in a power cord?
    a. Yes.
    b. No.
    c. Only if it is single phase.
    d. If current is less than one-half capacity of meter scale.
    e. Only if d-c is used.

2. What is the voltage of the motor-starter relay coil?
    a. 6V.
    b. 12V.
    c. 24V.
    d. 120V.
    e. 240V.

3. Where is the temperature control located in a 4-horsepower system?
    a. In the main power circuit.
    b. In the motor-starter relay circuit.
    c. Either circuit.
    d. Condenser fan circuit.
    e. Evaporator fan circuit.

4. How is the high-pressure limit control connected into the circuit?
    a. In series with the motor compressor relay.
    b. In series with the motor starter relay.
    c. In parallel with the oil pressure limit control.
    d. In series with the temperature control.
    e. In parallel with the temperature control.

5. What does it mean when a voltmeter reads 120V, when the leads are touched
    to two terminals?
    a. Closed circuit.
    b. Open circuit.
    c. Loose terminal.
    d. Corroded wire.
    e. Power is off.

MODERN REFRIGERATION AND AIR CONDITIONING
MODULE 3 - DOMESTIC REFRIGERATION LABORATORY TASKS

No.	NAME	TASK TEST GRADE	SIG.	TASK GRADE	SIG.	TASK DATE
3-1	Remove and Install Door Hardware					
3-2	Remove and Install Door Gaskets					
3-3	Remove and Install Breaker Strips					
3-4	Remove and Install a Chest Type Freezer Lid					
3-5	Add Oil to a Hermetic System					
3-6	Add Refrigerant to a Hermetic System					
3-7	Locate Trouble in a Manual Defrost Hermetic System					
3-8	Locate Trouble in an Electric Defrost Hermetic System					
3-9	Locate Trouble in a Hot Gas Defrost Hermetic System					
3-10	Install a Filter-Drier					
3-11	Repair or Replace a Capillary Tube					
3-12	Replace an Evaporator					
3-13	Replace a Condenser					
3-14	Wire a Domestic System					
3-15	Wire a Freezer System					
3-16	Remove and Install a Hermetic System					
3-17	Remove, Test, and Reinstall a Cabinet Mullion and Butter Heater System					
3-18	Remove a Hermetic Motor Compressor					
3-19	Dismantle and Check a Hermetic Motor Compressor					
3-20	Overhaul and Assemble a Hermetic Motor Compressor					

SAFETY WHEN SERVICING HERMETIC REFRIGERATORS

If any refrigerator is taken out of service, the door latch or THE DOOR MUST BE REMOVED IMMEDIATELY. Too often, children become trapped and are suffocated when they play in out-of-service refrigerators.

Do not permit oil from a hermetic unit to contact the skin; the oil may be acidic and cause severe burns.

The following is a basic safety rule to be observed in all cases when one works on a refrigerating unit: be sure that all the liquid refrigerant is removed and that the pressure is atmospheric (0 psi) in that part of the system being taken apart. Use gauges and thermometers as a check.

While doing any soldering, brazing or welding on refrigeration lines, the lines should be continuously purged with low-pressure CO_2 or nitrogen. Following soldering, brazing or welding, CO_2 or nitrogen should be used when testing for leaks.

Remove loose clothing, tuck in ties, roll up sleeves, wear a cap if one has long hair and wear goggles before working on a refrigeration system or near revolving or powered moving parts.

Report defective equipment to the instructor at once.

REMOVE AND INSTALL DOOR HARDWARE

OBJECTIVE: Given a refrigerator cabinet and the necessary tools: remove, replace and adjust
the door hardware to 100 percent operational standards.

REFERENCES: Required – Para. 2-62, 2-74, 10-41, 10-42, 10-45 and 11-9.
Supplementary – Para. 11-6, 11-19 and 11-82.

EQUIPMENT: A modern refrigerator with door hardware.

PREPARATION PROCEDURE:
1. Study the type of hardware on the domestic refrigerator. Study the reference paragraphs.
                                                                TEST√_____
2. Obtain: Tools – 1 pr. long-nosed pliers, 1 6-in. screwdriver, 1 extension cord with thin
wire and 40-watt test light.
3. Obtain: Instruments – 1 0.003-in. feeler gauge, 1 spirit level.
4. Obtain: Supplies – 1 wiping cloth, shim material for hinges, 1 safe cleaning solvent.

TASK PROCEDURE:
1. Use the spirit level and adjust the cabinet to a level position, check the door alignment,
and sealing ability of the gasket with either a feeler gauge or with the 40-watt test lamp.
2. If the door hardware is out of alignment, repair by changing the adjustment on the hinge
assembly.   1-2√_____
3. Check the gasket tightness again. If there is still a leakage, adjust the hinges again.
4. Check with a test light to determine fit.   3-4√_____

CLOSING THE STATION:
Clean the work station and return all material to the tool crib.

DATA:

Cabinet, Name:_____ Model _____
Hinge Mechanism, Type:_____

Remarks:

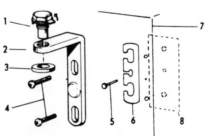

1. Pin for Top Hinge Bracket
2. Top Hinge Bracket
3. Nylon Bearing for Pin
4. Screw for Top Hinge Bracket to Cabinet
5. Tapping Plate Retainer Pin
6. Shim for Top Hinge Bracket
7. Cabinet Outer Shell
8. Tapping Plate for Top Hinge Bracket

Typical upper door hinge.

REMOVE AND INSTALL DOOR HARDWARE

Indicate the best answer for each question below by encircling its letter.

1. Can shims be used to raise the door?
   a. Yes.
   b. No.
   c. Door does not need to be raised.
   d. Only on the bottom hinge.
   e. Only on the middle hinge.

2. What type screw is used to hold the hinges in place?
   a. Studs.
   b. Cap screws.
   c. Machine screws.
   d. Sheet metal screws.
   e. Flat head machine screws.

3. What is the purpose of shims used under the hinge and the hinge bolt?
   a. To make the door square.
   b. To adjust the pressure needed to open the door.
   c. To adjust the distance between the door and the frame.
   d. To insure that no moisture will enter the system.
   e. To protect the finish of the cabinet.

4. If the bottom of the door is too far away from the frame, how is this adjusted?
   a. Remove a shim from the top hinge.
   b. Add a shim to the bottom hinge.
   c. Adjust the door liner screws.
   d. Loosen the top screws.
   e. Replace the gasket.

5. What kind of bushings are used in modern hinges?
   a. Nylon.
   b. Copper.
   c. Rubber.
   d. Steel.
   e. Bronze.

REMOVE AND INSTALL DOOR GASKETS

OBJECTIVE: Given one domestic refrigerator cabinet and the necessary tools: remove and replace the gasket to 90 percent quality.

REFERENCES: Required – Para. 10-41, 10-42, 10-45 and 11-9.
    Supplementary – Para. 11-6, 11-19 and 11-82.

EQUIPMENT: A refrigerator with a magnetic gasket.

PREPARATION PROCEDURE:
1. Study the gasket on the domestic refrigerator and the reference paragraphs.
                                                    TEST√_____
2. Obtain: Tools – 1 Gasket notcher, 1 Extension cord with thin wire and 40-watt test light, 2 putty knives.
3. Obtain: Instruments – 1 0.003-in. feeler gauge, 1 spirit level.
4. Obtain: Supplies – 1 replacement gasket, 1 wiping cloth, 1 safe cleaning solvent.

TASK PROCEDURE:
1. Check to see if the cabinet is level. Check the door alignment and sealing ability of the gasket with either a feeler gauge or with the 40-watt test lamp.
2. If the door hardware is out of alignment, repair by changing the adjustment on the hinge assembly.
                                                    1-2√_____
3. Repeat step No. 1. If there is still a leakage, replace the gasket.
4. Remove the old gasket and clean all surfaces. Be sure plastic strips are warm (ambient temperature) before prying on them with putty knives.
5. Replace the gasket with same style gasket, making certain that all corners fit properly by using gasket notcher.
6. Check with a test light to determine fit.
                                                    3-6√_____

CLOSING THE STATION:
    Clean the work station and return all the material to the tool crib.

DATA:

Refrigerator, Name _____ Model _____
Gasket, Type _____ Material _____
Method of Holding Gasket: Staples _____ Inner Panel _____ Adhesive _____

Remarks:

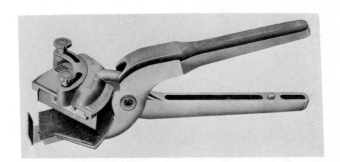

REMOVE AND INSTALL DOOR GASKETS.

Indicate the best answer for each question below by encircling its letter.

1. What tool is useful for removing the plastic sheet inner door panel?
   a. Screwdriver.
   b. Putty knife.
   c. Chisel.
   d. Knife.
   e. Thickness gauge.

2. What is the maximum pull allowed to open a domestic unit door?
   a. 8-12 lbs.
   b. 10-12 lbs.
   c. 13-15 lbs.
   d. 17-19 lbs.
   e. 20-25 lbs.

3. Why must the gasket be a tight fit to the door jamb?
   a. To reduce odors.
   b. To keep some air pressure in cabinet.
   c. To reduce air flow.
   d. To reduce moisture flow.
   e. To reduce both air and moisture flow.

4. What interval should be allowed if checking the gasket to see if it is sealing by opening the door twice in rapid succession?
   a. 5-10 second intervals.
   b. 10-14 second intervals.
   c. 15-20 second intervals.
   d. 25-30 second intervals.
   e. 1 minute to 2 minute intervals.

5. What is the main purpose of the magnets in the gasket?
   a. To keep the door closed.
   b. To have a good gasket fit.
   c. To comply with a Federal Safety Law.
   d. Less expensive than a latch and strike.
   e. Self closing.

REMOVE AND INSTALL A BREAKER STRIP

OBJECTIVE: Given the tools, materials and equipment listed below: remove and install a
breaker strip, that has been previously installed, using the clip method.

REFERENCES: Required – Para. 10-41, 10-42, 10-45 and 11-9.
Supplementary – Para. 11-6, 11-19 and 11-82.

EQUIPMENT: One domestic refrigerator cabinet.

PREPARATION PROCEDURE:
1.   Study the reference paragraphs, the illustrations and the refrigerator cabinet.
TEST√ _____

2.   Obtain: Tools – 2 putty knives, 2 plastic strip removers.
3.   Obtain: Supplies – 1 roll 1-in. masking tape, 1 wiping cloth.

TASK PROCEDURE:
1.   Open the door and warm the breaker strips. They must be room temperature (75 to 100° F).
2.   Place masking tape around the putty knives.
3.   If there are cornerpieces, remove by gently prying with putty knives.
4.   Insert the knives gently between the inner liner and the breaker strip.
5.   Gradually warp the breaker strip from its position. Be careful not to scratch or nick the
plastic or the metal shell edges.   1-5√ _____
6.   Replace the breaker strip gently.   6√ _____

CLOSING THE STATION:
Clean the work station and return all material to the tool crib.

DATA:

Refrigerator, Make _____ Model _____

Tools for removing plastic strips from cabinets and doors.

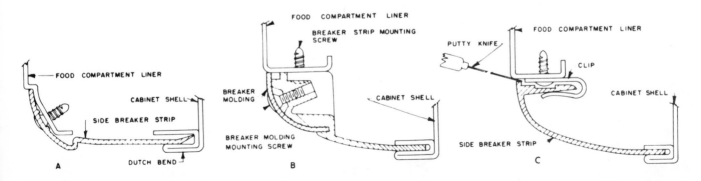

Three methods of attaching breaker strips to a cabinet. A—Visible sheet metal screw. B—Breaker strip and moulding method. C—Clip method.

REMOVE AND INSTALL A BREAKER STRIP.

Indicate the best answer for each question below by encircling its letter.

1. Why must the breaker strip be warm?
   a. Does not scratch easily.
   b. It is more flexible.
   c. To be sure there is no ice on other side.
   d. It does not have to be warm.
   e. It expands and loosens.

2. Why are breaker strips not made of metal?
   a. Some are.
   b. Too stiff.
   c. May corrode.
   d. Conducts heat.
   e. Too heavy.

3. If a breaker strip cracks or breaks, what must be done?
   a. Glue it.
   b. Weld it.
   c. Repair with tape.
   d. Replace it.
   e. Breaker strips do not break.

4. Is the joint between the shell edge and the breaker strip leak proof?
   a. Yes.
   b. No.
   c. It does not have to be.
   d. If it is not, ice will collect in the insulation.
   e. Air must circulate back of the breaker strip.

5. How can a breaker strip be heated before it is installed?
   a. Electric resistance heat.
   b. Radiant heat.
   c. Gently with a torch.
   d. Hot water.
   e. An air torch.

REMOVE AND INSTALL CHEST TYPE FREEZER LID

OBJECTIVE: Given the tools, materials and equipment listed below: remove and install a chest type freezer lid to satisfactory condition.

REFERENCES: Required – Para. 2-67, 10-32, 10-33, 10-34, 10-41 and 10-45.
Supplementary – Para. 11-6, 11-19 and 11-82.

EQUIPMENT: One chest type freezer cabinet.

PREPARATION PROCEDURE:
1. Study the cabinet hinges, illustration and reference paragraphs.   TEST√ _____
2. Obtain: Tools – 1 set screwdrivers, 1 pair of 6-in. slim nose pliers.
3. Obtain: Supplies – 1 wiping cloth.

TASK PROCEDURE:
1. Remove the covers over the hinges.
2. Mark position of spring adjustment, then loosen the counter balance springs built into the hinges. (See illustration below.) BE CAREFUL! If spring adjustment is turned out too far, the spring and adjusting screw will fly.
3. Remove the machine screws. (BE CAREFUL of counter balance springs – the hinges may fly loose.)   1-3√ _____
4. Remove the hinge from the lid.
5. Inspect for hinge pin wear. If worn, replace.
6. Install the hinge. Carefully align the lid before tightening the screws.
7. Adjust the counter balance spring.   4-7√ _____

CLOSING THE STATION:
Clean the station and return all materials to the tool crib.

DATA:

Freezer, Make _____ Model _____ Year _____
      Capacity _____ Hinge Material _____
      Type of Assembly Screws _____ Size _____

Remarks:

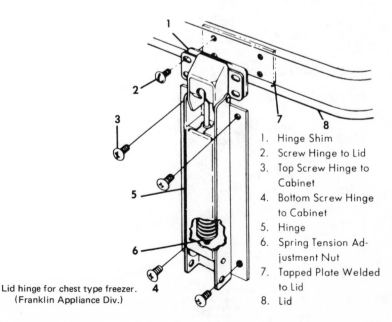

Lid hinge for chest type freezer.
(Franklin Appliance Div.)

1. Hinge Shim
2. Screw Hinge to Lid
3. Top Screw Hinge to Cabinet
4. Bottom Screw Hinge to Cabinet
5. Hinge
6. Spring Tension Adjustment Nut
7. Tapped Plate Welded to Lid
8. Lid

REMOVE AND INSTALL CHEST TYPE FREEZER LID.

Indicate the best answer for each question by encircling its letter.

1. Why is the chest design freezer used?
   a. Less expensive.
   b. Uses less space.
   c. The food is easier to reach.
   d. Less cold air is lost when opened.
   e. The refrigerating system is more efficient.

2. What is the purpose of the hinge spring?
   a. To open the lid.
   b. To close the lid.
   c. It makes the gasket tighter.
   d. It is easier to close the lid.
   e. It holds the lid open.

3. Why is the spring loosened before the hinge is removed?
   a. It is not.
   b. It is not adjustable.
   c. To prevent injury.
   d. Hinge cannot be removed otherwise.
   e. To avoid stripping the machine screw threads.

4. How many springs are used?
   a. One.
   b. Two.
   c. Three.
   d. As many as there are hinges.
   e. Some hinges use two springs.

5. What is done before a spring adjustment is loosened?
   a. Threads are oiled.
   b. Position of adjustment is marked.
   c. Nothing.
   d. The lid is opened.
   e. The lid is closed.

Task No. 3-5 Task Grade _____
Name _____
Date _____ Class _____

ADD OIL TO HERMETIC SYSTEM

OBJECTIVE: Given a hermetic system, a supply of refrigerant oil and the necessary tools: add oil to the system to approved standards.

REFERENCES: Required – Para. 2-70, 9-31, 9-36, 11-26 through 11-33, 11-47 and 11-65.
     Supplementary – Para. 11-82.

EQUIPMENT: An operating hermetic type household refrigerator.

PREPARATION PROCEDURE:
1.   Study the hermetic system assigned and study the reference paragraphs. TEST√_____
2.   Obtain: Tools – 1 charging cylinder, 1 valve attachment kit, 1 8-in. adj. wrench, 1 pr. goggles.
3.   Obtain: Instruments – 1 manifold gauge set and 3 lines, 1 vacuum pump.
4.   Obtain: Supplies – 1 wiping cloth, 1 20-oz. glass container of refrig. oil, 1 clamp-on service valve, 1 oil cylinder, 1 refrigerant cylinder.

TASK PROCEDURE (WEAR GOGGLES):
1.   Attach the gauge manifold to the service valve adaptor or to the clamp-on service valve. Purge all the attached lines using the refrigerant cylinder.
2.   Add oil in one of two ways:
     Method a: Evacuate the system, add oil using system vacuum and then recharge the system.
     Method b: Build up a refrigerant pressure in an oil cylinder higher than the system pressure and force the oil into the system.   1-2√_____
3.   Start system and check operating pressures and temperatures.
4.   Close valves and remove the gauge manifold.   3-4√_____

CLOSING THE STATION:
     Clean the work station and return all the materials to the tool crib.

DATA:

Hermetic System, Name_____ Model _____
Service Valves, Type used_____
Refrigerant, Kind_____ Amount _____
Operating Pressures, High Side_____ Low Side _____
Maximum Amount of Oil in System_____
Oil, Type Added_____ Amount Added _____
Method Used to Add Oil_____

Remarks:

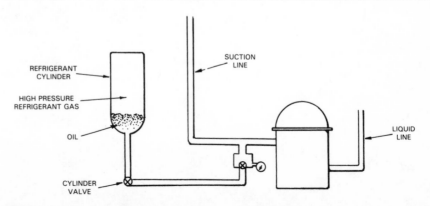

REFRIGERANT CYLINDER
HIGH PRESSURE REFRIGERANT GAS
OIL
CYLINDER VALVE
SUCTION LINE
LIQUID LINE

ADD OIL TO HERMETIC SYSTEM.

Indicate the best answer for each question below by encircling its letter.

1. How may oil be added if the system cannot be made to produce a vacuum?
   a. It cannot.
   b. Pour it directly into the compressor.
   c. Build up a pressure in an oil charged cylinder.
   d. Remove all the refrigerant.
   e. It is not important to have the correct oil charge.

2. What precautions must be taken when adding oil to a system which has service valves and the vacuum method, using a bottle, is used?
   a. Always keep the end of the hose submerged in oil.
   b. Draw a vacuum, open the unit and pour the oil in through a funnel.
   c. Produce a vacuum and add oil to the high side of system.
   d. Remove all refrigerant, then add oil.
   e. Always purge the high side of the system of air first.

3. What is the primary purpose of oil in a refrigeration system?
   a. Cooling and lubricating.
   b. Lubricating and quietness.
   c. Removing of heat.
   d. To act as a catalyst to the refrigerant.
   e. To prevent oxidation of parts.

4. What is one of the chief properties required of a good refrigerant oil?
   a. It must separate from the refrigerant at high temperatures.
   b. It must circulate with the refrigerant.
   c. It should flow at low temperatures.
   d. It must have high viscosity.
   e. It must have high pour point.

5. What is the meaning of "pour point" of oil?
   a. Its ability to lubricate at high temperatures.
   b. The ability to not solidify at the lowest temperatures in the system.
   c. The ability of the oil to not congeal at the highest temperature.
   d. The temperature at which it will pour the fastest.
   e. It is the lowest temperature at which the oil will flow.

ADD REFRIGERANT TO A HERMETIC SYSTEM

OBJECTIVE: Given a hermetic system and the necessary tools and supplies: charge and test the system to acceptable quality.

REFERENCES: Required - Para. 9-21 through 9-30, 9-33, 9-35, 9-36, 11-45 and 11-46.
Supplementary - Para. 9-34, 11-26 through 11-43.

EQUIPMENT: An operating hermetic system.

PREPARATION PROCEDURE:
1. Study the hermetic system assigned and study the reference paragraphs. TEST✓ _____
2. Obtain: Tools - 1 oiler with refrigerating oil, 1 charging board, 1 8-in. adjustable open end wrench, 1 complete service valve attachment and adapters, 1 pr. safety goggles.
3. Obtain: Instruments - 1 gauge manifold with refrigerant lines, 1 leak detector.
4. Obtain: Supplies - 1 small service cylinder with proper refrigerant (see system label), 1 wiping cloth.

TASK PROCEDURE (WEAR GOGGLES):
1. Start the system and allow it to run for at least 15 minutes, and check for frost line in the evaporator. Check for leaks.
2. Install the service valve attachment or clamp-on valve on the suction line (low side). Install the gauge manifold.   1-2✓ _____
3. Connect the refrigerant cylinder. Purge the lines, using cylinder gas. Test for leaks.
4. Charge the system. Open the valves and heat the service cylinder by placing it in a bucket of hot water. The cylinder must be upright. Keep the low-side pressures in the normal range.   3-4✓ _____
5. Check the system by running the unit and by testing for leaks.
6. Remove the gauge manifold and lines. Test for leaks.   5-6✓ _____

CLOSING THE STATION:
Clean the work station and return all the material to the tool crib.

DATA:
Hermetic System, Name _____ Model _____ Year _____
Refrigerant, Kind _____ Pounds _____
Normal Head Pressure _____ Normal Low-Side Pressure _____
Refrigerant Control, Make _____ Type _____

Testing	At Start	After 15 minutes
Low-Side Pressure		
High-Side Pressure		
Cooling Temperature		
Suction Line Temperature		
Liquid Line Temperature		
Noise, Compressor		
Evaporator		
Frost Line on Evaporator		
Charging: Amount of Refrigerant Added		

ADD REFRIGERANT TO A HERMETIC SYSTEM

Indicate the best answer for each question below by encircling its letter.

1. What is the most common indication of a shortage of refrigerant in a hermetic system?
    a. Excessive head pressure.
    b. Shorter running part of cycle.
    c. Lowering of frost line on the evaporator.
    d. Warmer cabinet.
    e. Excessive frosting.

2. What is the most important thing to do if a shortage of refrigerant is discovered?
    a. Charge the unit.
    b. Stop the unit.
    c. Overhaul the unit.
    d. Find the leak.
    e. Check the quantity of oil in the unit.

3. What is considered the best way to heat a service cylinder?
    a. Use a welding torch.
    b. Use a gas-air torch.
    c. Use a blow torch.
    d. Use hot water.
    e. Use hot gas.

4. How may one determine when the unit has been charged with the correct amount of refrigerant?
    a. By the head pressure.
    b. By the low-side pressure.
    c. By the liquid line temperature.
    d. By the suction line temperature.
    e. By the frost line on the evaporator.

5. What is the best leak testing method?
    a. Soap suds.
    b. Ammonia.
    c. Halide torch.
    d. Oil trace.
    e. Electronic sniffer.

LOCATE TROUBLE IN A MANUAL DEFROST HERMETIC SYSTEM

OBJECTIVE: Given a poorly operating hermetic system and the necessary tools and supplies:
   locate the trouble and repair it to satisfactory operation.

REFERENCES: Required - Para. 7-11, 7-13, 7-14, 7-25, 7-27, 7-50, 11-1 through 11-43, 11-49
   through 11-57, 11-61 through 11-64, 11-75, 11-76 and 11-82.
   Supplementary - Para. 11-44 through 11-48, 11-58 and 11-59.

EQUIPMENT: A charged but poorly operating hermetic system.

PREPARATION PROCEDURE:
   1.   Study the hermetic system assigned, and study the reference paragraphs.   TEST√_____
   2.   Obtain: Tools - 1 hermetic service valve attachment kit, 1 8-in. adjustable
        wrench, 1 4-in. screwdriver 1/4 in. x 1/32 in. blade end, 1 pr. safety goggles.
   3.   Obtain: Instruments - 1 hermetic analyzer or test light, 1 thermometer, 1 gauge
        manifold with refrigerant lines.
   4.   Obtain: Supplies - 1 12-in length of 1/8 in. dia. 50-50 solder, 1 clamp-on service
        valve, 1 can soldering flux.

TASK PROCEDURE (WEAR GOGGLES):
   1.   Start the system. If it will not start: (a) Check the electrical circuit, wall receptacles,
        thermostat, relay, capacitor and wiring. (b) If internal trouble is indicated, a shop
        overhaul or replacement is necessary.   1 √_____
   2.   If the system starts but shuts off almost immediately, this trouble indicates an overload.
        The motor overload device is opening the circuit. Locate the trouble, repair if external
        or a major overhaul is necessary.   2 √_____
   3.   If the system refrigerates and then defrosts repeatedly, there is moisture in the system.
        Install a new filter-drier.   3 √_____
   4.   If the unit refrigerates, but not satisfactorily, check for lack of refrigerant.
   5.   If the unit over-refrigerates (too cold), check the motor control thermostat.
                                                                 4-5 √_____

CLOSING THE STATION
     Clean the work station and return all the material to the tool crib.

DATA:

System, Make _____ Model _____ Year _____ -
Refrigerant, Kind _____ Amount, Lb. _____ Oz. _____
Normal Head Pressure _____ Normal Low-Side Pressure _____
Trouble _____
Repair _____

Remarks:

LOCATE TROUBLE IN A MANUAL DEFROST HERMETIC SYSTEM.

Indicate the best answer for each question below by encircling its letter.

1. What is probably wrong if the cabinet is too cold and the unit runs continuously?
   a. Faulty thermostat.
   b. Faulty relay.
   c. Nothing.
   d. Out of refrigerant.
   e. An open circuit.

2. How does one check the electrical power outlet for the unit?
   a. Ammeter.
   b. Test light.
   c. If cabinet light will not work, power is off.
   d. If house lights work, the power is all right.
   e. Ohmmeter.

3. Why must the condenser surface be kept clean?
   a. To prevent overheating the fan motor.
   b. To keep the head pressure down.
   c. To prevent dust in the room.
   d. For sanitation purposes.
   e. To keep moisture out of the system.

4. What is an indication that there is moisture in the system?
   a. It will not start.
   b. It will run noisily.
   c. It will freeze and defrost intermittently.
   d. It will run but will not freeze.
   e. The suction line will sweat or frost.

5. What is an indication that there is too much refrigerant in the system?
   a. The unit will not start.
   b. The unit will not freeze.
   c. The suction line will sweat or frost.
   d. The cabinet will get too cold.
   e. The relay will burn out.

LOCATE TROUBLE IN AN ELECTRIC DEFROST SYSTEM

OBJECTIVE: Given a hermetic system with an electric defrost problem, and the necessary tools:
   locate the trouble and repair it to satisfactory operation.

REFERENCES: Required – Para. 3-24, 8-29, 8-30, 8-35, 8-43, 10-15, 10-16, 10-17, 10-27,
   10-28 and 11-21.
   Supplementary – Para. 10-45, 11-82, 12-32, 12-44 and 12-74.

EQUIPMENT: 1 refrigerating system with electric defrost and 1 replacement heater of proper type
   and rating.

PREPARATION PROCEDURE:
   1.   Study the refrigerating system assigned, study the reference paragraphs.   TEST√_____
   2.   Obtain: Tools – 1 Phillips head screwdriver, 1 4-in. screwdriver, 1 linesman's pliers,
        1 breaker trim remover, 1 pr. safety goggles.
   3.   Obtain: Instruments – 1 combination voltmeter, ammeter and ohmmeter (multimeter), 1 test light.
   4.   Obtain: Supplies – 1 wiping cloth, 1 roll 1/2-in. electrical tape, 1 bottle water-
        proofing liquid, 1 box solderless connections.

TASK PROCEDURE (WEAR GOGGLES):
   1.   Check the unit and determine visually and by checking for moisture and ice, if heater
        coils are functioning. Also check the mullion door jamb heater, drain warmer, butter
        conditioner, etc.
   2.   Check electrical circuits with ohmmeter (power off). Refer to manufacturer's wiring
        diagram for heater values.   1-2√_____
   3.   Locate defective heater or heater coil switch. To service heater, remove cabinet
        parts and breaker trim if necessary.
   4.   Disconnect electrical wires and retest electrical heater. If defective, replace with
        correct replacement.
   5.   Install heater using solderless connectors or other fastening devices to insure water-
        proof electrical connections.
   6.   Install cabinet parts and operate system.   3-6√_____

CLOSING THE STATION:
   Clean the work station and return all the material to the tool crib.

DATA:

System, Make _____ Model _____
System, Type _____
Heater, Type _____ Wattage _____
Replaced Heater, Type _____
Reason for Replacement _____
Heater Control, Make _____ Model _____ Type _____

Remarks:

LOCATE TROUBLE IN AN ELECTRIC DEFROST SYSTEM.

Indicate the best answer for each question below by encircling its letter.

1. What temperature range is the heating element in a butter conditioner supposed to maintain?
   a. 15-32° F.
   b. 25-35° F.
   c. 35-45° F.
   d. 40-55° F.
   e. 50-60° F.

2. How is the heating element in a butter conditioner connected into the system?
   a. In parallel with the other accessories.
   b. In series with the other accessories.
   c. Independent of the motor.
   d. In series-parallel with the other accessories.
   e. In series with the motor.

3. Why is a plug fuse inadequate protection for a motor?
   a. It is not accurate.
   b. It is too large for the running current.
   c. It must be large enough for the starting current.
   d. It is too small.
   e. It is too expensive.

4. How is the light switch and light wired?
   a. In series with the motor.
   b. In parallel with the motor.
   c. Independent of the motor.
   d. In series with the thermostat.
   e. In series with the mullion heater.

5. What is the purpose of the freezer door heater?
   a. Prevents condensation from forming and freezing.
   b. Provides enough heat to give an adequate seal to the door.
   c. Keeps the gasket pliable.
   d. Prevents moisture from dripping on the floor.
   e. Promotes defrosting on the off cycle.

LOCATE TROUBLE IN A HOT GAS DEFROST HERMETIC SYSTEM

OBJECTIVE: Given a hermetic system with a poorly operating hot gas defrost system and the necessary tools: locate the trouble and repair it to satisfactory operation quality.

REFERENCES: Required - Para. 3-23, 5-19, 5-20, 5-32, 8-29, 8-30, 8-31, 8-43, 10-18, 10-19, 10-20, 10-45, 11-21, 11-54, 11-82 and 12-29.
Supplementary - Para. 12-44 and 12-74.

EQUIPMENT: One hermetic system with hot gas defrost.

PREPARATION PROCEDURE:
1. Study the hermetic system and the reference paragraphs.   TEST√_____
2. Obtain: Tools - 1 set screwdrivers, 1 set pliers, 1 set socket wrenches, 1 8-in. adjustable wrench, 1 pr. safety goggles.
3. Obtain: Instruments - 1 combination voltmeter, ammeter and ohmmeter (multimeter), 1 test light.
4. Obtain: Supplies - 1 wiping cloth.

TASK PROCEDURE (WEAR GOGGLES):
1. Operate system for 10 to 15 minutes. Then start up defrost system. Carefully touch the hot gas line. If warm, solenoid valve is open and defrost problem must be in the electrical circuit. If defrost line is cold, it may be stuck solenoid or open electrical circuit.
2. Test the electrical circuit with the voltmeter. If found open, repair it.
                                                                      1-2√_____
3. If solenoid magnetic coil is open, replace it.
4. If defrost control is faulty, replace it.   3-4√_____
5. If valve is stuck closed, the valve body will have to be replaced. See instructor.
                                                                      5√_____

CLOSING THE STATION:
Clean up the work station and return all the material to the tool crib.

DATA:

System, Make_____ Model_____ Type_____
Solenoid Valve, Make_____ Model_____ Voltage_____ Size of Tubing_____
Defrost Control, Make_____ Model_____
Trouble_____
Repair_____

Remarks:

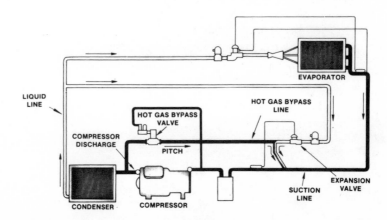

LOCATE TROUBLE IN A HOT GAS DEFROST HERMETIC SYSTEM.

Indicate the best answer for each question below by encircling its letter.

1. What valve controls the hot gas flow to the evaporator?
    a. Pressure valve.
    b. Temperature valve.
    c. Solenoid valve.
    d. Motorized valve.
    e. Thermostatic expansion valve.

2. How is the hot gas valve closed (end of defrost cycle)?
    a. Timer.
    b. Thermostat.
    c. Timer or thermostat.
    d. Refrigerator thermostat.
    e. Pressurestat.

3. Where does the "hot gas" come from?
    a. Compressor and condenser.
    b. Compressor.
    c. Condenser.
    d. Suction line.
    e. From electric heaters.

4. Will rapping the body of the valve to open it be a good repair?
    a. No.
    b. Yes.
    c. Action will ruin the valve.
    d. May cause a leak.
    e. It is less expensive than replacing the valve.

5. Does the compressor run during the "hot gas" defrost operation?
    a. No.
    b. Yes.
    c. Only part of the time.
    d. Only if the hot gas cools.
    e. Just until the end of the defrost part of the cycle.

INSTALL A FILTER-DRIER

OBJECTIVE: Given a hermetic system with a clogged filter-drier and the necessary tools: replace the filter-drier and return system to satisfactory operation.

REFERENCES: Required – Para. 11-26 through 11-33, 11-35, 11-51, 11-52, 11-53, 11-63, 11-75 and 11-82.
Supplementary – Para. 11-36.

EQUIPMENT: A hermetic system.

PREPARATION PROCEDURE:
1. Study the system assigned and study the reference paragraphs.   TEST√_____
2. Obtain: Tools – 1 leak detector, 1 8-in. adjustable open end wrench, 1 vacuum pump, 1 brazing outfit, 1 valve attachment kit, 1 pr. safety goggles.
3. Obtain: Instruments – 1 6-in steel rule, 1 gauge manifold with refrigerant lines.
4. Obtain: Supplies – 1 bottle mineral spirits, 1 wiping cloth, 1 jar brazing flux, 1 4-in. square sandpaper, 1 refrigerant cylinder, 1 valve adaptor or piercing valve, 1 filter-drier, 1 length of brazing filler metal, 1 filler.

TASK PROCEDURE (WEAR GOGGLES):
1. Install valve adaptor or piercing valve. Connect gauge manifold. Remove refrigerant from system. VENTILATE WELL.
2. Clean the joints, flux the joints, heat. Remove the drier. Record the size of the fittings. Handle hot parts with pliers.
3. Install the new drier in the system carefully. Flux and braze. Use the refrigerant cylinder to create a 70 to 90 psi head pressure. Test for leaks.   1-3√_____
4. If no leaks, evacuate the system for at least an hour.
5. Charge the system and operate the system for 20 minutes. If the drier heats or gets warm, it means it is absorbing moisture.
6. Remove the gauge manifold from the system. BE CAREFUL! Test the system for leaks again.   4-6√_____

CLOSING THE STATION
Clean the station and return all material to the tool crib.

DATA:

System, Make_____ Model_____ Size_____
Name of Drier_____ Size_____
Chemical_____
Inlet Fitting, Size and Type_____
Outlet Fitting, Size and Type_____
Test for Leaks, Method_____ Pressure_____

Remarks:

INSTALL A FILTER-DRIER.

Indicate the best answer for each question below by encircling its letter.

1. How can one tell when a drier without an indicator is absorbing moisture?
   a. The drier will become cold when the unit is operating.
   b. The drier will become warm when the unit is operating.
   c. The head pressure will rise.
   d. The head pressure will fall.
   e. The drier will frost when the unit is operating.

2. What is a strainer screen supposed to remove?
   a. Solid impurities.
   b. Acid.
   c. Oil.
   d. Moisture.
   e. Sludge.

3. What does moisture do in an R-12 system?
   a. Stops the compressor.
   b. Produces a noisy refrigerator.
   c. Causes the system to corrode.
   d. Freezes at the refrigerant control.
   e. Freezes in the compressor.

4. Where is the most common place to install a drier in the system?
   a. In the liquid line.
   b. Between compressor and condenser.
   c. Between the condenser and liquid receiver.
   d. Between the refrigerant control and the evaporator.
   e. Anywhere.

5. What is a popular drier chemical?
   a. Silica gel.
   b. Zinc moss.
   c. Iron oxide.
   d. Cupric oxide.
   e. Sodium hydroxide.

REPAIR OR REPLACE A CAPILLARY TUBE

OBJECTIVE: Given a hermetic system with a clogged capillary tube, and the necessary tools:
remove and repair or replace the capillary tube to satisfactory operation.

REFERENCES: Required - Para. 3-9, 4-17, 4-18, 4-61, 5-26, 5-27, 5-28, 5-32, 11-35 through
11-43, 11-51, 11-52, 11-53, 11-63, 11-75 and 11-82.

EQUIPMENT: A hermetic system which has a capillary tube.

PREPARATION PROCEDURE:
1.   Check the assigned hermetic system and study the reference paragraphs.

                                                                                         TEST√_____
2.   Obtain: Tools - 1 capillary tube cleaner, 1 8-in. adjustable open end wrench,
1 vacuum pump, 1 leak detector, 1 brazing outfit, 1 valve attachment kit, 1 pr.
safety goggles.
3.   Obtain: Instruments - 1 6-in. steel rule, 1 gauge manifold complete with lines.
4.   Obtain: Supplies - 1 wiping cloth, 1 bottle mineral spirits, 1 jar of brazing flux,
1 4-in. square sandpaper, 1 cylinder refrigerant, 1 valve adaptor or piercing valve,
1 capillary tube, 1 length of brazing filler metal.

TASK PROCEDURE (WEAR GOGGLES):
1.   Install the valve adaptor or piercing valve. Connect the gauge manifold. Purge the lines.
Test for leaks. Test the unit.
2.   Remove the capillary tube. Remove the refrigerant by SAFELY purging (use good
ventilation). Balance the pressure, clean the capillary tube connection, put flux
on joints and heat. Remove the capillary tube and filter-drier (some may be
soldered or brazed) and plug the openings if possible.   1-2√_____
3.   Repair the capillary tube by using a capillary tube cleaner. If necessary, replace
with a new one. Always install a new filter-drier.
4.   Install the capillary tube and filter-drier into the unit. Clean and dry the connections.
Flux the joints. Braze. Clean off the flux with warm water. Pressurize system with
refrigerant and test for leaks. Evacuate by the deep vacuum or triple vacuum method.
Charge with the correct amount of refrigerant (in vapor form into low side). Test for
leaks.
5.   Operate the system.   3-5√_____

CLOSING THE STATION:
Clean the work station and return all the material to the tool crib.

DATA:
System, Make_____ Model _____ Type_____
Capillary Tube, Material_____ ID_____ OD_____ Length_____
Filter-drier, Material_____ Diameter_____ Length_____

Remarks:

REPAIR OR REPLACE A CAPILLARY TUBE.

Indicate the best answer for each question below by encircling its letter.

1. Of what material is a capillary tube made?
    a. Steel.
    b. Brass.
    c. Stainless steel.
    d. Aluminum.
    e. Copper.

2. What effect does internal moisture have on a capillary tube system?
    a. None.
    b. It makes it frost back.
    c. It makes it defrost.
    d. It makes it colder.
    e. It stops the motor.

3. What is the most popular refrigerant control in domestic refrigerators?
    a. TEV
    b. AEV
    c. LSF
    d. HSF
    e. Capillary tube.

4. Why is a filter put at the inlet of the capillary tube?
    a. To remove moisture.
    b. To remove oil.
    c. To remove air.
    d. To remove solid foreign particles.
    e. To prevent gas from entering the capillary tube.

5. What happens when a capillary tube system is overcharged?
    a. Nothing.
    b. It has a high head pressure.
    c. It will partially defrost.
    d. It will sweat and frost back.
    e. It will have below normal low-side pressure.

REPLACE AN EVAPORATOR

OBJECTIVE: Given a hermetic system and the necessary tools and supplies: remove and replace the evaporator to satisfactory operation.

REFERENCES: Required – Para. 4-5, 4-6, 10-45, 11-25 through 11-33, 11-38 through 11-42, 11-48, 11-55, 11-56, 11-62, 11-75 and 11-82.
Supplementary – Para. 10-12.

EQUIPMENT: A hermetic system and a replacement evaporator.

PREPARATION PROCEDURE:
1. Study the hermetic system assigned and study the reference paragraphs.
TEST√_____
2. Obtain: Tools – 1 pr. 8-in. pliers, 1 8-in. adjustable open end wrench, 1 4-in. screwdriver 1/4-in. x 1/32-in. blade end, 1 tube cutter, 1 wire brush or steel wool, 1 leak detector, 1 pr. safety goggles, 1 brazing outfit, 1 vacuum pump.
3. Obtain: Instruments – 1 gauge manifold complete with refrigerant lines, 1 thermometer.
4. Obtain: Supplies – 1 length of brazing filler metal, 1 jar brazing flux, 1 wiping cloth, 1 refrigerant cylinder, 1 valve adaptor or piercing valve.

TASK PROCEDURE (WEAR GOGGLES):
1. Remove the parts to expose the evaporator.
2. Attach the adaptor or piercing valve. Install the gauge manifold, purge the manifold lines and check for leaks.
3. Purge the refrigerant from the system (ventilate).
4. Cut the refrigerant lines at the evaporator. Clean and dry the tubing at the cutting positions. Cut the lines at a place that permits brazing of the lines to the new unit. Plug the lines connected to the system.   1-4√_____
5. Remove the evaporator by unbolting it from the cabinet, and install the new evaporator.
6. Clean the tubing. Swage the tubing or use couplings. Braze the connections, using the correct brazing procedure.
7. Remove and install a new filter-drier.
8. Pressurize the system and test for leaks.
9. Evacuate using a vacuum pump. Use either the deep vacuum method or triple vacuum method to remove the air and moisture.   5-9√_____
10. Charge the unit. Use the exact weight of refrigerant charge, if known, or charge until the evaporator is frosted over but NOT down the suction line.   10√_____

CLOSING THE STATION:
Clean the work station and return all material to the tool crib.

DATA:
System, Make_____ Model_____ Year_____
Refrigerant, Kind_____ Amount, Lb._____ Oz._____
Compressor Type_____ How Assembled_____
Evaporator Type_____ Where Located_____ Condition_____

Remarks:

REPLACE AN EVAPORATOR.

Indicate the best answer for each question below by encircling its letter.

1. What type of evaporator is used with a capillary tube?
    a. Dry.
    b. Brine.
    c. Tubular.
    d. Flooded.
    e. Any type.

2. Why should the service valve attachment installation be checked for leaks?
    a. To save needed refrigerant.
    b. To provide practice in making connections.
    c. To help one practice leak testing.
    d. To check if impurities can enter the system.
    e. To prevent low high-side pressures.

3. Why is the tubing cut with a tube cutter instead of being cut with a hacksaw?
    a. It is easier.
    b. To keep copper chips out of the refrigerant lines.
    c. It is faster.
    d. To keep air out of the tubing.
    e. To help one determine the tubing material.

4. What tubing lines are cut?
    a. Suction tubing only.
    b. Suction and condenser tubing.
    c. Capillary tubing.
    d. Capillary tubing and suction tubing.
    e. Capillary tubing and condenser tubing.

5. What action should be taken when removing the refrigerant from the system?
    a. Save the refrigerant.
    b. Purge it into a sewer.
    c. Purge it out a window and through an oil trap.
    d. Pump it into an open crock.
    e. Purge it into a special purge line into a ventilation hood.

REPLACE A CONDENSER

OBJECTIVE: Given a hermetic system with a faulty condenser, and the necessary tools and supplies: remove and replace the condenser to satisfactory operation quality.

REFERENCES: Required - Para. 4-13, 4-61, 11-26 through 11-33, 11-38 through 11-43, 11-55, 11-56, 11-61, 11-75 and 11-82.
Supplementary - Para. 11-76 and 11-77.

EQUIPMENT: One hermetic system and a replacement condenser.

PREPARATION PROCEDURE:
1. Study the assigned hermetic system and study the reference paragraphs.

TEST√ _____

2. Obtain: Tools - 1 8-in. adjustable open end wrench, 1 set screwdrivers, 1 tube cutter, 1 wire brush or steel wool, 1 leak detector, 1 pr. safety goggles, 1 brazing outfit, 1 hermetic service valve attachment kit or piercing valve, 1 pr. of 8-in. pliers, 1 vacuum pump.
3. Obtain: Instruments - 1 gauge manifold complete with flexible lines, 1 thermometer.
4. Obtain: Supplies - 1 length 1/16-in. brazing alloy, 1 jar brazing flux, 1 wiping cloth, 1 refrigerant cylinder.

TASK PROCEDURE (WEAR GOGGLES):
1. Remove condenser shroud and fan.
2. Attach the valve adaptor or piercing valve, install the gauge manifold, purge the manifold lines. Test for leaks.
3. Purge the refrigerant from the system to 0-5 psi. Ventilate. Trap the oil mist from the purged vapor.
4. Cut the refrigerant lines at outlet to condenser and outlet of filter-drier. Clean and dry the tubing before cutting. Cut the lines at places where brazing will be easier later. Immediately plug the lines still connected to the system.   1-4√ _____
5. Remove the condenser and filter-drier. Install new condenser and filter-drier.
6. Clean the tubing. Swage the tubing or use couplings. Flux and then braze the joints. Remove the flux.
7. Pressurize the system and test for leaks.
8. Evacuate the system using the vacuum pump. Use either the deep vacuum method or the triple vacuum method.
9. Charge the unit with vapor refrigerant. Charge with exact amount of refrigerant or charge until suction line sweats or frosts (then purge a little).   5-9√ _____

CLOSING THE STATION:
Clean the work station and return all material to the tool crib.

DATA:

System, Make _____ _____ Model _____ Serial No. _____ Type _____
Condenser, Type _____ Inlet Size _____ Outlet Size _____
Filter-drier _____ Length _____ Inlet Size _____ Outlet Size _____ __
Refrigerant, Kind _____ Amount _____

Remarks:

REPLACE A CONDENSER.

Indicate the best answer for each question below by encircling its letter.

1. What is the most common fault with condensers?
    a. Clogged.
    b. Undersize.
    c. Leaks.
    d. Oil bound.
    e. Overcharged.

2. When does a condenser fan operate?
    a. All the time.
    b. Only during the "on" part of cycle.
    c. Only during the "off" part of cycle.
    d. Only when the compressor is running.
    e. Only when the thermostat points are open.

3. What is the most frequent service operation performed on a condenser?
    a. Replacing it.
    b. Purging it.
    c. Straightening the fins.
    d. Cleaning it.
    e. Connecting gauge manifold to it.

4. Why should one avoid bending a condenser fan blade?
    a. Reduces air flow.
    b. Blade will break.
    c. Fan will vibrate.
    d. Fan will hit condenser.
    e. Fan will hit motor.

5. How does one know there is air in the system?
    a. There is no way to find out.
    b. The condenser will gurgle on "off" cycle.
    c. The bottom tube of condenser will be hot.
    d. The motor overload will open.
    e. The head pressure will be above normal.

WIRE A DOMESTIC SYSTEM

OBJECTIVE: Given a domestic system without wires, and the necessary tools and supplies: wire all circuits and operate system to approved standards.

REFERENCES: Required - Para. 6-5, 6-7, 6-8, 6-9, 6-29, 6-30, 8-1, 10-9, 10-17, 10-20, 10-24, 10-28, 10-31 and 11-10.
    Supplementary - Para. 6-74 through 6-80, 7-34, 7-48, 7-50, 8-2, 8-4, 8-23, 8-37, 8-41, 8-42, 8-43 and 11-21.

EQUIPMENT: A complete operating hermetic system from which some or all of the wiring has been removed.

PREPARATION PROCEDURE:
1. Inspect the system and locate the wiring diagram. Study the reference paragraphs.
    TEST√_____
2. Obtain: Tools - 1 set insulated screwdrivers, 1 set terminal socket wrenches, 1 pr. diagonal cutting pliers, 1 wire stripper, 1 eyelet plier.
3. Obtain: Instruments - 1 test light, 1 ohmmeter.
4. Obtain: Supplies - 1 roll 1/2-in. plastic tape, 1 coil #14 stranded plastic covered wire, 1 box electrical eyelets, 1 wiping cloth, 1 box solderless connectors.

TASK PREPARATION:
1. Sketch the circuits and parts and indicate where new wires are to be installed.
    1 √_____
2. Determine size and type of wire to be replaced. Follow color code, if possible.
3. Cut new wire to proper length.
4. Strip insulation off each end of wire without injuring metal.
5. Install terminals on new wire. Both the wire and the terminals must be clean. Use the same types which are used on other wires of the system. Make sure all terminals are adequately taped where necessary.
6. Install the new wires tightly on the cleaned proper terminals to make all circuits complete. Check each circuit with ohmmeter before fastening to power terminals.
7. Reinspect all circuits and connections. Make sure all metal parts are grounded.
    2-7√_____
8. Connect electrical system to power and check its operation, also the operation of each control and accessory. 8 √_____

CLOSING THE STATION:
    Clean the work station and return material to the tool crib.

DATA:
System, Make_____ Model_____
Condensing Unit, Make_____ Model_____ Starting Amps._____
        Running Amps._____ Voltage_____ Phase_____
        Hertz_____ Overload, Make_____ Type_____
                    Relay, Make_____ Type_____
Refrigerant Control_____
Accessories, Butter Conditioner, etc. List of_____
Motor Control, Make_____ Type_____ Location_____

Remarks:

WIRE A DOMESTIC SYSTEM.

Indicate the best answer for each question below by encircling its letter.

1. What may be housed in the junction box on some units?
    a. Relay.
    b. Thermostat.
    c. Mullion heater.
    d. Defrost control.
    e. Light switch.

2. What instrument should be used to check for a short circuit?
    a. Voltmeter.
    b. Ohmmeter.
    c. Ammeter.
    d. Wattmeter.
    e. Megohmmeter.

3. How many terminals are used on most hermetic units which operate at 3,400 rpm?
    a. Three.
    b. Four.
    c. Two.
    d. Five.
    e. Six.

4. What instrument should be used to check the receptacle outlet?
    a. Ohmmeter.
    b. Megohmmeter.
    c. Voltmeter.
    d. Ammeter.
    e. None of the above.

5. How is the light switch and light connected into the electrical circuit?
    a. In series with the motor.
    b. In series with the motor fan.
    c. On a separate circuit from the junction box.
    d. On two separate circuits.
    e. Wired into a separate junction box.

WIRE A FREEZER SYSTEM

OBJECTIVE: Given a hermetic freezer system without wiring and the necessary tools and supplies: wire and operate the system to satisfactory operating condition.

REFERENCES: Required – Para. 6-5 through 6-9, 6-29, 6-30, 6-64, 6-66, 8-1, 8-23, 10-33, 10-34, 10-36, 10-37, 10-45 and 11-10.
   Supplementary – Para. 6-74 through 6-80, 7-34, 7-48, 7-50, 8-2, 8-4, 8-37, 8-41, 8-43 and 11-82.

EQUIPMENT: An operating chest type freezer with some or all of the wiring (leads) missing.

PREPARATION PROCEDURE:
1. Inspect the hermetic freezer system, locate the wiring diagram. Study the reference paragraph.   TEST √ _____
2. Obtain: Tools – 1 set insulated screwdrivers, 1 set terminal socket wrenches, 1 pr. diagonal cutting pliers, 1 wire stripper, 1 eyelet plier.
3. Obtain: Instruments – 1 test light, 1 combination voltmeter, ammeter and ohmmeter (multimeter).
4. Obtain: Supplies – 1 roll 1/2-in. plastic tape, 1 coil #14 standard plastic covered wire, 1 box electrical eyelets, 1 wiping cloth, 1 box solderless connectors.

TASK PROCEDURE:
1. Sketch the circuits and parts. Mark where new wires (leads) are to be installed.
                                                     1 √ _____
2. Determine size and type of wire to be replaced. Use same color code as wiring diagram, if possible.
3. Cut new wire to proper length.
4. Strip insulation from each end of wire without injuring metal.
5. Install terminals on new wire. Both wire and the terminal must be clean. Use the same types which are used on other wires of the system. Make sure all terminals are adequately taped where necessary.
6. Install the new wires tightly on the cleaned proper terminals to make all circuits complete. Check each circuit with ohmmeter before connecting to power terminals.
7. Recheck all circuits and connections. Make sure all metal parts are grounded.
                                                     2-7 √ _____
8. Note the method of operation of freezer alarm if used.
9. Connect electrical system to power and check its operation; also, the operation of each control and accessory.   8-9 √ _____

CLOSING THE STATION:
   Clean the work station and return all material to the tool crib.

DATA:
System, Make _____ Model _____ Serial No. _____
Condesning Unit, Make _____ Model _____ Amperage _____
   Voltage _____ Phase _____ Hertz _____
   Relay, Make _____ Type _____
   Overload, Make _____ Type _____
Refrigerant Control _____
Accessories, Freezer Alarm _____ Voltage _____
Motor Control, Type _____ Location _____

WIRE A FREEZER SYSTEM.

Indicate the best answer for each question below by encircling its letter.

1. Which type of evaporator is most used on chest type freezers?
    a. Shell liner.
    b. Plate on shelf.
    c. Open coils.
    d. Flooded.
    e. Combination of two or more of the above.

2. What is the recommended temperature range for a chest type food freezer?
    a. 0° F to 10° F.
    b. -20° F to -10° F.
    c. -30° F to -25° F.
    d. -40° F to -30° F.
    e. -10° F to -20° F.

3. What type of refrigerant control is in common use on small domestic freezers?
    a. Capillary tube.
    b. Automatic expansion valve.
    c. Thermostatic expansion valve.
    d. Low-side float.
    e. High-side float.

4. Which of the following alarm circuits is best?
    a. Alarm in parallel with the thermostat.
    b. Alarm in series with the thermostat.
    c. Alarm in parallel with the motor.
    d. A separate battery circuit.
    e. Alarm in series with the relay.

5. How is the frost disposed of in an upright frost-free freezer?
    a. Out a heated drain - to a building drain.
    b. Evaporated in the motor-compressor-condenser compartment.
    c. Evaporated by a freezer compartment fan.
    d. No frost accumulates.
    e. Caught in a bucket.

REMOVE AND INSTALL A HERMETIC SYSTEM

OBJECTIVE: Given a cabinet with a hermetic system, and the necessary tools: remove and replace the hermetic system to approved manufacturer's standards.

REFERENCES: Required - Para. 3-9, 7-48, 7-50, 10-8, 11-48 and 11-82.
   Supplementary - Para. 7-47, 10-12, 10-16, 10-19, 10-27, 10-30, 10-33, 10-34, 10-36, 10-37, 10-41, 10-42 and 10-45.

EQUIPMENT: 1 mounting stand for system, 1 cabinet with hermetic system.

PREPARATION PROCEDURE:
1. Study the system and the installation. Study the reference paragraphs. Determine what special tools are necessary to remove and install the system.   TEST√_____

2. Obtain: Tools - 1 set of screwdrivers, 1 set of sockets and ratchet drive, 1 set of pliers, 1 breaker trim remover, 1 pr. safety goggles.
3. Obtain: Instruments - 1 combination voltmeter, ammeter and ohmmeter (multimeter).
4. Obtain: Supplies - 1 wiping cloth, 1 roll 1/2-in. electrical tape, 1 tube caulking compound.

TASK PROCEDURE (WEAR GOGGLES):
1. Determine how the evaporator, condenser, and motor compressor are to be removed... from the front, or rear, etc.
2. Remove breaker trim. Breaker strip must be warm.
3. Remove evaporator panels, fan and motor, electric heating elements and mounting device. Label all electrical connections. Use masking tape. Put all parts in a tray.
4. Remove the electrical parts fastened to evaporator.
5. Remove evaporator mounting devices.
6. Remove motor compressor mounting devices and disconnect the electrical leads (identify with a tag).
7. Remove condenser mounting devices, if necessary.   1-7√_____
8. Remove motor compressor, evaporator and condenser being careful not to pinch or kink the refrigerant tubing.
9. Place the system in the mounting (shipping) stand.   8-9√_____
10. Install the system, reversing the above removal process. Tighten all assembly devices.
11. Install the electrical parts and wires (leads).
12. Plug in and operate the system.   10-12√_____

CLOSING THE STATION:
   Clean the station. Return all material to the tool crib.

DATA:

System, Make_____	Model_____	Serial No._____	Year_____
Compressor, Type_____	How Mounted_____	Assembly device_____	
Condenser, Type_____	Where Located_____	Assembly device_____	
Refrigerant Control_____	Where Located_____	Assembly device_____	
Evaporator, Type_____	Where Located_____	Assembly device_____	
Motor Control_____	Where Located_____	Assembly device_____	
Report any damage_____		_____	

REMOVE AND INSTALL A HERMETIC SYSTEM.

Indicate the best answer for each question below by encircling its letter.

1. Which is the most popular insulation?
    a. Styrofoam.
    b. Cellotex.
    c. Cork.
    d. Glass wool.
    e. Rigid urethane.

2. What type of evaporator is used in the frost-free refrigerator?
    a. Plate.
    b. Air spill-over.
    c. Secondary refrigerant system.
    d. Forced convection.
    e. Two temperature.

3. Of what material are cabinet breaker strips usually made?
    a. Steel.
    b. Plastic.
    c. Aluminum.
    d. Copper.
    e. Plexiglass.

4. Where is the mullion strip located?
    a. In the freezer door.
    b. In the provision door.
    c. Next to the evaporator.
    d. Between the freezer compartment and the fresh food compartment.
    e. None of the above.

5. Of what material is the inner shell of most of the domestic refrigerators made?
    a. Sheet steel.
    b. Aluminum.
    c. Fiberglass.
    d. Plastic.
    e. Iron.

REMOVE, TEST, INSTALL A CABINET MULLION HEATER
AND A BUTTER HEATER SYSTEM

OBJECTIVE: Given a refrigerator cabinet and the necessary tools: test, remove and install the mullion heater and the butter heater to original manufacturer's standards.

REFERENCES: Required – Para. 6-21, 6-28, 6-29, 6-79, 6-80, 8-1, 8-2, 8-42, 8-43, 10-17 and 10-40.
   Supplementary – Para. 6-15, 6-19, 6-20, 6-30, 6-64, 6-66, 6-76, 10-20, 10-24, 10-28, 10-29, 10-31, 10-36, 10-37, 10-41, 10-42, 10-45, 11-21 and 11-82.

EQUIPMENT: A refrigerator cabinet with a mullion heater and butter heater.

PREPARATION PROCEDURE:
1. Study the refrigerator system, locate the wiring diagram and study the reference paragraphs.   TEST√_____
2. Obtain: Tools – 1 set screwdrivers, 1 set pliers, 1 breaker strip tool.
3. Obtain: Instruments – 1 combination voltmeter, ammeter and ohmmeter (multimeter), 1 test light.
4. Obtain: Supplies – 1 wiping cloth, 1 roll plastic tape, 1 roll masking tape.

TASK PROCEDURE:
1. Remove cabinet parts necessary to expose wire terminals for both the mullion heater and the butter heater. POWER OFF!
2. Locate the junction box ends of the mullion heater wires (leads).
3. Locate the mullion heater and the butter heater end of the wires.
4. Locate any controls or switches and their terminals.
5. Disconnect the junction wire terminals. Use masking tape to identify wires and terminals. Also use color code.   1-5√_____
6. Test the two circuits with the ohmmeter.
7. Remove the two heaters.
8. Replace the two heaters.
9. Test the two circuits with the ohmmeter.
10. Connect the wires to the junction box terminals.
11. Test for continuity with test light.
12. Operate the system.   6-12√_____

CLOSING THE STATION:
   Clean the work station and return all materials to the tool crib.

DATA:
System, Make_____ Model_____ Serial No._____ Type_____
Mullion Heater, Watts_____ Butter Heater, Watts_____
Circuit Controls, Type_____ Location_____ Circuit_____

Remarks:

REMOVE, TEST, INSTALL A CABINET MULLION HEATER
AND A BUTTER HEATER SYSTEM.

Indicate the best answer for each question below by encircling its letter.

1. When is the mullion heater circuit open?
   a. Never.
   b. During "off" part of cycle.
   c. When thermostat points are open.
   d. When plug is pulled.
   e. When ambient air is over 80° F.

2. Which uses more electricity, the mullion heater or the butter heater?
   a. Neither use any.
   b. The mullion heater.
   c. The butter heater.
   d. They use the same amount.
   e. The amount is insignificant.

3. Why do some cabinets have two mullion heaters located in the same place?
   a. To increase the heat.
   b. To allow adjustment for different climates.
   c. To permit use of two small heaters.
   d. In case one fails, the other can be used.
   e. To allow either a 120V or 240V connection.

4. How does a mullion heater prevent condensation?
   a. It evaporates the moisture.
   b. It heats the mullion above the dew point temperature.
   c. It keeps the mullion below the dew point temperature.
   d. It heats the air above the dew point temperature.
   e. It is only useful in a warm, dry room.

5. Do single door refrigerators have mullion heaters?
   a. Yes.
   b. No.
   c. Only those over 15 cu. ft.
   d. Only those under 15 cu. ft.
   e. They are an optional accessory.

REMOVE A HERMETIC MOTOR COMPRESSOR

OBJECTIVE: Given a hermetic system with a faulty motor compressor and the necessary tools : remove the compressor neatly and safely.

REFERENCES: Required – Para. 4-25, 11-1 through 11-4, 11-25 through 11-33, 11-39 through 11-42, 11-55 through 11-59 and 11-82.

EQUIPMENT: Hermetic system with faulty motor compressor.

PREPARATION PROCEDURE:
1. Study system assigned and determine special tools and equipment necessary. Study the reference paragraphs.   TEST ✓ _____
2. Obtain: Tools – 1 oxyacetylene brazing outfit or 1 air-acetylene brazing outfit, 1 8-in. adjustable open end wrench, 1 set open end wrenches, 1 set socket wrenches, 1 set screwdrivers, 1 pinch-off tool (parallel jaw), 1 tube cutter, 1 pr. safety goggles.
3. Obtain: Instruments – 1 gauge manifold complete with refrigerant lines, 1 hermetic service valve attachment or clamp-on valve.
4. Obtain: Supplies – 1 jar of brazing flux, 1 wiping cloth, 1 wire brush or steel wool.

TASK PROCEDURE (WEAR GOGGLES):
1. Attach the valve attachment or clamp-on, purge the lines, and check for leaks.
2. Purge the refrigerant from the system. VENTILATE. Trap the oil mist.
                                                                                1-2 ✓ _____
3. Remove the electrical connections and the overload protection and relay if mounted on the motor compressor.
4. Cut the refrigerant lines, unbolt the motor compressor and remove it. Tape or plug the system lines to keep moisture and dirt out of the system. Do not touch or spill the oil, it may be acidic.
5. Pinch the tubing stubs connected to the motor compressor.
                                                                                3-5 ✓ _____
6. Carefully store the removed motor compressor. It will be reused in Tasks 3-19 and 3-20.

CLOSING THE STATION:
Clean the station and return the materials to the tool crib.

DATA:

System, Make _____ Model _____ Serial No. _____ Type _____
Condenser Line, Dia. _____ Suction Line, Dia. _____ Process Tube _____

Remarks:

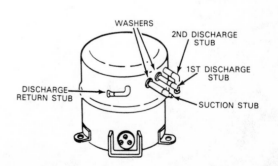

REMOVE A HERMETIC MOTOR COMPRESSOR.

Indicate the best answer for each question below by encircling its letter.

1. What should be done to a capacitor before removing it?
    a. Nothing.
    b. Short it.
    c. Unsolder the connections.
    d. Record its capacity.
    e. Check its temperature.

2. Why must one be careful when handling the old compressor oil?
    a. To keep it clean.
    b. It may be hot.
    c. It may be acidic.
    d. It may spill.
    e. It may cause the motor compressor unit to slip out of one's hands.

3. What size motor compressor is used as a replacement?
    a. One size larger.
    b. One size smaller.
    c. 1/20 hp more.
    d. The same size.
    e. 1/10 hp more.

4. Why are tubing connections silver brazed?
    a. They are not.
    b. To keep out soft solder flux.
    c. To anneal the tubing during the brazing.
    d. Because it is easier.
    e. To produce stronger joints.

5. Why is it dangerous to braze while there is air in the system?
    a. An explosive mixture may be formed in the system.
    b. The air will expand and prevent tight joints.
    c. The air will cause corrosion.
    d. The air cannot be evacuated.
    e. More flux is needed when there is air in the system.

DISMANTLE AND CHECK A HERMETIC MOTOR COMPRESSOR

OBJECTIVE: Given a hermetic motor compressor (reciprocating type) and the necessary tools: dismantle the motor compressor and check all electrical and mechanical parts to approved manufacturer's standards.

REFERENCES: Required – Para. 4-25 through 4-33, 4-36, 4-39, 4-40, 4-61, 11-64 through 11-67, 11-82, 14-36, 14-43 and 14-109.

EQUIPMENT: Hermetic motor compressor, compressor dome grinding machine, cleaning tank, work bench.

PREPARATION PROCEDURE:

1. Study the motor compressor. Study reference paragraphs.   TEST√_____
2. Obtain: Tools – 1 set socket wrenches, 1 set screwdrivers, 1 set pliers, 1 pr. safety goggles, 1 pr. rubber gloves, 1 tube cutter, 1 set Vee blocks.
3. Obtain: Instruments – 1 6-in. steel rule, 1 0-1 in. micrometer, 1 dial indicator, 1 vacuum cup, 1 combination voltmeter, ammeter and ohmmeter (multimeter) 1 megohmmeter.
4. Obtain: Supplies – several wiping cloths, 1 cleaning brush, 1 pan of safe cleaning fluid, 1 package of litmus paper.

TASK PROCEDURE (WEAR GOGGLES):

1. Cut pinched suction line stub. WEAR RUBBER GLOVES. If odor of vapor from open stub is obnoxious, OIL MAY BE DANGEROUSLY ACID.
2. Test oil with litmus paper. If acidic, all oil must be CAREFULLY disposed of and the oil should not be touched or spilled.   1-2√_____
3. After removing oil, place motor compressor in special grinding stand and remove the weld metal holding the dome halves together.
4. Separate the dome halves and disconnect the electrical leads. Some tubing joints to dome may have to be unbrazed. If system is acidic, thoroughly wash the interior with a safe cleaner to remove all trace of oil.   3-4√_____
5. Dismantle the motor. Test the motor electrically for grounds, shorts and open circuit. Check the motor bearing for wear (dial indicator).
6. Dismantle the compressor. Check bearings, crankshaft (dial indicator and micrometer) piston and cylinder, and valves and valve plate (vacuum cup). Inspect all oil and refrigerant passages.   5-6√_____
7. Carefully store the dismantled motor compressor. It will be reused in Task 3-20.

CLOSING THE STATION:

Clean the station, store all parts, and return the materials to the tool crib.

DATA:

Motor Compressor, Make_____ Model_____ Serial No._____ Type_____
Compressor Dome Grinder, Make_____ Model_____ Serial No._____
Capacity_____ Grinding Specifications_____
Condition of parts diagnosis: Motor_____ Motor Bearings_____
Valve plate_____ Intake Valve_____ Discharge Valve_____
Crankshaft_____ Piston(s)_____ Cylinder(s)_____

Remarks:

DISMANTLE AND CHECK A HERMETIC MOTOR COMPRESSOR.

Indicate the best answer for each question below by encircling its letter.

1. What electrical instrument is best for testing for motor winding grounds?
    a. Voltmeter.
    b. Ammeter.
    c. Ohmmeter.
    d. Megohmmeter.
    e. Test light.

2. How may one detect a worn main bearing?
    a. Micrometer.
    b. Dial indicator.
    c. Moving manually.
    d. Tapping with brass mallet.
    e. Watch for oil being squeezed out of shaft as it is turned.

3. How may the compressor dome be opened?
    a. Use a dome grinder.
    b. Use a cutting torch.
    c. Use an arbor press.
    d. Use a hacksaw.
    e. Use a hammer and cold chisel.

4. Do the valve seats have to be inspected?
    a. Yes.
    b. No.
    c. Only if they are made of cast iron.
    d. Only if they are removable.
    e. Only if the valve is faulty.

5. What is probably the reason for breakage of exhaust valve?
    a. Not enough oil.
    b. Refrigerant vapor had no oil mist.
    c. Liquid refrigerant allowed to enter the compressor.
    d. Refrigerator ran too cold.
    e. Refrigerator ran too hot.

OVERHAUL AND ASSEMBLE A MOTOR COMPRESSOR

OBJECTIVE: Given a cut-open reciprocating type hermetic motor compressor and the necessary tools: repair the motor and compressor, and assemble the unit to manufacturer's original specification.

REFERENCES: Required - Para. 4-25, 4-27 through 4-33, 4-36, 4-39, 4-40, 11-68, 11-69, 11-71, 11-72, 11-73, 11-82, 14-36, 14-37, 14-39, 14-40, 14-43 and 14-109.
Supplementary - Para. 14-91 and 14-92.

EQUIPMENT: 1 opened hermetic motor compressor, 1 motor compressor test bench, 1 arbor press, 1 small gas tungsten arc welder (GTAW), complete.

PREPARATION PROCEDURE:
1. Inspect motor compressor and determine special tools and equipment needed. Study reference paragraphs.   TEST√_____
2. Obtain: Tools - 1 set adjustable open end wrenches, 1 set open end wrenches, 1 set screwdrivers, 1 pr. safety goggles, 1 lapping block.
3. Obtain: Instruments - 1 dial indicator, 1 0-1 in. micrometer, 1 megohmmeter.
4. Obtain: Supplies - 1 wiping cloth, 1 can of mineral spirits, 1 gallon refrigerant oil, 1 wire brush, 1 can lapping compound.

TASK PROCEDURE (WEAR GOGGLES):
1. Replace motor windings if faulty (stator).
2. Grind and lap valve seat. Use new valves.
3. Replace crankshaft if worn out.
4. Replace piston and cylinder if worn.
5. Clean all parts.   1-5√_____
6. Assemble the compressor and motor in lower half of dome. Torque all assembly devices. Put proper oil in bottom half of dome.
7. Operate motor and compressor. Check for pumping efficiency.   6-7√_____
8. Connect the electrical system.
9. Weld dome halves together.   8-9√_____
10. Flow low pressure nitrogen or CO_2 through the dome during arc welding.
11. Test on motor compressor test bench.   10-11√_____

CLOSING THE STATION:
   Clean the station and return all material to the tool crib.

DATA:
System, Make_____ Model_____ Serial No._____ Type_____
Oil, Viscosity_____Ounces of Oil_____
Testing First Assembly, Results_____
Testing after Welding, Results_____
Electrical Testing: First Assembly, Results_____
Electrical Testing: After Welding, Results_____

Remarks:

OVERHAUL AND ASSEMBLE A MOTOR COMPRESSOR.

Indicate the best answer for each question below by encircling its letter.

1. What must be removed from the dome in addition to the tubing connection?
   a. The evaporator.
   b. The electrical connections.
   c. The thermostat.
   d. The fan.
   e. The liquid line.

2. What should be done with the oil after removing it from the dome?
   a. It is redistilled.
   b. It is saved.
   c. It is measured and tested for acid.
   d. It is put in the sewer.
   e. Nothing.

3. Why should the unit be run before the dome is put in place?
   a. To check the operating pressure.
   b. To wear in the new parts and check the motor.
   c. To remove the dirt.
   d. To see if the assembly operates correctly.
   e. To check for loose parts.

4. How may one best clean the mechanism before assembly?
   a. Cloth.
   b. Brush.
   c. Wash with water.
   d. Wash with gasoline.
   e. Wash with mineral spirits.

5. What service is recommended for compressor valves?
   a. Lapping.
   b. Grinding.
   c. Filing.
   d. Sanding.
   e. Replacing.

MODERN REFRIGERATION AND AIR CONDITIONING
MODULE 4 - COMMERCIAL REFRIGERATION LABORATORY TASKS

NO.	NAME	TASK TEST GRADE	SIG.	TASK GRADE	SIG.	TASK DATE
4-1	Remove, Test, Install and Adjust a Thermostatic Expansion Valve					
4-2	Remove, Test, Install and Adjust a Pressure-Operated Water Valve					
4-3	Dismantle, Inspect, Assemble and Test a Two-Temperature Valve					
4-4	Remove, Clean, Install and Operate an Oil Separator					
4-5	Remove, Inspect, Install and Adjust a Commercial Type Pressure Motor Control					
4-6	Install Electrical Circuit on a Multiple Cabinet System					
4-7	Install a Chilled Water Cooling System.					
4-8	Install a Display Case System with Doors					
4-9	Install a Reach-In Cabinet System					
4-10	Install a Low-Temperature System (Open Cases)					
4-11	Install a Walk-In Cooler System					
4-12	Install a Multiple-Temperature System.					
4-13	Install an Evaporative Condenser or a Cooling Tower					
4-14	Install a Remote Air-Cooled Condenser.					
4-15	Install an Electric Defrost System					
4-16	Install a Hot Gas Defrost System					
4-17	Install and Test a Roof-Top System					
4-18	Locate Trouble in a Water-Cooled System					
4-19	Locate Trouble in an Ice Maker					
4-20	Locate Trouble in a Low-Temperature System					

SAFETY IN SERVICING COMMERCIAL REFRIGERATORS

Heat tar (hydrolene) only with hot water. Use goggles to protect the eyes. Open flames or a high temperature may cause a violent fire.

Moisture is always a hazard to refrigerating mechanisms. Keep everything which is to be connected to the refrigerant part of the system completely dry. Always pull a vacuum before charging a unit.

Make certain that all the connections are in good condition and tightened prior to operating a system to keep the joints from separating under high pressures. WEAR GOGGLES!

Prior to running a system, make certain all the nuts, bolts and capscrews have been carefully torqued to the proper tension so that the assembled parts will not leak under high pressure.

Always charge refrigerant vapor into a system. Liquid refrigerant entering a compressor may injure the compressor and may even cause the unit to burst (explode).

Frost and ice should be removed by low temperature heating (hot water or electric heat). The use of a knife or a metal scraper may puncture the unit.

Pressure and temperature relief devices are installed on the units for equipment protection, user protection, and service technician protection. They should be kept in good condition and accurate. Always keep them in operation.

NEVER USE CYLINDER OXYGEN TO TEST ANY DEVICE FOR LEAKS. An explosion will take place. USE REFRIGERANT, LOW PRESSURE CARBON DIOXIDE OR NITROGEN. When blowing out lines and/or pressure testing with carbon dioxide or nitrogen, use an accurate pressure regulator and a relief valve designed to open at 180 psi. One should not exceed 170 psi for CO_2 or nitrogen while testing. (See figure below.) A cylinder pressure of 900 psi carbon dioxide or 3000 psi nitrogen will burst the system!

Heavy units should be handled with hand trucks and lifts. When removing mechanisms, be careful not to drop them (they may be slippery). Wear safety shoes on the job. Avoid carrying a heavy or bulky object if the floor is wet, oily, or if the floor is cluttered.

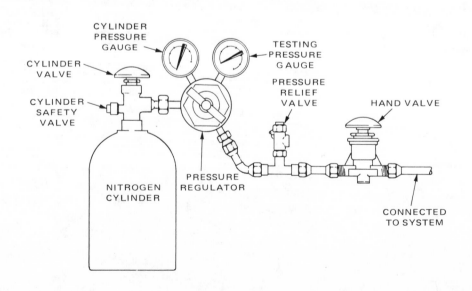

REMOVE, TEST, INSTALL AND ADJUST A THERMOSTATIC EXPANSION VALVE

OBJECTIVE: Given a conventional TEV system, diagnose and adjust it to the proper low-side pressure and temperature at the sensing element.

REFERENCES: Required – Para. 3-8, 5-7 through 5-14, 5-21, 5-32, 14-67, 14-69, 14-71, 14-72, 14-73 and 14-109.
Supplementary – Para. 14-62 through 14-66, 14-68 and 14-70.

EQUIPMENT: A complete operating unit using a thermostatic expansion valve.

PREPARATION PROCEDURE:
1. Study the illustration shown in Fig. 14-82. Study the reference paragraphs.
                                                                    TEST√_____
2. Obtain: Tools – 1 1/2 in. open end wrench, 1 8-in. adjustable wrench, 1 8-in screwdriver, 1 valve ratchet wrench, 1 large-mouth thermos bottle, 1 pr. safety goggles.
3. Obtain: Instruments – 1 thermometer, 1 complete gauge manifold.
4. Obtain: Supplies – 1 flange gasket, 1 bottle of oil, 1 wiping cloth, 1 carton of ice, 1 bottle of safe cleaning fluid.

TASK PROCEDURE (WEAR GOGGLES):
1. Install the gauge manifold.
2. Start the unit and note the low-side pressure after the unit has run 20 minutes.
3. Adjust the service valves preparatory to removing the thermostatic expansion valve.
                                                                    1-3√_____
4. Remove the thermostatic expansion valve.
5. Clean the TEV, including the screen.
6. Test the valve.
7. Connect it to an air line.
8. Put the power element in an ice and water bath.
9. Test the needle with oil against a 90-pound air pressure.
10. Adjust to a 10° F superheat setting.
11. Install TEV in system, purge and/or evacuate.   4-11 √_____
12. Build up pressure and test for leaks.
13. Start the unit and, after running it for 20 minutes, record the low-side pressure and the temperature at the power element location.   12-13√_____

CLOSING THE STATION:
Clean the work station and return all materials to the tool crib.

DATA:
Valve Manufacturer_____ Type_____ Model_____
Capacity_____ Capillary Tube Length_____
Fitting Size and Kind: Inlet_____ Outlet_____ Orifice Size_____
Screen Location_____ Mesh_____
Superheat Setting_____ Low-Side Pressure_____ Bulb Temperature_____
One Turn of Adjustment Changes the Superheat Setting_____ °F
Valve Leaks: Yes_____ No_____ Bulb Charged, Yes_____ No_____
Condition of Valve_____

REMOVE, TEST, INSTALL AND ADJUST A THERMOSTATIC EXPANSION VALVE.

Indicate the best answer for each question below by encircling its letter.

1. Where is the power bulb located when controlling an air-cooling evaporator?
    a. On the evaporator.
    b. On the liquid line.
    c. On the suction line near the evaporator.
    d. On the suction line outside the cabinet.
    e. Anywhere inside the cabinet.

2. What does the thermostatic expansion valve control?
    a. The temperature of the refrigerant in the evaporator.
    b. The quantity of refrigerant in the evaporator.
    c. The pressure in the evaporator.
    d. The temperature of the evaporator.
    e. The high-side pressure.

3. How may the needle and seat be tested for leaks?
    a. High pressure air.
    b. Vacuum.
    c. Turning the adjustment all the way out.
    d. Cooling the power bulb and using air pressure.
    e. With water.

4. What will happen to the evaporator if the TEV adjustment screw is turned out?
    a. Starve.
    b. Flood.
    c. Become warmer.
    d. Become colder.
    e. Nothing.

5. What will happen to the evaporator if the power element is located in a warm air stream?
    a. Flood.
    b. Starve.
    c. Nothing.
    d. Unit will not run.
    e. Unit will run constantly.

REMOVE, TEST, INSTALL AND ADJUST A PRESSURE-OPERATED WATER VALVE

OBJECTIVE: Given a water-cooled condensing unit, adjust and set a water control valve to give the correct water pressure and operation.

REFERENCES: Required – Para. 12-57 through 12-60, 12-74, 14-55 through 14-61 and 14-109.

EQUIPMENT: One water-cooled condensing unit with a pressure-controlled water valve.

PREPARATION PROCEDURE:
1. Study the system assigned. Study the reference paragraphs.   TEST√_____
2. Obtain: Tools – 1 8-in. adjustable wrench, 1 6-in. screwdriver, 1 refrigeration ratchet wrench, 1 1-in. open end wrench, 1 3/4-in. open end wrench, 1 pr. safety goggles.
3. Obtain: Instruments – 1 thermometer, 1 gauge manifold.
4. Obtain: Supplies – 1 can grinding compound, 1 can of cleaning fluid, 1 4-in. square sheet sandpaper (fine), 1 wiping cloth.

TASK PROCEDURE (WEAR GOGGLES):
1. Install the gauge manifold. Start the unit and, after 15 minutes of running, record the inlet and outlet water temperatures. Inlet_____ Outlet_____.
2. Adjust the service valves before removing the water valve.   1-2√_____
3. Remove the water valve.
4. Dismantle and clean the valve.
5. Assemble the valve carefully and install it in system.   3-5√_____
6. Start the unit and adjust the water valve to the correct opening pressure according to the water "IN" temperature and the kind of refrigerant used.
7. Determine the change in opening pressure produced by one complete turn of the adjustment.
8. Determine if the water will shut off after the unit has stopped. (Wait at least one minute.)
                                                                6-8√_____

CLOSING THE STATION:
Clean the work station and return all materials to the tool crib.

DATA:
Water Valve Make_____ Model No._____
Water Connections: Inlet Size_____ Outlet Size_____
Refrigerant Connection Size_____
Strainer: Yes_____ No_____ Area_____ Mesh_____ Material_____
One Turn of the Adjustment Changes the Setting_____ psi
Adjusted for an R-_____ Refrigerant Charge
Circulating Water Temp.: In_____ Out_____ Water Pressure of_____ psi
Leak Test: Pressure Used_____ OK_____ Not OK_____

Remarks:

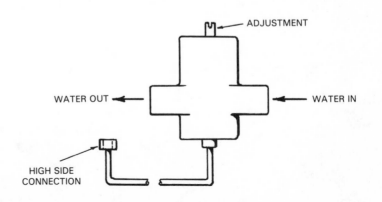

REMOVE, TEST, INSTALL AND ADJUST A PRESSURE-OPERATED WATER VALVE.

Indicate the best answer for each question below by encircling its letter.

1. What is one main advantage of a pressure-operated water valve?
   a. No cost of operation.
   b. Turns the water on and off.
   c. Easiest to install.
   d. Varies the rate of water flow.
   e. Will operate satisfactorily under high water pressure.

2. Where is the refrigerant line to the water valve usually connected into the system?
   a. Suction line.
   b. Compressor crankcase.
   c. Receiver.
   d. Compressor head.
   e. Condenser.

3. What is the usual termperature difference between the water outlet and the water inlet?
   a. 0° F.
   b. 10° F.
   c. 30° F.
   d. 40° F.
   e. None.

4. What happens to the water flow when the condensing unit stops?
   a. Stops instantly.
   b. Keeps on running.
   c. Continues running but at a lower rate of flow.
   d. Stops quickly.
   e. Increases.

5. What is one of the advantages of an electric water valve?
   a. Easy to install.
   b. Turns the water on and off.
   c. No cost of operation.
   d. Can operate under high pressure.
   e. Varies the rate of water flow.

DISMANTLE, INSPECT, ASSEMBLE AND TEST
A TWO-TEMPERATURE VALVE

OBJECTIVE: Given a refrigerating system that has two boxes that require different temperatures: inspect, assemble, test and adjust a two-temperature valve to give the proper operating conditions.

REFERENCES: Required - Para. 12-46 through 12-51, 12-74, 14-74, 14-75 and 14-109.

EQUIPMENT: 1 Refrigerating mechanism which provides two evaporators which operate at different temperatures, 1 Pressure operated metering two-temperature valve, 1 Thermostatic two-temperature valve, 1 Pressure operated snap-action two-temperature valve, 1 Electric two-temperature valve.

PREPARATION PROCEDURE:
1. Study the system assigned. Study the reference paragraphs.   TEST√_____
2. Obtain: Tools - 1-in. open end wrench, 1 6-in. screwdriver, 1 8-in. adjustable end wrench, 1 can refrigerant oil, 1 pr. safety goggles.
3. Obtain: Instruments - 1 combination voltmeter, ammeter and ohmmeter (multimeter), 1 gauge manifold complete with hoses.
4. Obtain: Supplies - 1 pt. bottle safe cleaning fluid, 1 wiping cloth, 1 can refrigerant oil.

TASK PROCEDURE (WEAR GOGGLES):
1. Inspect each valve and take it apart if possible.
2. Clean the parts thoroughly.
3. Inspect the parts and record data required.   1-3√_____
4. Assemble the valves carefully.
5. Test the valve for leaks using air pressure and adjust.
6. Install the pressure metering type valve in a system, purge, and/or evacuate.
7. Test for leaks.
8. Operate the system for at least 20 minutes.   4-8√_____

CLOSING THE STATION:
    Clean the work station and return all materials to the tool crib.

DATA:

Make	Metering	Snap-Action	Thermostatic	Electric
Connections--inlet				
-outlet				
-gauge				
Range Adj. psi/turn				
Differential Adj. - psi/turn				
Condition				

Remarks:

DISMANTLE, INSPECT, ASSEMBLE AND TEST A TWO-TEMPERATURE VALVE.

Indicate the best answer for each question below by encircling its letter.

1. For what kind of service is a pressure operated type two-temperature valve usually used?
   a. When a small temperature difference is desired.
   b. When a large temperature difference is desired.
   c. For water-cooler and ice-cream installations.
   d. Any multiple system.
   e. Only on display cases.

2. For what kind of service is a snap-action two-temperature valve usually used?
   a. Where a small temperature difference is desired.
   b. Where a large temperature difference is desired.
   c. In small and large cabinet combination installations.
   d. Anywhere in a multiple installation.
   e. In the main suction line.

3. Where should the check valve be located when used in two-temperature installations?
   a. In the warmest evaporator suction line.
   b. In the coldest evaporator suction line.
   c. In the liquid line.
   d. At the compressor.
   e. In the main suction line.

4. What is used in combination with a thermostat to produce a two-temperature valve?
   a. A motor.
   b. A pressure switch.
   c. An electric solenoid valve.
   d. A float valve.
   e. A thermostatic expansion valve.

5. In a two-temperature installation, what is the purpose of the accumulator?
   a. To store liquid refrigerant.
   b. To catch overflow liquid refrigerant.
   c. An oil reservoir.
   d. Vapor storage in the main suction line.
   e. A hot vapor reservoir.

REMOVE, CLEAN, INSTALL AND OPERATE AN OIL SEPARATOR

OBJECTIVE: Given a commercial condensing unit, remove and install an oil separator.

REFERENCES: Required – Para. 3-11, 3-12, 3-22, 12-55 and 12-74.

EQUIPMENT: One commercial unit complete with an oil separator.

PREPARATION PROCEDURE:
1. Study the system assigned. Study the reference paragraphs. TEST√ _____
2. Obtain: Tools – 1 ratchet valve wrench, 1 1/2-in. open end wrench, 1 3/4-in. open end wrench, 1 1-in. open end wrench, 1 pr. safety goggles.
3. Obtain: Instruments – 1 complete gauge manifold and hoses.
4. Obtain: Supplies – 1 wiping cloth, 1 bottle mineral spirits, 2 18-in. copper tubes 1/4-in. dia., complete with nuts, 2 1/4 MF x 1/8 MP brass half unions.

TASK PROCEDURE (WEAR GOGGLES):
1. Check the unit.
2. Install the gauge manifold.
3. Remove the refrigerant from the system. Balance pressures. Remove the oil separator.
   1-3√ _____
4. Dismantle and clean the separator.   4√ _____
5. Assemble the separator.   5√ _____
6. Install the separator. Test for leaks. Evacuate system. Charge the system.
7. Run the unit for at least 20 minutes.   6-7√ _____

CLOSING THE STATION:
   Clean. the work station and return all materials to the tool crib.

DATA:
Oil Separator Make _____ Model _____
Fittings, Refrigerant Inlet, Size _____
Fittings, Refrigerant Outlet, Size _____
Fittings, Oil Return, Size _____
Assembly Devices, Kind _____ Number _____ Size _____ Wrench Size _____
Condition _____

Remarks:

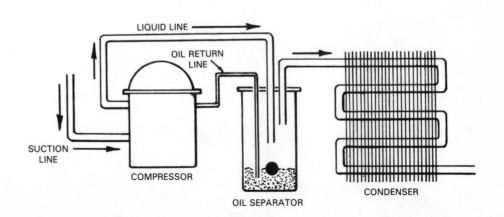

REMOVE, CLEAN, INSTALL AND OPERATE AN OIL SEPARATOR.

Indicate the best answer for each question below by encircling its letter.

1. Where is the oil separator located in the system?
   a. Between the condenser and the liquid line.
   b. Between the receiver and the liquid line.
   c. Between the compressor and the condenser.
   d. Between the suction line and the compressor.
   e. Between the liquid line and the evaporator.

2. Why are most oil separators insulated?
   a. To keep the oil warm.
   b. To keep any moisture in the separator from freezing.
   c. To keep the refrigerant from condensing in the separator.
   d. Only hot oil will separate from refrigerant.
   e. To minimize noise.

3. What will happen if the oil separator float collapses?
   a. Nothing.
   b. The valve will stay open.
   c. The valve will stay closed.
   d. The liquid refrigerant will short circuit into the crankcase.
   e. The head pressure will become excessive.

4. What is one advantage of an oil separator?
   a. Keeps the oil in the compressor.
   b. Low cost.
   c. Easy to service.
   d. Traps the moisture.
   e. May be used as a service cylinder.

5. How must an oil separator be mounted?
   a. Any position.
   b. Level.
   c. Suspend from the condenser line.
   d. Below the compressor.
   e. Above the compressor.

REMOVE, INSPECT, INSTALL AND ADJUST A
COMMERCIAL TYPE PRESSURE MOTOR CONTROL

OBJECTIVE: Given a commercial refrigerating system: remove, inspect, install and adjust a commercial type pressure motor control that will provide the desired box temperature.

REFERENCES: Required – Para. 8-20, 8-21, 8-22, 8-43, 12-37, 12-38, 12-40, 14-94 and 14-109.
Supplementary – Para. 12-39 and 12-74.

EQUIPMENT: 1 Commercial pressure control with a high-pressure safety cut-out, 1 commercial refrigerating system.

PREPARATION PROCEDURE:
1. Study the system assigned. Study the reference paragraphs.   TEST√_____
2. Obtain: Tools – 1 4-in. screwdriver, 1 refrigeration ratchet wrench, 1 3/4-in. open end wrench, 1 1-in. open end wrench, 1 pr. safety goggles.
3. Obtain: Instruments – 1 complete gauge manifold, 1 hydraulic pump and gauge, 1 hand pressure and vacuum pump.
4. Obtain: Supplies – 1 4-in. sheet of #1/2 sandpaper, 1 wiping cloth, 1 bottle cleaning fluid.

TASK PROCEDURE (WEAR GOGGLES):
1. Examine the control and determine the cut-in and cut-out settings. (Understand them thoroughly.)
2. Determine the safety control settings using a hydraulic pump and gauge. Record_____.
3. Determine the low-side control settings using a vacuum pump with a compound gauge. Record_____.
4. Adjust the cut-in and cut-out points.   1-4√_____
5. Install the control in the system.
6. Operate the system for 20 minutes.   5-6√_____

CLOSING THE STATION:
Clean the work station and return all materials to the tool crib.

DATA:
Control, Make_____ Type_____ Model_____
Capacity_____ Overload Protection_____
Low-Pressure Connection, Size_____ Kind_____
High-Pressure Connection, Size_____ Kind_____
Original Setting: Cut-in_____ Cut-out_____ Safety Cut-out_____
One Turn of Range Adj. Changes Setting: Cut-in_____ Cut-out_____
One Turn of Differential Adj. Changes Setting: Cut-in_____ Cut-out_____
Control Adjusted to Cut-in_____ Cut-out_____
Condition of Control_____

Remarks:

REMOVE, INSPECT, INSTALL AND ADJUST A COMMERCIAL
TYPE PRESSURE MOTOR CONTROL.

Indicate the best answer for each question below by encircling its letter.

1. Why are high-pressure safety motor cut-outs used?
    a. To cycle the unit.
    b. To economize on power consumption.
    c. To protect the motor control.
    d. To protect the unit from high pressures.
    e. To keep the high pressure up to normal.

2. Where should the low-side connection of the pressure motor control be connected
    into the system?
    a. To the suction line of the warmest evaporator.
    b. To the compressor high side.
    c. To the crankcase.
    d. To the liquid receiver.
    e. Anywhere on the low-pressure side.

3. Where is a high-pressure safety motor cut-out line connected into the system?
    a. At the condenser.
    b. At the compressor head.
    c. To the liquid line.
    d. To the evaporator.
    e. To the suction line.

4. What are the relative pressures in the low-pressure side while the unit is running?
    a. The same throughout.
    b. Higher at the evaporator.
    c. Lower at the evaporator.
    d. Higher at the suction service valve.
    e. Higher as the termperature drops.

5. What is the most common pressure motor control trouble which will cause the system
    to short cycle?
    a. Lack of refrigerant.
    b. Low-pressure setting too low.
    c. Clogged screen.
    d. Too low a range.
    e. Too low a high-pressure cut-out setting.

INSTALL ELECTRICAL CIRCUIT ON A MULTIPLE CABINET SYSTEM

OBJECTIVE: Given a multiple cabinet system, install the electrical circuit in accordance with local electrical code.

REFERENCES: Required – Para. 7-13 through 7-22, 7-27, 7-28, 7-50 and 12-46.
Supplementary – Para. 7-47, 8-23, 8-43, 14-6, 14-74 and 14-109.

EQUIPMENT: One multiple cabinet system with a hermetic unit, a blower evaporator, and a condenser fan.

PREPARATION PROCEDURE:
1. Study system assigned. Study the reference paragraphs.   TEST√ _____
2. Obtain: Tools – 1 pr. terminal pliers, 1 pr. 6-in. pliers, side cutting, 1 6-in. reg. screwdriver, 1 pr. safety goggles.
3. Obtain: Instruments – 1 test light, 1 combination voltmeter, ammeter and ohmmeter (multimeter).
4. Obtain: Supplies – 1 wiping cloth, 1 5-ft. length #12 wire, 1 roll 1/2-in. plastic tape, 1 set of terminals.

TASK PROCEDURE (WEAR GOGGLES):
1. Study the electrical circuitry of the system.
2. Make an electrical diagram of the system and fill out the data sheet.   1-2√ _____
3. Dismantle the electrical system. (BE SURE THE POWER IS DISCONNECTED.)
4. Rewire the electrical system.
5. Operate the system for 20 minutes. Use the instruments to check the voltage and current.
                                                                          3-5√ _____

CLOSING THE STATION:
Clean the work station and return all materials to the tool crib.

DATA:
Compressor Motor, Make _____ Model _____ rpm _____
   Voltage _____ Phase _____ Rated Current, Start _____ Run _____
Starting Capacitor, Make _____ Voltage _____ Mfd _____
Running Capacitor, Make _____ Voltage _____ Mfd _____
Evaporator Blower Motor, Make _____ Model _____ rpm _____
   Voltage _____ Phase _____ Rated Current _____
Condenser Fan Motor, Make _____ Model _____ rpm _____
   Voltage _____ Phase _____ Rated Current _____
Motor Control, Make _____ Model _____ Capacity, Voltage _____ Current _____
Relay, Make _____ Model _____ Rating _____
Overload Protectors, Make _____ Model _____ Rating _____
Voltage Checks _____ Current Checks _____
Condition _____ _____

Remarks:

INSTALL ELECTRICAL CIRCUIT ON A MULTIPLE CABINET SYSTEM.

Indicate the best answer for each question below by encircling its letter.

1. How many external parallel circuits are needed to wire a system with an evaporator fan, a condenser fan, a motor-compressor with a current relay, two defrost circuits, an oil heater circuit and a thermostatic motor starter?
   a. 6
   b. 7
   c. 8
   d. 9
   e. 10

2. If a junction box has 12 wires, how many circuits is it likely to have?
   a. 5
   b. 6
   c. 9
   d. 10
   e. 11

3. How many circuits are possible if two wires are fastened to one terminal?
   a. 1
   b. 2
   c. 3
   d. 4
   e. 5

4. What could be wrong if a voltage exists between the motor-compressor housing and a water pipe when the power is turned on?
   a. An open circuit.
   b. A closed circuit.
   c. A short.
   d. A ground.
   e. Nothing.

5. How are the external overload protector and the internal overload protector electrically connected?
   a. In series.
   b. In parallel.
   c. Either parallel or series.
   d. Both series and parallel.
   e. They are not connected.

INSTALL A CHILLED WATER COOLING SYSTEM

OBJECTIVE: Given a beverage cooler with a multiple evaporator, install and operate.

REFERENCES: Required - Para. 12-21 through 12-24, 12-74, 13-15, 13-16, 14-17, 14-23, 14-25 and 14-109.
     Supplementary - Para. 13-33, 14-16 and 14-24.

EQUIPMENT: One beverage cooler with a multiple evaporator.

PREPARATION PROCEDURE:
1. Study water cooling systems. Study the reference paragraphs.   TEST√ _____
2. Obtain: Tools - 1 25-ft. extension cord, 1 refrigeration ratchet wrench, 1 3/4-in. open end wrench, 1 1-in. open end wrench, 1 1/4-in. tube bender, 1 1/2-in. tube bender, 1 hand water valve, 1 pr. safety goggles.
3. Obtain: Instruments - 1 combination voltmeter, ammeter and ohmmeter (multimeter), 1 complete gauge manifold, 1 thermometer.
4. Obtain: Supplies - 1 refrigerant oil can, 1 tube thread compound, 1 bottle oil, 1 wiping cloth, 1 coil 3/8-in. copper tubing, 1 assortment tubing, pipe fittings and clips, 1 manual water valve.

TASK PROCEDURE (WEAR GOGGLES):
1. Install the gauge manifold.
2. Check the operation of the unit.
3. Dismantle the water and drain lines.   1-3√ _____
4. Reinstall the water-in and drain lines.
5. Operate the unit.   4-5√ _____

CLOSING THE STATION:
   Clean the work station and return all materials to the tool crib.

DATA:

Beverage Cooler, Make _____ Model _____ Serial No. __ _____ Type _____
Motor Control, Make _____ Model _____
Motor Relay, Type _____
Refrigerant, Kind _____ Quantity _____
Suction Line, Size _____ Liquid Line, Size _____
Condenser, Type _____ Evaporator, Type _____
Voltage _____ Starting Amperes _____ Running Amperes _____
Condition _____

Remarks:

INSTALL A CHILLED WATER COOLING SYSTEM.

Indicate the best answer for each question below by encircling its letter.

1. What is used to make a sweet water bath?
   a. Tap water.
   b. A salt brine.
   c. No brine.
   d. An alcohol brine.
   e. A sugar solution.

2. What is the lowest temperature at which the refrigerant may be operated in a direct water cooler?
   a. 40° F.
   b. 35° F.
   c. 30° F.
   d. 32° F.
   e. 28° F.

3. To what temperature should water for restaurants be cooled?
   a. 55° F.
   b. 40° F.
   c. 45° F.
   d. 35° F.
   e. 32° F.

4. How do water coolers increase their efficiency with a heat exchanger?
   a. Use a water-cooled condenser.
   b. Cool the incoming water with a heat transfer from the drain water.
   c. Use the drain water to cool the condenser.
   d. Use the incoming water to cool the condenser.
   e. Run the liquid line through the cooled water.

5. How many Btu's must be removed to cool twenty gallons of water from 80° F to 40° F?
   a. 1000 Btu.
   b. 2000 Btu.
   c. 5550 Btu.
   d. 6672 Btu.
   e. 7777 Btu.

INSTALL A DISPLAY CASE SYSTEM WITH DOORS

OBJECTIVE: Given a refrigerated display case: install, operate and test for leaks.

REFERENCES: Required - Para. 12-16 through 12-20, 12-74, 13-5 through 13-9, 14-1 through
    14-7, 14-9 through 14-13, 14-15 through 14-19, 14-23, 14-24 and 14-109.
      Supplementary - Para. 12-21, 12-22, 12-23, 13-10, 14-8, 14-14, 14-20, 14-21 and 14-22.

EQUIPMENT: 1 display case, 1 condensing unit, 1 evaporator.

PREPARATION PROCEDURE:
1. Study the display case system assigned. Study the reference paragraphs.

                                                              TEST√_____

2. Obtain: Tools - 1 flaring outfit, 1 8-in. adjustable end wrench, 1 refrigeration ratchet
wrench, 1 6-in. screwdriver, 1 purging line, 1 complete air-acetylene soldering outfit,
1 pr. safety goggles.
3. Obtain: Instruments - 1 combination voltmeter, ammeter and ohmmeter (multimeter), 1 complete
gauge manifold, 1 leak detector.
4. Obtain: Supplies - 1 can refrigerant oil, 1 filter-drier, 1 1/2-in. hand shut-off valve, 1 sight
glass, 1 roll 1/8 dia. 50-50 solder wire, 1 jar of flux, 1 sheet #00 sandpaper, 1 lb. box of
sealing compound, 50 ft. 1/4 OD copper tubing, 50 ft. 1/2 OD copper tubing, 25 ft.
extension cord, 12 1/2-in. pipe straps.

TASK PROCEDURE (WEAR GOGGLES):
1. Install the condensing unit and evaporator.
2. Install the suction line and liquid line.
3. Install the electrical wiring to code standards.   1-3√_____
4. Evacuate the system and charge with vapor to 25 psi.
5. Test for leaks.
6. Deep evacuate the system or triple evacuate the system.
7. Install filter-drier and sight glass.
8. Start the unit, charge, test for leaks. Run for 20 minutes.
9. Remove gauge manifold.   4-9√_____

CLOSING THE STATION:
    Clean the station and return all materials to the tool crib.

DATA:
Condensing Unit: Manufacturer_____ Model_____ Capacity_____
Current_____ Voltage_____ Phase_____ Hertz_____
Liquid Line Size_____ Suction Line Size_____
Motor Control, Manufacturer_____ Type_____ Model_____
Evaporator, Manufacturer_____ Model_____ Year_____
Thermostatic Expansion Valve, Manufacturer_____ Model_____ Capacity_____
Refrigerant, Kind_____ Charge_____
Drier, Manufacturer_____ Capacity_____ Desiccant_____
Condition_____

Remarks:

INSTALL A DISPLAY CASE SYSTEM WITH DOORS.

Indicate the best answer for each question below by encircling its letter.

1. What should be done to the opening through which the tubing enters the cabinet?
    a. Does not need to be sealed.
    b. It is too small to seal.
    c. Should be sealed with sealing compound.
    d. Should be taped.
    e. Must be left open for ventilation.

2. When should the suction line tubing be installed?
    a. Before the liquid line.
    b. After the liquid line.
    c. At the same time the liquid line is installed.
    d. Anytime.
    e. Before the evaporator is installed.

3. How should a dry evaporator be mounted?
    a. In a level position.
    b. In the center of the cabinet.
    c. 3 in. from the top of the cabinet.
    d. At a slant toward the suction line.
    e. As low as possible.

4. Before starting an installed unit, what should be done to the thermostatic expansion valve adjustment?
    a. Turned out.
    b. Turned in.
    c. Nothing.
    d. Turn to left.
    e. Turn to right.

5. How should the suction line and the liquid line be protected from chafing?
    a. Straps.
    b. Tape.
    c. Wire.
    d. Nails.
    e. Wood screws.

Task No. 4-9 Task Grade _____
Name _____
Date _____ Class _____

INSTALL A REACH-IN CABINET SYSTEM

OBJECTIVE: Given a reach-in cabinet system, install and operate according to the
manufacturer's recommended operating conditions.

REFERENCES: Required - Para. 12-1 through 12-4, 12-6, 12-7, 12-15 through 12-20, 12-74,
13-2, 13-4, 14-1 through 14-7, 14-9 through 14-13, 14-15 through 14-19, 14-23, 14-24
and 14-109.
Supplementary - Para. 12-9 through 12-14, 13-33, 14-8, 14-14, 14-20, 14-21 and 14-22.

EQUIPMENT: 1 blower evaporator, 1 condensing unit, 1 reach-in cabinet, 1 thermostatic expansion
valve, 1 solenoid valve.

PREPARATION PROCEDURE:
1. Study the system assigned. Study the reference paragraphs.   TEST√_____
2. Obtain: Tools - 1 tube cutter, 1 8-in. adjustable open end wrench, 1 6-in. screwdriver,
1 air-acetylene soldering torch, complete, 1 pr. safety goggles.
3. Obtain: Instruments - 1 combination voltmeter, ammeter and ohmmeter (multimeter), 1 complete
gauge manifold, 1 leak detector.
4. Obtain: Supplies - 1 refrigerant oil spout can, 1 filter-drier, 1 wiping cloth, 1 sight glass,
1 roll 1/8-in. dia. solder wire, 1 can solder flux, 1 25-ft. length #14 wire extension,
25-ft. length 1/2 copper tubing, 25-ft. length 1/4 copper tubing, 1/4 soldering fittings,
1/2 soldering fittings.

TASK PROCEDURE (WEAR GOGGLES):
1. Install the condensing unit and evaporator.
2. Install the thermostatic expansion valve. Connect the blower motor to a 120V a-c source
(follow the local code). Install the solenoid valve.
3. Install the suction line and liquid line.
4. Install the electrical wiring.
5. Install the evaporator drain.
6. Install the gauge manifold.   1-6√_____
7. Either evacuate or purge the evaporator, or both.
8. Test for leaks.
9. Produce a deep vacuum or use the triple vacuum system.
10. Charge the system.
11. Operate for 15 minutes. Test for leaks.
12. Remove the gauge manifold.   7-12√_____

CLOSING THE STATION:
Clean the work station and return all materials to the tool crib.

DATA:
Condensing Unit, Manufacturer_____ Model_____ Year_____
Voltage_____ Amperage_____ Hertz_____ Phase_____
Motor Control, Manufacturer_____ Model_____ Capacity_____
Refrigerant, Kind_____ Amount_____
Evaporator, Manufacturer_____ Model_____ Year_____
Refrigerant Control, Manufacturer_____ Model_____ Year_____
Condition_____

INSTALL A REACH-IN CABINET SYSTEM.

Indicate the best answer for each question below by encircling its letter.

1. What is the average temperature difference between the evaporator refrigerant and the cabinet air?
    a. 0° F.
    b. 10° F.
    c. 20° F.
    d. 30° F.
    e. 40° F.

2. How frequently does the blower motor usually run?
    a. Only while the condensing unit is off.
    b. Only while the condensing unit is running.
    c. All the time.
    d. Either all the time or while the condensing unit is running.
    e. Either all the time or while the condensing unit is not running.

3. Where should the thermostat be located?
    a. On the evaporator.
    b. In back of the evaporator.
    c. On the cabinet wall.
    d. Just outside the door.
    e. On the condensing unit.

4. What is one of the advantages of a blower evaporator?
    a. It requires little space.
    b. It does not dry up foods.
    c. The air movement is slow.
    d. It is cheaper to operate.
    e. It is easier to install.

5. How fast does the air flow over the typical blower evaporator?
    a. 1000 ft./min.
    b. 3000 ft./min.
    c. 6000 ft./min.
    d. 9000 ft./min.
    e.   25 ft./min.

INSTALL A LOW-TEMPERATURE SYSTEM (OPEN CASES).

OBJECTIVE: Given a frozen foods system, install and operate according to the manufacturer's recommended operating conditions.

REFERENCES: Required - Para. 12-1 through 12-4, 12-6, 12-7, 12-15, 12-28 through 12-34, 12-52, 12-55, 12-74, 13-9 through 13-12, 14-3, 14-4, 14-15 through 14-19, 14-23, 14-24 and 14-109.
    Supplementary - Para. 12-5, 12-8 through 12-14, 12-61 through 12-72.

EQUIPMENT: 1 frozen food cabinet, 1 low-temp. evaporator, 1 low-temp. condensing unit.

PREPARATION PROCEDURE:
1. Study the system assigned. Study the reference paragraphs.   TEST√_____
2. Obtain: Tools - 1 valve ratchet wrench, 1 8-in. adjustable open end wrench, 1 set cleaning brushes, 1 brazing outfit, 1 tube cutter, 1 pr. safety goggles.
3. Obtain: Instruments - 1 combination voltmeter, ammeter, ohmmeter (multimeter), 1 gauge manifold, 1 leak detector.
4. Obtain: Supplies - 1 cylinder refrigerant, 1 filter-drier, 2 lengths copper tubing, 1 sight glass, 1 silver brazing wire, 1 assortment of tube fittings, 1 jar silver brazing flux.

TASK PROCEDURE (WEAR GOGGLES):
1. Inspect the equipment and determine the tools and supplies needed to install system.
2. Position the cabinet and condensing unit.
3. Connect the suction line, liquid line, and electrical power.   1-3√_____
4. Evacuate the system, charge to 25 psi refrigerant pressure and test for leaks.
5. If no leaks are found, charge to 75 to 100 psi pressure and test for leaks.
6. If no leaks are found, evacuate using the deep vacuum method or triple vacuum system.
7. Balance pressures, remove liquid line connection of condensing unit end and install drier and sight glass.
8. Purge the liquid line.
9. Charge the system.
10. Operate the unit for 10 to 20 minutes and check the pressures and temperatures.
11. Remove the gauge manifold.   4-11√_____

CLOSING THE STATION:
    Clean the work station. Return tools, instruments and unused supplies to tool crib.

DATA:
Cabinet, Make_____ Model_____ Dimensions____ x ____ x ____ Area____ Volume____
Condensing Unit, Make_____ Model_____ Type____ Capacity____
    Voltage_____ Amperage_____ Hertz_____ Phase____
Evaporator, Make_____ Model_____ Type____ Capacity____
Refrigerant Control, Make_____ Model_____ Type____ Capacity____
Motor Control, Make_____ Model_____ Type____ Capacity____
Liquid Line Size_____ Suction Line Size_____
Refrigerant, R-_____ Amount_____
Running Conditions, Pressures: High_____ Low_____
    Temperature, Cabinet_____ Evaporator_____ Condenser_____

Remarks:

INSTALL A LOW-TEMPERATURE SYSTEM (OPEN CASES).

Indicate the best answer for each question below by encircling its letter.

1. How may door gaskets be tested for a tight fit?
    a. Air pressure.
    b. Press on lid.
    c. With a strip of paper.
    d. By the running time of the unit.
    e. By the frost accumulation in the cabinet.

2. Where should a frozen foods cabinet be coldest?
    a. In the center of the cabinet.
    b. At the top rear inner wall.
    c. At the top center of cabinet.
    d. On the evaporator surface.
    e. The temperature should be same all over.

3. What is a good source of electrical energy for an alarm system?
    a. Kitchen light circuit.
    b. Cabinet power circuit.
    c. Batteries.
    d. Radio power circuit.
    e. Garage power circuit.

4. What is considered a good frozen foods temperature?
    a. 32° F.
    b. 15° F.
    c. 5° F.
    d. -10° F.
    e. -32° F.

5. What is considered a good fast-freezing temperature?
    a. 32° F.
    b. 10° F.
    c. 5° F.
    d. -10° F.
    e. -20° F.

INSTALL A WALK-IN COOLER SYSTEM

OBJECTIVE: Given a walk-in cooler system: install, test for leaks and operate.

REFERENCES: Required – Para. 12-1 through 12-4, 12-6, 12-7, 12-15, 12-16, 12-20, 12-74, 13-3, 14-1 through 14-7, 14-9 through 14-13, 14-15 through 14-19, 14-23, 14-24 and 14-109. Supplementary – Para. 12-5, 12-8 through 12-14, 12-17 through 12-20, 14-8, 14-14, 14-20 through 14-22.

EQUIPMENT: 1 walk-in cabinet, 1 condensing unit, 1 evaporator.

PREPARATION PROCEDURE:
1. Study the system assigned. Study the reference paragraphs.   TEST √ _____
2. Obtain: Tools – 1 valve ratchet wrench, 1 8-in. adjustable open end wrench, 1 tube cutter, 1 set cleaning brushes, 1 brazing outfit, 1 pr. safety goggles.
3. Obtain: Instruments – 1 gauge manifold, 1 combination voltmeter, ammeter, and ohmmeter (multimeter).
4. Obtain: Supplies – 1 length 1/4-in. copper tubing, 1 length 1/2-in. copper tubing, 1 filter-drier, 1 cylinder refrigerant, 1 sight glass, 1 jar of brazing flux, 1 container safe cleaning fluid, 1 wiping cloth, 1 roll brazing wire.

TASK PROCEDURE (WEAR GOGGLES):
1. Inspect equipment, and determine tools and supplies needed to install the system.
2. Position the cabinet and condensing unit.
3. Connect the suction line, the liquid line, the water lines, and the electrical service.
                                                                                 1-3 √ _____
4. Evacuate the system, charge to 25 psi and test for leaks.
5. If no leaks are found, charge to 75 psi and test for leaks.
6. If no leaks are found, use the deep vacuum method or the triple vacuum system.
7. Balance the pressures, remove the liquid line connection at the condensing unit, and install the drier and sight glass.
8. Purge the liquid line.
9. Charge the system.
10. Operate the system for 10 to 20 minutes, check the pressures and temperatures.
11. Remove the gauge manifold.   4-11 √ _____

CLOSING THE STATION:
    Clean the station. Return the tools, instruments and unused supplies to tool crib.

DATA:

Cabinet, Make _____ Model _____ Dimensions _____ x _____ x _____ Floor Area _____
        Volume _____
Condensing Unit, Make _____ Model _____ Type _____ Capacity _____
        Voltage _____ Amperage _____ Phase _____ Hertz _____
Evaporator, Make _____ Model _____ Type _____ Capacity _____
Refrigerant Control, Make _____ Model _____ Type _____ Capacity _____
Motor Control, Make _____ Model _____ Type _____ Capacity _____
Refrigerant, R- _____ Amount _____ Suction Line Size _____
                                                        Liquid Line Size _____
Operating Data: Pressures, High Side _____ Low Side _____
        Temperature, Cabinet _____ Evaporator _____ Condenser _____

INSTALL A WALK-IN COOLER SYSTEM.

Indicate the best answer for each question below by encircling its letter.

1. What is probably wrong if the liquid line frosts?
   a. The system is short of refrigerant.
   b. A float needle is leaking.
   c. The system is too cold.
   d. The screen in the liquid receiver is partially clogged.
   e. There is too much refrigerant in the line.

2. What partial pinching causes the greatest decrease in the capacity of the unit?
   a. The suction line.
   b. The liquid line.
   c. The condenser line.
   d. The evaporator tube.
   e. They are all equal.

3. What happens to oil as it becomes colder?
   a. It is thicker.
   b. It is thinner.
   c. It congeals.
   d. It precipitates.
   e. It loses its lubricating properties.

4. Why are the drier and the sight glass put in the system last?
   a. They should be put in when system is dry.
   b. A vacuum cannot be pulled if they are in the system.
   c. A vacuum ruins the desiccant.
   d. A vacuum ruins the moisture indicator chemical.
   e. To keep the drier and indicator free of impurities.

5. How can a nearby surface be protected from being scorched during a joint brazing operation?
   a. Use a low temperature flame.
   b. Bend the pipe away from the surface.
   c. Use a metal plate shield.
   d. Use flared connections.
   e. Refinish scorched surface.

Task No. 4-12 Task Grade _____

Name _____

Date _____ Class _____

INSTALL A MULTIPLE-TEMPERATURE SYSTEM

OBJECTIVE: Given a multiple temperature system, install to conform to local code requirements.

REFERENCES: Required - Para. 12-45 through 12-52, 12-74, 14-24, and 14-109.
   Supplementary - Para. 12-5 through 12-8, 12-54, 12-55, 12-56, 12-65 through
   12-72, 14-1 through 14-13, 14-15 through 14-19, and 14-23.

EQUIPMENT: 2 dry evaporators, 2 cabinets, 1 condensing unit, air-cooled.

PREPARATION PROCEDURE:
1.   Study the system assigned. Study the reference paragraphs.   TEST ✓ _____
2.   Obtain: Tools - 1 16 oz. ball peen hammer, 1 8-in. adjustable end wrench, 1 valve
   ratchet wrench, 1 6-in. screwdriver, 1 purging line, 1 brazing outfit, 1 pr. safety goggles.
3.   Obtain: Instruments - 1 gauge manifold, complete, 1 combination voltmeter, ammeter,
   and ohmmeter (multimeter), 1 vacuum pump system, 1 leak detector.
4.   Obtain: Supplies - 2 thermostatic expansion valves, 1 1/2-in. valve manifold, 1 1/4 in.
   valve manifold, 2 1/4-in. 3-way valves, 2 1/2-in. 3-way valves, 1 oiler, refrig, oil,
   50 ft. 1/4-in. copper tubing, 50 ft. 1/2-in. copper tubing, 25 ft. 3/8-in. copper pipe,
   25 ft. super service extension cord, 1 jar of brazing flux, 1 filter-drier, 1 roll of 1/16-in.
   silver brazing wire, 1 sight glass, 6 1/4-in. soldered fittings, 6 1/2-in. soldered fittings,
   4 3/8-in. soldered fittings, 6 1/2-in. pipe straps, 1 roll of 3/4-in. plastic tape.

TASK PROCEDURE (WEAR GOGGLES):
1.   Position the cabinets and the condensing unit.
2.   Install the tubing to the evaporators, to the manifold valves, and to the condensing unit.
                                                                          1-2 ✓ _____
3.   Install the electrical wiring. Use the local code requirements.
4.   Evacuate the system, vapor charge it to 25 psi and test for leaks. All hand valves must
   be open.
5.   When system is without leaks, install the drier and sight glass and charge the system.
6.   Start the unit using the hand valves to operate one evaporator first and then both evaporators.
7.   Record pressures in the system and temperatures of each evaporator after 20 minutes of operation.
8.   Purge the condenser to remove any residual air.
9.   Remove the gauge manifold.   3-9 ✓ _____

CLOSING THE STATION:
   Clean the work station. Return tools, instruments and unused supplies to tool crib.

DATA:
Cabinet #1, Make _____ Model _____ Type _____ Size _____
      #2, Make _____ Model _____ Type _____ Size _____
Condensing Unit, Manufacturer _____ Model _____ Type ____ Capacity _____
Motor, Voltage _____ Amperage _____ Hertz _____ Phase _____
Motor Control, Manufacturer _____ Model _____ Capacity _____
Refrigerant, R- _____ Amount _____

Evaporators	Evaporator #1	Evaporator #2
Name		
Type		
Size		
Refrigerant Control		
Name		
Model		
Capacity		

INSTALL A MULTIPLE-TEMPERATURE SYSTEM.

Indicate the best answer for each question below by encircling its letter.

1. What is the first thing to be done to the lines and evaporator after the system is installed?
    a. Purged.
    b. Purged then evacuated.
    c. Tested for leaks.
    d. Insulated.
    e. Oiled.

2. Why is a filter-drier installed in a new system?
    a. To remove the copper chips.
    b. To remove any moisture that may be in the system.
    c. To keep moisture in the system from freezing.
    d. To remove the air.
    e. To keep the oil in the compressor.

3. Where should the hand operated valves be installed?
    a. At the compressor.
    b. Near each evaporator.
    c. In the suction line at each evaporator.
    d. In the liquid line at each evaporator.
    e. On the wall adjacent to the condensing unit.

4. What type of tubing connections should one use on evaporators?
    a. Ordinary nuts.
    b. Frost-proof nuts.
    c. Weatherhead fittings.
    d. Double flare connections.
    e. Shellacked fittings.

5. How should the suction line be installed?
    a. Slanted upward toward the compressor.
    b. Horizontally.
    c. Have vertical loops.
    d. Have no loops.
    e. Installed horizontally and vertically only.

INSTALL AN EVAPORATIVE CONDENSER OR A COOLING TOWER

OBJECTIVE: Given an evaporative condenser or cooling tower, install to proper operating conditions.

REFERENCES: Required – Para. 12-9 through 12-15, 12-40, 12-57 through 12-60, 12-74, 14-1, 14-3, 14-8 through 14-13, 14-109, 19-3 and 19-14.
Supplementary – Para. 14-2, 14-18, 14-21, 14-22, 14-23 and 19-25.

EQUIPMENT: 1 evaporative condenser or cooling tower, 1 water pump, 1 water-cooled condensing unit.

PREPARATION PROCEDURE:
1. Study the system assigned. Study the reference paragraphs.   TEST√_____
2. Obtain: Tools – 1 pipe cutter, 2 12-in. pipe wrenches, 1 pr. safety goggles.
3. Obtain: Supplies – 1 length 3/8-in. galvanized pipe, 1 assortment of pipe fittings and unions, 1 can pipe thread compound, 2 3/8-in. hand water valves.

TASK PROCEDURE (WEAR GOGGLES):
1. Position the evaporative condenser or cooling tower and the circulating pump.
2. Install the piping, the make-up water pipe and the electrical wiring.
3. Fill the system with water and check the piping for leaks.
4. Operate the system and check operation.   1-4√_____
5. Shut down the system.

CLOSING THE STATION:
    Clean up the work station. Return tools and unused supplies to tool crib.

DATA:

Evaporative Condenser, Make_____ Model_____ Capacity_____
Water Pump, Make_____ Model_____ Capacity_____
    Voltage_____ Amperage_____ Hertz_____ Phase_____
Condensing Unit, Make_____ Model_____ Capacity_____
    Voltage_____ Amperage_____ Hertz_____ Phase_____
Piping Size, To Condensing Unit_____ From Condensing Unit_____
    Make Up Water_____
Operation Data, Temperature In_____ Out_____ Make Up_____
Cooling Tower, Make_____ Model_____ Capacity_____

Remarks:

INSTALL AN EVAPORATIVE CONDENSER OR A COOLING TOWER.

Indicate the best answer for each question below by encircling its letter.

1. In an evaporative condenser, how are the coils cooled?
   a. Submerged in water.
   b. Sprayed with water.
   c. Air-cooled.
   d. Forced air.
   e. None of these.

2. What is the most likely cause of poor water flow through an evaporative condenser?
   a. Water shut off at the source.
   b. Float valve water-logged.
   c. Plumbing connected wrong.
   d. Water too warm.
   e. Screen clogged.

3. What is meant by calibrating a float?
   a. Adjusting to provide the proper water level.
   b. Heating in order to test for leaks in the float.
   c. Dehydrating the float.
   d. Measuring the float size.
   e. Weighing the float.

4. Why must water be added when using an evaporative condenser?
   a. It is cooler.
   b. Some is evaporated.
   c. It is cleaner.
   d. It is circulated faster.
   e. It is under higher pressure.

5. What is the static head of a cooling tower system?
   a. The height of the unit.
   b. The length of the pipe to the condenser.
   c. The length of the pipe from the condenser.
   d. The vertical height of the piping.
   e. The water pressure when the pump is running.

Task No. 4-14 Task Grade
Name _____
Date _____ _____ Class ____

INSTALL A REMOTE AIR-COOLED CONDENSER

OBJECTIVE: Given a remote air-cooled condenser: properly install, operate and test.

REFERENCES: Required - Para. 12-1 through 12-8, 12-74, 14-1, 14-2, 14-3, 14-109 and 19-11.
   Supplementary - Para. 14-4 through 14-24.

EQUIPMENT: 1 remote air-cooled condenser, 1 motor compressor.

PREPARATION PROCEDURE:
1. Study the system assigned. Study the reference paragraphs.   TEST√_____
2. Obtain: Tools - 1 tube cutter, 1 brazing outfit, 1 pr. safety goggles.
3. Obtain: Instruments - 1 gauge manifold, 1 combination voltmeter, ammeter and ohmmeter (multimeter), 1 leak detector, 1 vacuum pump.
4. Obtain: Supplies - 1 coil copper tubing, 1 assortment copper tube fittings, 1 coil silver brazing wire, 1 jar brazing flux, 1 wiping cloth, 1 cylinder of refrigerant.

TASK PROCEDURE (WEAR GOGGLES):
1. Position the remote air-cooled condenser and the compressor unit.
2. Install the condenser line and the return line. (Make sketch first.)
3. Connect the electric devices. (Make sketch first.)   1-3√_____
4. Evacuate the system, charge with vapor refrigerant to 25 psi, test for leaks.
5. If no leaks are found, charge to 75 psi and test for leaks.
6. Use local code requirements.
7. If no leaks are found, evacuate by the deep evacuation method or the three-step evacuation method.
8. Charge the system.
9. Operate the system for 10 to 20 minutes.
10. Remove the gauge manifold.   4-10√_____
11. Shut down the system.

CLOSING THE STATION:
   Clean the work area. Return tools, instruments and unused supplies to tool crib.

DATA:

Compressor, Make_____	Model_____	Type_____	Capacity_____
Remote Condenser, Make_____	Model_____	Type____	Capacity_____
Compressor Limiter Device, Make_____		Model____	Type_____
Line Sizes, Condenser_____		Return_____	
Refrigerant, R-_____	Amount_____	Leak Test Method____ ____	
Operating Conditions, Head Pressure_____		Liquid Line Temp._____	

Remarks:

INSTALL A REMOTE AIR-COOLED CONDENSER.

Indicate the best answer for each question below by encircling its letter.

1. What temperature should the head pressure correspond to when the unit is running?
    a. 70° F.
    b. 10° F above the room temperature.
    c. 30° F below room temperature.
    d. 30° F above room temperature.
    e. It is independent of the temperature.

2. What does it indicate when the liquid line is warmer than the room temperature?
    a. An overcharge of refrigerant.
    b. A stuck-open TEV.
    c. A lack of refrigerant.
    d. Too much oil.
    e. Too high a low-side pressure.

3. Is there any oil in the condenser?
    a. Yes.
    b. Only if the system is water-cooled.
    c. Only if too much oil is in the system.
    d. No.
    e. Only when the unit is being pumped down.

4. What causes a condensing unit to operate for longer periods of time?
    a. It is undersize.
    b. It is ready to shut off.
    c. It has air in the condenser.
    d. It is oversize.
    e. It is not level.

5. How is a normal head pressure maintained in sub-zero weather?
    a. By an undersized condenser.
    b. By overcharging the system.
    c. By restricting the air flow over the condenser.
    d. No change has to be made.
    e. By using an electric heater.

INSTALL AN ELECTRIC DEFROST SYSTEM

OBJECTIVE: Given an electric defrost system on a commercial unit, properly install and test.

REFERENCES: Required – Para. 12-32, 12-74 and 14-64.
    Supplementary – Para. 12-18, 12-19, 12-20, 12-27, 14-63 and 14-109.

EQUIPMENT: 1 cabinet, 1 condensing unit, 1 evaporator, 1 set of electric defrost accessories.

PREPARATION PROCEDURE:

1. Study the system assigned. Study the reference paragraphs.   TEST √ _____
2. Obtain: Tools – 1 valve ratchet wrench, 1 8-in. adjustable wrench, 1 copper tube cutter, 1 copper pipe wire brush, 1 pr. safety goggles.
3. Obtain: Instruments – 1 gauge manifold with flexible hoses, 1 combination voltmeter, ammeter and ohmmeter (multimeter), 1 leak detector, 1 vacuum pump, 1 thermometer, 1 test light.
4. Obtain: Supplies – necessary copper tubing, 1 jar brazing flux, 1 box of tube fittings, 1 refrigerant cylinder, 1 wiping cloth, 1 roll plastic tape, 1 brazing material.

TASK PROCEDURE (WEAR GOGGLES):

1. Position the cabinet, condensing unit, and install the evaporator.
2. Install the suction and liquid lines.
3. Make a wiring diagram.   1-3 √ _____
4. Attach electrical heating resistors under the drain pan and along the drain pipe.
5. Install the timer, thermostatic or pressure control, and refrigerant solenoid if required.
6. Wire the system.   4-6 √ _____
7. Evacuate the unit, then vapor charge to 25 to 30 psi and test for leaks.
8. If no leaks are found, vapor charge to 75 to 100 psi and test for leaks.
9. If no leaks are found, evacuate by either deep evacuation or triple evacuate the system.
10. Charge the system.
11. Operate the system through several defrost cycles.
12. Remove gauge manifold.   7-12 √ _____

CLOSING THE STATION:

Clean the work station. Return tools, instruments and unused supplies to tool crib.

DATA:

Cabinet, Make _____ Model _____ Type _____ Size _____
Condensing Unit, Make _____ Model _____ Type _____ Capacity _____
    Voltage _____ Phase _____
    Hertz _____ Current Loads, Min. _____
    Max. _____
Evaporator, Make _____ Model _____ Type _____ Size _____
Evaporator Blower Motor, Make _____ Model _____ Type _____ Size _____
Operating Temperatures, Evaporator _____
    Suction Line _____ Liquid Line _____
    Pressures, High Side _____ Low Side _____
Defrosting Temperatures, Evaporator _____
    Suction Line _____
    Pressures, High Side _____ Low Side _____

Remarks:

INSTALL AN ELECTRIC DEFROST SYSTEM.

Indicate the best answer for each question below by encircling its letter.

1. What must be the condition in the operating cycle before the defrost electrical circuit is completed?
   a. The system is automatically pumped down.
   b. The electrical circuit is turned off.
   c. The refrigerator is put on defrost.
   d. The evaporator must be frosted over.
   e. The condensing unit must be running.

2. Why does the electrical resistance heater operate only when the low side is pumped down?
   a. It does not.
   b. Cannot operate while condensing unit is running.
   c. To prevent liquid refrigerant from moving from the evaporator to the compressor.
   d. Requires a high temperature.
   e. Requires a low temperature.

3. What device ends the electrical defrost cycle?
   a. Thermostat on the evaporator.
   b. Pressure motor control.
   c. Weight of ice accumulation.
   d. Thickness of ice accumulation.
   e. Low-side pressure.

4. Where should the drain pan under the evaporator be placed?
   a. Below the condensing unit.
   b. At the coldest place on the condensing unit.
   c. At the warmest place on the condensing unit.
   d. So it will drain.
   e. Drain pan not needed.

5. Why do some electrical defrost systems have a heating element at the drain pan?
   a. To keep the condenser compartment warm.
   b. To save electricity.
   c. To serve as a heating anticipator.
   d. To keep the condensate from freezing.
   e. To balance the electrical load.

INSTALL A HOT GAS DEFROST SYSTEM

OBJECTIVE: Given a hot gas defrost system on a commercial unit, properly install and operate.

REFERENCES: Required - Para. 12-25, 12-26, 12-27, 12-29, 12-30, 12-33, 12-34 and 12-74.
Supplementary - Para. 12-28, 12-31, 12-32, 12-44, 14-1 through 14-24 and 14-109.

EQUIPMENT: 1 cabinet, 1 condensing unit, 1 evaporator, 1 set of hot gas defrosting accessories.

PREPARATION PROCEDURE:
1. Study the system assigned. Study the reference paragraphs. TEST✓_____
2. Obtain: Tools - 1 valve ratchet wrench, 1 8-in. adjustable wrench, 1 brazing outfit, 1 copper tube cutter, 1 copper pipe wire brush, 1 pr. safety goggles.
3. Obtain: Instruments - 1 gauge manifold with flexible hoses, 1 combination voltmeter, ammeter and ohmmeter (multimeter), 1 leak detector, 1 vacuum pump, 1 thermometer.
4. Obtain: Supplies - 1 refrig. cylinder, 1 wiping cloth, 1 brazing filler material, 1 jar brazing flux, 1 box of tube fittings, 1 coil copper tube.

TASK PROCEDURE (WEAR GOGGLES):
1. Position the cabinet, condensing unit, and install the evaporator.
2. Install the suction and liquid lines.
3. Install the condenser line bypass valve.
4. Install the suction line accumulator.
5. Make sketch of the wiring diagram.
6. Wire the unit. 1-6 ✓_____
7. Evacuate the unit, then vapor charge to 25 to 30 psi and test for leaks.
8. If no leaks are found, vapor charge to 75 to 100 psi and test for leaks.
9. If no leaks are found, evacuate by either deep evacuation or triple evacuate the system.
10. Charge the system.
11. Operate the system through several defrost cycles.
12. Remove the gauge manifold. 7-12 ✓_____
13. Shut down the system.

CLOSING THE STATION:
Clean the work station. Return tools, instruments and unused supplies to the tool crib.

DATA:

Cabinet, Make _____ Model _____ Type _____ Size _____

Condensing Unit, Make _____ Model _____ Type _____ Capacity _____

Voltage _____ Phase _____ Hertz _____ Current Loads, Min. _____

Max. _____

Evaporator, Make _____ Model _____ Type _____ Size _____

Evaporator Blower Motor, Make _____ Model _____ Type _____ Size _____

Operating Temperatures, Evaporator _____ Suction Line _____

Liquid Line _____

Pressures, High Side _____ Low Side _____

Defrosting Temperatures, Evaporator _____ Suction Line _____

Hot Gas Line Temp. _____ °F

Pressures, High Side _____ Low Side _____

Remarks:

INSTALL A HOT GAS DEFROST SYSTEM.

Indicate the best answer for each question below by encircling its letter.

1. What happens to the "hot gas" as it enters the evaporator?
    a. It becomes warmer.
    b. It condenses.
    c. It cools.
    d. It evaporates.
    e. It sub-cools.

2. What minimizes the return of liquid refrigerant to the compressor?
    a. A suction pressure valve.
    b. An oil trap.
    c. A liquid line heat exchanger.
    d. An accumulator tank.
    e. The thermostatic expansion valve.

3. What happens to the low-side pressure when the hot gas bypass valve opens?
    a. Stays the same.
    b. Rises.
    c. Lowers.
    d. First it lowers, then it rises.
    e. It equals the head pressure.

4   How many pipes or tubes are connected to the evaporator in a hot gas defrost system?
    a. Two.
    b. Three.
    c. Four.
    d. Five.
    e. Six.

5. How is the defrost water kept from freezing in the drain pan and drain tubes?
    a. There is no danger of freezing.
    b. It drains away too fast to freeze.
    c. The heat in the liquid line.
    d. The hot gas line.
    e. By electrical resistance heaters.

INSTALL AND TEST A ROOFTOP SYSTEM

OBJECTIVE: Given a commercial rooftop unit, install and operate.

REFERENCES: Required – Para. 12-5, 12-8, 12-74, 14-14 through 14-18, 14-20 through 14-24, 14-109, 23-26, 23-27, 23-28 and 23-39.
  Supplementary – Para. 14-19.

EQUIPMENT: 1 rooftop condensing unit, 1 cabinet, 1 evaporator.

PREPARATION PROCEDURE:
1. Study the system assigned. Study the reference paragraphs.   TEST√_____
2. Obtain: Tools – 1 valve ratchet wrench, 1 tube cutter, 1 8-in. adjustable open end wrench, 1 set cleaning brushes, 1 brazing outfit, 1 pr. safety goggles.
3. Obtain: Instruments – 1 combination voltmeter, ammeter and ohmmeter (multimeter), 1 gauge manifold, 1 leak detector.
4. Obtain: Supplies – 1 length 1/4-in. copper tubing, 1 length 1/2-in. copper tubing, 1 cylinder refrigerant, 1 jar of brazing flux, 1 container of safe cleaning fluid, 1 wiping cloth, 1 roll brazing wire.

TASK PROCEDURE (WEAR GOGGLES):
1. Inspect the equipment and determine the tools and supplies needed to install the system.
2. Position the evaporator in the proper position.
3. Position the rooftop condensing unit and check level of installation.
4. Connect suction line, liquid line, and electrical service.
5. Install gauge manifold.   1-5√_____
6. Evacuate the system, charge to 25 psi and test for leaks.
7. If no leaks are found, increase charge to 75 psi and test for leaks.
8. If no leaks are found, use a deep vacuum method or triple vacuum system.
9. Balance the pressures, remove the liquid line connections at the condensing unit, and install the drier and sight glass.
10. Purge the liquid line.
11. Recharge the system.
12. Operate the system for 15 to 30 minutes; check the pressures and temperatures.
13. Remove the gauge manifold.
14. Shut down the system.   6-14√_____

CLOSING THE STATION:
  Clean the work station and return all materials to the tool crib.

DATA:
Condensing Unit, Make_____ Model_____ Serial No. _____ Type_____
Motor-Compressor, Voltage_____ Starting Amperes_____ Running Amperes_____
Suction Tubing, Size_____ Liquid Line Tubing, Size_____
Liquid Line Filter-Drier, Make_____ Fittings_____
Suction Line Filter-Drier, Make_____ Fittings_____
Sight Glass, Make_____ Fittings_____
Refrigerant_____ Pounds_____
Control Circuit Voltage_____ Thermostat, Make _____
Evaporator, Make_____ Model_____ Serial No. _____ Type_____

INSTALL AND TEST A ROOFTOP SYSTEM.

Indicate the best answer for each question below by encircling its letter.

1. What is one of the advantages of an outdoor air-cooled condensing unit?
   a. A savings in plumbing for water circuits.
   b. Cheap to operate.
   c. It requires less power.
   d. Better in hot weather.
   e. Eliminates danger of moisture entering the system.

2. What device is required on a rooftop unit which is exposed to temperatures below operating temperatures?
   a. The unit must have a head pressure control.
   b. An electrical defrost is required.
   c. A rain gauge.
   d. A two-temperature valve in the refrigerant line.
   e. None of these.

3. How should the housing be installed on a rooftop unit?
   a. In a housing open at the top for ventilation.
   b. No housing is required.
   c. In an airtight housing.
   d. In a weatherproof housing.
   e. With screened-in sides.

4. What will low ambient temperatures cause?
   a. High head pressure.
   b. Low head pressure.
   c. Failure of pressure motor control.
   d. Short cycling.
   e. Too long cycle running time.

5. What should be the capacity of the liquid receiver on a rooftop unit?
   a. Capacity to flood most of the condenser in winter.
   b. Should be empty of refrigerant in winter.
   c. Capable of holding all the refrigerant in the system.
   d. No reserve capacity required.
   e. Capacity not important.

LOCATE TROUBLE IN A WATER-COOLED SYSTEM

OBJECTIVE: Given a water-cooled system: locate, solve and correct the problems most frequently found.

REFERENCES: Required - Para. 12-9 through 12-12, 12-74, 14-25 through 14-32, 14-49 through 14-52 and 14-109.
Supplementary - Para. 14-53, 14-55 and 14-56.

EQUIPMENT: One condensing unit and evaporator with a water-cooled condenser.

PREPARATION PROCEDURE:
1. Study the system assigned. Study the reference paragraphs.   TEST √_____
2. Obtain: Tools - 1 brazing outfit, 1 complete service kit, consisting of necessary wrenches, pliers, tube cutters, flaring tools, soldering equipment, 1 pr. safety goggles.
3. Obtain: Instruments - 1 combination voltmeter, ammeter and ohmmeter (multimeter), 1 gauge manifold, 1 leak detector, 1 water flow meter, 1 thermometer.
4. Obtain: Supplies - 1 6-in. square of #00 sandpaper, 1 wiping cloth, 1 jar of brazing flux, 1 roll brazing wire.

TASK PROCEDURE (WEAR GOGGLES):
1. Install gauge manifold.
2. Record the operating pressures after 15 minutes of operation.   1-2 √_____
3. Check temperature of water leaving condenser.
4. Determine proper operating pressures for unit.
5. Check the temperatures.
6. Record suction and liquid line temperatures.
7. Record water-in and water-out temperatures.
8. Check and record water flow in gpm.   3-8 √_____
9. Test system and also water leaving the condenser for leaks.
10. Determine and record the cycling pressures, temperatures, and troubles--if any--in the system.
11. Remove the gauge manifold.   9-11 √_____
12. Shut down the unit.

CLOSING THE STATION:
Clean the work station. Return the tools, instruments, and unused supplies to tool crib.

DATA:
Water-Cooled Condenser, Type _____
Condensing Unit, Manufacturer _____ Model _____ Type _____ Capacity _____
Motor, Manufacturer _____ Model _____ Type _____ H.P. _____
    Voltage _____ Phase _____ Hertz _____ Amperage _____
Motor Control, Manufacturer _____ Model _____ Type _____
Cut-in Pressure _____ Cut-out Pressure _____ High Cut-out Pressure _____
Refrigerant, R- _____ Amount _____ Liquid Level Indicator _____

	Start	After 15 Min.	After Adjusting
Evaporator Temperature			
Condensing Unit Head Pressure			
Low-Side Pressure			
Water, Rate of Flow			
Water Temperature: In -			
Out -			

LOCATE TROUBLE IN A WATER-COOLED SYSTEM.

Indicate the best answer for each question below by encircling its letter.

1. What should be the approximate water rate of flow through a water-cooled condenser?
    a. As rapid as possible.
    b. Rate not important.
    c. 5 fpm.
    d. 200 fpm.
    e. 400 fpm.

2. How is a shell and tube condenser constructed?
    a. Straight tubes inside receiver with a manifold on both ends.
    b. Circular tubes on the condenser.
    c. One large pipe with water flowing through it and a smaller refrigerant pipe on the inside.
    d. A coil within a tank.
    e. Tubes soldered together.

3. What will be the results of scaling in a water-cooled condenser?
    a. An increase in heat transfer.
    b. A reduction in heat transfer.
    c. An increase in water velocity.
    d. An increase in suction line pressure.
    e. A decrease in suction line pressure.

4. How does water flow in a tube-within-a-tube condenser?
    a. Both refrigerant and water flow in the same direction.
    b. Water flows only on the off cycle.
    c. Water flow stops on the off cycle.
    d. Refrigerant and water flow in opposite directions.
    e. Water flow stops on the running cycle.

5. What is the rate of heat removal in a water-cooled condenser?
    a. Same as air-cooled.
    b. More rapidly than air-cooled condenser in cold weather.
    c. Depends on the barometer reading.
    d. 15 times more rapidly than air.
    e. 10 times more slowly than air.

LOCATE TROUBLE IN AN ICE MAKER

OBJECTIVE: Given an ice maker: locate, solve and correct the problems found, and obtain the proper operating conditions.

REFERENCES: Required - Para. 3-14, 8-17, 8-32, 8-43, 12-25, 12-74, 13-17, 14-8, 14-13, 14-27, 14-28, 14-30, 14-31, 14-41, 14-54, 14-59, 14-81, 14-82, 14-99 and 14-109.
Supplementary - Para. 14-23, 14-32, 14-36, 14-39, 14-43 through 14-53, 14-55, 14-56, 14-58, 14-60, 14-61, 14-62 and 14-102 through 14-106.

EQUIPMENT: One ice maker.

PREPARATION PROCEDURE:
1. Study the system assigned. Study the reference paragraphs.　　　　TEST √ _____
2. Obtain: Tools - 1 service technician's tool kit, 1 pr. safety goggles.
3. Obtain: Instruments - 1 -40° F to +230° F calibration thermometer, 1 gauge manifold, 1 combination voltmeter, ammeter and ohmmeter (multimeter).
4. Obtain: Supplies - 1 wiping cloth, 1 oiler, SAE 30.

TASK PROCEDURE (WEAR GOGGLES):
1. Check the water system.
2. Test the water-in temperature, the float controlling the water level, the cleanliness of the water control devices.
3. Check the water pump.
4. Check the mechanism, clean the condenser, oil fan motors, and install the gauge manifold.　　　　1-4 √ _____
5. Check the defrost system.
6. Test for leaks.
7. Check the ice-making cycle.
8. Record pressures after 15 minutes of operation.
9. Remove gauge manifold.　　　　5-9 √ _____
10. Shut down system.

CLOSING THE STATION:
Clean the work station. Return tools, instruments and unused supplies to tool crib.

DATA:
Ice Cube Maker, Make _____ Model _____ Type of Ice Cube _____ Capacity _____
Evaporator, Type _____ Refrigerant Control _____
Defrost System, Type _____
Motor Control, Make _____ Type _____ Capacity _____
Liquid Line, Size _____ Suction Line, Size _____
Suction Line Temperature _____ °F Liquid Line Temperature _____ °F
Head Pressure _____ Low-Side Pressure _____

Remarks:

LOCATE TROUBLE IN AN ICE MAKER.

Indicate the best answer for each question below by encircling its letter.

1. How do ice makers produce clear ice cubes?
   a. Distilled water is used.
   b. The water is boiled first.
   c. Flowing water is frozen.
   d. The water is warmed by electrical heaters.
   e. The water is cooled to -10° F.

2. How is the ice cube making stopped automatically?
   a. A bin operated control is used.
   b. The system produces a certain number of ice cubes and then stops.
   c. The system stops when the water is used up.
   d. A timer is used.
   e. A pressure control is used.

3. What type of ice is produced when an auger is used?
   a. Large sheets of ice.
   b. Solid cubes.
   c. Round hollow cubes.
   d. Ice chips.
   e. Cone shaped cubes.

4. Of what material is the evaporator usually made?
   a. Aluminum.
   b. Copper.
   c. Plastic.
   d. Brass.
   e. Stainless steel.

5. What type of defrost system is used when solid cubical ice cubes are made?
   a. Hot gas.
   b. Electric.
   c. Thermal liquid.
   d. Electric and hot gas.
   e. Electric and thermal liquid.

LOCATE TROUBLE IN A LOW-TEMPERATURE SYSTEM

OBJECTIVE: Given a low-temperature commercial system with either a single or multiple
   evaporator, obtain the proper operating temperatures.

REFERENCES: Required – Para. 14-25 through 14-27 and 14-109.
   Supplementary – Para. 14-83, 14-84, 14-85, 14-88 through 14-91, 14-94, 14-98 through 14-106.

EQUIPMENT: One commercial system.

PREPARATION PROCEDURE:
   1.   Study the system assigned. Study the reference paragraphs.   TEST√_____
   2.   Obtain: Tools – 1 vacuum pump, 1 complete service kit, consisting of necessary
        wrenches, pliers, tube cutters, flaring tools, soldering equipment, 1 pr. safety goggles.
   3.   Obtain: Instruments – 1 test light, 1 combination voltmeter, ammeter and ohmmeter
        (multimeter), 1 gauge manifold, 1 leak detector.
   4.   Obtain: Supplies – 1 6-in. square of #00 sandpaper, 1 wiping cloth.

TASK PROCEDURE (WEAR GOGGLES):
   1.   Install the gauge manifold.
   2.   Determine proper operating pressures for the system.
   3.   Run the unit for at least 15 minutes and check low-side and high-side pressure.
                                                                      1-3√_____
   4.   Check the evaporator temperature.
   5.   Test for leaks.
   6.   Repair if necessary.
   7.   Remove gauge manifold.   4-7√_____
   8.   Shut down the system.

CLOSING THE STATION:
   Clean the work station. Return the tools, instruments and unused supplies to tool crib.

DATA:
Condensing Unit, Make_____ Model_____ Serial No._____ Type_____
Voltage_____ Hertz_____ Phase_____ Starting Amperes_____ Running Amperes_____
Refrigerant_____ Pounds_____
Suction Line Size_____ Liquid Line Size_____
Evaporator, Make_____ Model_____ Serial No._____ Type_____
Liquid Line Filter-Drier, Make_____
Suction Line Filter-Drier, Make_____
Sight Glass, Make_____

	At the Beginning	After 15 Minutes
Low-Side Pressure		
High-Side Pressure		
Suction Line Temp., Approx.		
Liquid Line Temp., Approx.		
Evaporator #1 Temperature		

Remarks:

LOCATE TROUBLE IN A LOW-TEMPERATURE SYSTEM.

Indicate the best answer for each question below by encircling its letter.

1. If tested by touch, what should be the temperature of the suction line?
    a. Cool.
    b. Warm.
    c. At ambient temperature.
    d. Too hot to touch.
    e. Very cold and frosting over.

2. What happens when the system is low on refrigerant?
    a. The liquid line becomes warm or the sight gauge will show bubbles.
    b. The head pressure is high.
    c. The liquid receiver becomes cold all over.
    d. The suction line will sweat.
    e. The liquid line will frost.

3. How is moisture in the system indicated?
    a. It freezes in the evaporator.
    b. A change of color in the indicator glass on the filter-drier.
    c. It freezes in the drier.
    d. It collects on the surface of the liquid refrigerant.
    e. It clogs the TEV valve screen.

4. What type of refrigerant control is used in most multiple dry systems?
    a. Pressure-operated expansion valve.
    b. Thermostatic expansion valves.
    c. A capillary tube.
    d. Low-side float.
    e. High-side float.

5. How may one detect if too much refrigerant is in the system?
    a. Liquid line will frost over.
    b. The low-side pressure will be excessive.
    c. The head pressure will be above normal.
    d. Liquid line will be warm.
    e. The suction line will be warm.

NAME_____ NUMBER_____

MODERN REFRIGERATION AND AIR CONDITIONING
MODULE 5 – CLIMATE CONTROL–COMFORT COOLING LABORATORY TASKS

NO.	NAME	TASK TEST GRADE	SIG.	TASK GRADE	SIG.	TASK DATE
5-1	Measure Relative Humidity and Dew Point					
5-2	Measure Noise Levels					
5-3	Measure Air Velocity in a Duct using an Anemometer					
5-4	Install and Use a Water Manometer ...					
5-5	Measure Air Velocity in a Duct using a Pitot Tube					
5-6	Measure Air Velocity in a Duct using a Velocimeter					
5-7	Measure Air Velocity and an Airflow Pattern in an Open Room using a Smoke Draft Indicator					
5-8	Measure Air Velocity and an Airflow Pattern at a Grille Opening using an Anemometer					
5-9	Measure Pressure Drop through a Filter					
5-10	Install and Operate Air Flow Controls					
5-11	Install a Window Type Comfort Cooler					
5-12	Install a Self-Contained Comfort Cooler (Console)					
5-13	Install a Residential Central Cooling System					
5-14	Install a Rooftop Comfort Cooling System					
5-15	Install a Heat Pump					
5-16	Locate Trouble in a Window Type Comfort Cooler					
5-17	Locate Trouble in a Heat Pump.........					
5-18	Locate Trouble in a Residential Central Comfort Cooling System					
5-19	Locate Trouble in a Water Chiller (Air Conditioning)					
5-20	Calculate the Comfort Cooling Heat Load for an Assigned Space					

SAFETY IN SERVICING CLIMATE CONTROL EQUIPMENT
(COMFORT COOLING)

It is important that air conditioners provide enough fresh air to keep the oxygen content of the air within healthy limits.

The service technician should make certain that the electrical power source of an electronic filter is disconnected before servicing the unit.

Ultraviolet rays should be shielded from the persons who use or service the system.

Always check the power circuit voltage at the air conditioner. It should be at least 95 percent of the rated voltage.

Fans, belts and pulleys must have guards in place.

WEAR SAFETY GOGGLES if there is danger of flying particles or leaking refrigerant.

Wear safety shoes if heavy objects must be carried or if heavy objects may fall.

Keep hands, hair, and loose clothing away from a moving fan and away from a moving pulley and/or belt.

When servicing rooftop units:

    Observe all safety rules for ladders:
        Safety fastened at bottom.
        Safety fastened at top.
        Ladder should extend above roof edge.
        Do not carry objects in hands when moving up
        or down a ladder. Instead, use a rope hoist,
        with rope control from both top and bottom
        (a two-person job!).

    Safety on the roof:
        Avoid removing system panels in a high wind.
        Avoid standing in water when checking or
        working on electrical circuits.

Task No. 5-1 Task Grade _____

Name _____

Date _____ Class _____

MEASURE RELATIVE HUMIDITY AND DEW POINT

OBJECTIVE: Given a wet bulb and dry bulb thermometer, obtain a 100 percent accurate dew point reading, both indoor and outdoor.

REFERENCES: Required – Para. 1-39, 1-58, 1-61, 1-62, 18-4, 18-5 through 18-9, 18-11, 18-12, 18-14, 18-15 and 18-16.
   Supplementary – Para. 1-64, 18-52 and 28-33.

EQUIPMENT: None, only instruments are required. The instructor will give directions to the place where the humidity measurements and dew point measurements are to be made.

PREPARATION PROCEDURE:
1. Study the construction and operation of the sling psychrometer and the instruments and methods used to measure dew point. Study the reference paragraphs.   TEST√_____
2. Obtain: Tools – 1 6-in. screwdriver.
3. Obtain: Instruments – 1 sling psychrometer, 1 wall psychrometer, 1 dew point indicator apparatus, 1 aspirator bulb and tubing, 2 120° F thermometers.
4. Obtain: Supplies – pencil and paper, 1 bottle of ether, 1 bottle of distilled water.

TASK PROCEDURE:
1. Make an indoor and outdoor relative humidity measurement: Wet wicks with distilled water. Swing sling psychrometer, chest high, several times (600 ft./min. approx.). Record the readings. Repeat until five (5) readings are recorded. (At least the last two must be the same to insure correct readings.) Record readings of wall psychrometer. Determine the other six (6) values for the air from the psychrometric chart.   1√_____
2. Make an indoor and outdoor dew point measurement: Clean dew point apparatus thoroughly. Connect pump to inlet of the dp apparatus. Fill well one-half full of ether. DANGER, ETHER IS EXPLOSIVE! VENTILATE WELL AND DO NOT HAVE ANY SPARKS OR OPEN FLAMES NEAR THE UNIT.
3. Mount thermometers. Suspend one thermometer inside thermometer well extending into the ether. Mount other thermometer in special bracket built on dp apparatus.
4. Obtain readings. (The slower the ether temperature lowers, the more accurate the results will be.) Work pump gently, forcing air slowly through the ether. Watch the glass window. As soon as a mist appears, read thermometer suspended in the ether. Warm the unit, and when the fog or mist disappears, record the reading.   2-4√_____

CLOSING THE STATION:
   Clean the station and return all materials to the tool crib.

DATA:
DEW POINT AND HUMIDITY MEASUREMENT

INDOOR	1	2	3	4	5	av.
dry bt.						
dew pt.						

OUTDOOR	1	2	3	4	5	av.
dry bt.						
dew pt.						

INDOOR		1	2	3	4	5	Final	rh	dp	th	vp	Sp.Vol.	Grains/#dry air
Sling	db												
Psychrom.	wb												
Wall	db												
Psychrom.	wb												
OUTDOOR													
Sling	db												
Psychrom.	wb												
Wall	db												
Psychrom.	wb												

Reason for Discrepancies _____

MEASURE RELATIVE HUMIDITY AND DEW POINT

Indicate the best answer for each question below by encircling its letter.

1. How often should the wick be dipped in the water?
   a. Every three hours.
   b. Once each day.
   c. Just before each set of readings is obtained.
   d. Before each reading.
   e. Only when thoroughly dry.

2. What liquid should be used to wet the wick?
   a. Tap water.
   b. Salt water.
   c. Distilled water.
   d. Spring water.
   e. Warm water.

3. What produces the lower reading of the wet bulb?
   a. Cooling by evaporization.
   b. The thermometer is calibrated that way.
   c. The cloth and water forms a cooling solution.
   d. It does not read lower.
   e. Ice.

4. What law governs the moisture content in a confined body of air?
   a. Pascal's Law.
   b. Charles's Law.
   c. Dalton's Law.
   d. Boyle's Law
   e. Ohm's Law.

5. What does wet bulb depression mean?
   a. A cavity in the bulb.
   b. The wet bulb is located below the dry bulb.
   c. The difference in readings between the wet bulb thermometer
      and the dry bulb thermometer.
   d. The inaccuracy of the thermometer.
   e. The appearance of mercury in the thermometer.

Task No. 5-2 Task Grade _____
Name _____
Date _____ Class _____

MEASURE NOISE LEVELS

OBJECTIVE: Given a climate control–comfort cooling system, determine if it is operating
within the proper noise level.

REFERENCE: Required – Para. 18-49, 18-50, 18-52, 22-5, 22-25 and 22-40.
Supplementary – Para. 18-51 and 22-26.

EQUIPMENT: One residential central climate control and air conditioning system or window unit.

PREPARATION PROCEDURE:
1. Study to make certain the unit is properly operating and cooling the facility to the proper
temperatures. Study the reference paragraphs.   TEST√_____
2. Obtain: Tools – 1 pr. safety goggles.
3. Obtain: Instruments – 1 sound level meter.

TASK PROCEDURE (WEAR GOGGLES):
1. Allow system to operate for 15 minutes.
2. Determine original source of sound.   1-2 √_____
3. Check the standards for decibel ratings in the community and whether a dB(A) scale is
used which requires a filter "A" in the microphone circuit.
4. Using the sound level meter, measure and record the strength of sound 3 ft. from its source.
5. Using the sound level meter, measure and record the sound 25 ft. from its source.
6. Measure and record a street sound.
7. Measure and record a classroom sound.   3-7√_____

DATA:

System, Make _____ Model _____ Serial No. _____
  HP _____ Capacity, Btu's _____ Type _____

Community dB(A) Standards	1st Sound Reading		2nd Sound Reading	
	Min.	Max.	Min.	Max.
3 foot distance				
25 foot distance				

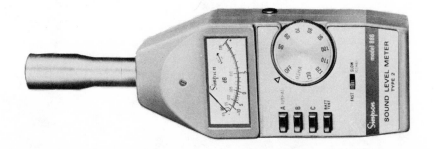

MEASURE NOISE LEVELS.

Indicate the best answer for each question below by encircling its letter.

1. What are the basic noise problems?
    a. Noise source.
    b. Noise carriers.
    c. Noise amplifiers or reflectors.
    d. All of the above.
    e. None of these.

2. Which of the following is not a common noise absorber?
    a. Insulation covered ducts.
    b. Insulation lined ducts.
    c. Drapes and curtains.
    d. Fabric-covered furniture.
    e. Smooth polished walls.

3. Where is the first measurement of the strength of sound usually taken?
    a. At the expected source.
    b. 3 ft. from its source.
    c. 10 ft. from its source.
    d. Over 50 ft. from its source.
    e. Anywhere.

4. At what sound level does objectionable sound begin?
    a. 30 dB.
    b. 50 dB.
    c. 90 dB.
    d. 120 dB.
    e. 190 dB.

5. What is the term used for sound measured under 50 ft. from its source?
    a. Frequency.
    b. Tone.
    c. Sound pressure.
    d. Sound strength.
    e. The total amount of sound coming from a unit.

MEASURE AIR VELOCITY IN A DUCT USING AN ANEMOMETER

OBJECTIVE: Given a fan and duct system, determine the correct air velocity in the duct.

REFERENCES: Required – Para. 18-19, 18-20, 18-52, 22-26 and 22-40.
      Supplementary – Para. 18-18.

EQUIPMENT: Fan and duct system with one inlet and one outlet opening.

PREPARATION PROCEDURE:
   1. Study the type of anemometer to be used. Study the reference paragraphs. TEST√_____
   2. Obtain: Tools - 1 6-in. screwdriver, 1 pr. safety goggles.
   3. Obtain: Instruments - 1 stop watch, 1 anemometer, 1 psychrometer.
   4. Obtain: Supplies - 1 wiping cloth.

TASK PROCEDURE (WEAR GOGGLES):
   1. Obtain the air velocities at one outlet grille and one inlet grille. Hold the anemometer in the correct position. Allow the anemometer fan to reach a constant speed. Start the anemometer readings and the stop watch at the same time. For high velocities, measure in 1/2-min. intervals. For low velocities, measure in 1-min. intervals. 1√_____
   2. Measure db and wb temperatures at inlet and outlet openings.
   3. Calculate air volume and air weight passing through openings. 2-3√_____

CLOSING THE STATION:
      Clean the work station and return all materials to the tool crib.

DATA:
Blower Inlet Dimensions:

_____ x _____ = area _____ sq. ft.

Inlet Readings	Outlet Reading
1. _____	1. _____
2. _____	2. _____
3. _____	3. _____
4. _____	4. _____
5. _____	5. _____

Total
Ave.

Blower Outlet Dimensions:

_____ x _____ = area _____ sq. ft.

Volume
   Air Inlet _____ cfm
   Air Outlet _____ cfm

Weight: Inlet   Outlet
   db _____   db _____
   wb _____   wb _____
   Sp. Vol. _____   Sp.Vol. _____
   Weight _____   Weight _____

Outlet: Dry Bulb Temp._____ Wet Bulb Temp._____
          Specific Volume _____

Outlet:
      Weight of Air Outlet = $\dfrac{\text{Outlet Vol.}}{\text{Outlet Sp. Vol.}}$ = _____

Remarks:

MEASURE AIR VELOCITY IN A DUCT USING AN ANEMOMETER.

Indicate the best answer for each question below by encircling its letter.

1. What does an anemometer measure?
   a. Feet.
   b. Feet per minute.
   c. Cubic feet.
   d. Cubic feet per minute.
   e. Temperature.

2. How is the anemometer held in reference to the air stream?
   a. At an angle.
   b. Square to the air stream.
   c. Moved with a slight oscillating motion.
   d. Moved back and forth in line with the air flow.
   e. At a 45 deg. angle.

3. What must happen before the readings may start?
   a. The stop watch must be started first.
   b. The anemometer must be turned on first.
   c. They must both start registering at the same time.
   d. Either one can be started first.
   e. Adjust the grille opening to 1/2 its normal opening.

4. How many start and zero level controls does an anemometer have?
   a. One.
   b. Two.
   c. Three.
   d. Four.
   e. Five.

5. What is wrong if the anemometer registers backwards?
   a. Nothing.
   b. The air flow is too slow.
   c. The anemometer is facing the wrong way.
   d. The anemometer gears are reversed.
   e. The air flow is too fast.

INSTALL AND USE A WATER MANOMETER

OBJECTIVE: Given a multiple duct system: using a water manometer, determine the velocity, pressures, and flow of air through the inlets, outlets and ducts.

REFERENCES: Required – Para. 18-18 through 18-21, 18-43, 18-52, 22-8, 22-9 and 22-14 through 22-26.
  Supplementary – Para. 22-10 through 22-13, 22-27, 22-28 and 22-40.

EQUIPMENT: Fan and duct system with one inlet and three outlet openings.

PREPARATION PROCEDURE:
1. Study the multiple duct system assigned. Study the reference paragraphs.   TEST√_____
2. Obtain: Tools – 1 pr. safety goggles.
3. Obtain: Instruments – 1 stem type dial thermometer, 1 stop watch, 1 anemometer, 1 manometer.
4. Obtain: Supplies – 1 wiping cloth.

TASK PROCEDURE (WEAR GOGGLES):
1. Check the grilles and duct work for obstructions.
2. Obtain the air velocities at all outlet grilles and the inlet grille, using an anemometer; record data and measure size of grille.
3. Measure the db and wb temperatures at the inlet and outlets and calculate the air volume and air weight passing through each opening.   1-3√_____
4. Install manometer to obtain duct pressure in inlet duct and in each of the three outlet ducts. Record data.   4√_____

CLOSING THE STATION:
  Clean station and return all materials to the tool crib.

DATA:

Blower Inlet Dimensions:

____ x ____ = area ____ sq. ft.

Anemometer Readings – Inlet Reading:

1. ____   4. ____
2. ____   5. ____
3. ____   6. ____

Blower Outlet Dimensions:

____ x ____ = area ____ sq. ft.

Outlet Readings (three outlets):

	#1	#2	#3		#1	#2	#3
1.				4.			
2.				5.			
3.				6.			

Average_____

Average_____

Volume of Air Inlet:
  Area of Inlet_____ x Average Velocity = _____(Cfm) Cu. ft. per min.
Volume of Air Outlet:
  Area of Outlet 1_____ x Average Velocity = _____(Cfm) Cu. ft. per min.
  Area of Outlet 2_____ x Average Velocity = _____(Cfm) Cu. ft. per min.
  Area of Outlet 3_____ x Average Velocity = _____(Cfm) Cu. ft. per min.
Inlet: Dry Bulb Temp._____Wet Bulb Temp._____Spec. Volume_____ ____

  Weight of Air Inlet = $\dfrac{\text{Inlet Vol.}}{\text{Inlet Sp. Vol.}}$ = _____

Outlet: Dry Bulb Temp._____Wet Bulb Temp_____Spec. Volume_____

  Weight of Air Outlet = $\dfrac{\text{Outlet Vol.}}{\text{Outlet Sp.Vol.}}$ = #1_____ = #2_____ = #3_____

Water Manometer Readings: Inlet Duct_____Outlet Duct #1_____ #2_____ #3_____

INSTALL AND USE A WATER MANOMETER.

Indicate the best answer for each question below by encircling its letter.

1. What are water manometers used for?
    a. To measure relative humidity.
    b. To measure barometric pressure.
    c. To measure small pressure differences.
    d. To measure high pressure differences.
    e. To measure velocity pressure.

2. How are water manometers usually used to measure air duct pressure?
    a. They are placed inside the duct.
    b. They are placed on top of the duct.
    c. They are placed below the duct.
    d. One end is connected to the duct with a rubber tube.
    e. Both ends are connected to the duct with a rubber tube.

3. Why not use mercury in a manometer used for measuring duct pressure?
    a. It pollutes the air.
    b. It is too expensive.
    c. It evaporates.
    d. It is too heavy.
    e. It is too difficult to handle.

4. Why is water usually used in a manometer used for measuring duct pressure?
    a. It is cheap.
    b. Does not pollute the air.
    c. It provides a sensitive manometer.
    d. Not affected by temperature.
    e. Easy to handle.

5. When measuring duct pressure with a water manometer, how many pressure readings should be taken?
    a. One, at the center of the duct.
    b. Four, at the four edges of the duct.
    c. Several, Lengthwise in the duct.
    d. Several, across the duct.
    e. Not important.

MEASURE AIR VELOCITY IN A DUCT USING A PITOT TUBE

OBJECTIVE: Given an air conditioning duct system: using a pitot tube, determine the velocity of air through the system.

REFERENCES: Required – Para. 18-18, 18-19, 18-22, 18-52, 22-11, 22-12, 22-16 and 22-40.

EQUIPMENT: A domestic air conditioning blower and duct system.

PREPARATION PROCEDURE:
1. Study the pitot tube system designated for the job. Study the reference paragraphs.

    TEST√ _____

2. Obtain: Tools – 1 pr. safety goggles, 1 6-in. screwdriver.
3. Obtain: Instruments – 1 pitot tube complete with necessary rubber tubing, 1 draft indicator, 1 wb-db thermometer.
4. Obtain: Supplies – 1 wiping cloth.

TASK PROCEDURE (WEAR GOGGLES):
1. Start up the unit and record the data.
2. Using a pitot tube, take the sixteen and/or twenty readings at both the inlet and outlet grilles.

    1-2√ _____

3. Measure the wb and db readings at both openings. Calculate the air weights for both the inlet and outlet openings.

    3√ _____

CLOSING THE STATION:
   Clean the station and return all materials to the tool crib.

DATA:
Duct Inlet Size _____ x _____ = _____ Area, sq. ft. Duct Outlet Size _____ x _____ = _____ Area, sq.ft.

INLET READINGS: Position

	1	2	3	4	5	6	7	8	9	10	11	12	13	14	15	16	17	18	19	20	Av.
Original																					
Final																					

                                        Average Difference _____

$v = 4050$ $\sqrt{hw}$ $= 4050 \times$ ___ = _____ ft/min   wt/min _____

OUTLET READINGS: Position

	1	2	3	4	5	6	7	8	9	10	11	12	13	14	15	16	17	18	19	20	Av.
Original																					
Final																					

                                        Average Difference _____

$v = 4050$ $\sqrt{hw}$ $= 4050 \times$ ___ = _____ ft/min   wt/min _____

MEASURE AIR VELOCITY IN A DUCT USING A PITOT TUBE.

Indicate the best answer for each question below by encircling its letter.

1. What does the inner pitot tube opening register?
   a. Total pressure.
   b. Velocity pressure.
   c. Static pressure.
   d. Total pressure minus velocity pressure.
   e. Total pressure minus static pressure.

2. What do the openings in the outer pitot tube register?
   a. Total pressure.
   b. Velocity pressure.
   c. Static pressure.
   d. Total pressure minus static pressure.
   e. Sea level pressure.

3. How many holes are located in the outer tube?
   a. One.
   b. Four.
   c. Eight.
   d. Sixteen.
   e. Twenty-four.

4. On what is the air velocity based?
   a. The total pressure.
   b. The static pressure.
   c. The total pressure minus the static pressure.
   d. The total pressure minus the velocity pressure.
   e. The velocity pressure minus the static pressure.

5. How should the pitot tube be held in reference to the air stream?
   a. Parallel.
   b. Perpendicular.
   c. At a 45 deg. angle.
   d. Its angle should be constantly changed.
   e. 90 deg.

MEASURE AIR VELOCITY IN A DUCT USING A VELOCIMETER

OBJECTIVE: Given a duct system with fan: using a velocimeter, determine the velocity of air in a duct.

REFERENCES: Required – Para. 18-18, 18-19, 18-21, 18-52, 22-11, 22-12 and 22-40.

EQUIPMENT: A duct system equipped with a fan.

PREPARATION PROCEDURE:
1. Study the velocimeter. Study the reference paragraphs.   TEST√ _____
2. Obtain: Tools – 1 6-in. screwdriver, 1 pr. safety goggles.
3. Obtain: Instruments – 1 velocimeter, scale 0-500 ft./min.
4. Obtain: Supplies – 1 wiping cloth.

TASK PROCEDURE (WEAR GOGGLES):
1. Record the velocimeter data. Be sure to use the correct air pick up jet.   1√ _____
2. Determine the average velocity of one outlet opening. Take the sixteen (16) or twenty (20) readings using the standard sectioning plan.
3. Determine the average velocity at the inlet opening. Take the sixteen (16) or twenty (20) readings.   2-3√ _____

CLOSING THE STATION:
Clean the station and return all materials to the tool crib.

DATA:
OUTLET VELOCITY:

	1	2	3	4	5	6	7	8	9	10	11	12	13	14	15	16	17	18	19	20
Reading Position																				
Reading Value																				

Average Reading _____

INLET VELOCITY:

	1	2	3	4	5	6	7	8	9	10	11	12	13	14	15	16	17	18	19	20
Reading Position																				
Reading Value																				

Average Reading _____

Remarks:

MEASURE AIR VELOCITY IN A DUCT USING A VELOCIMETER.

Indicate the best answer for each question below by encircling its letter.

1. What is another instrument used to obtain air velocity values?
    a. Hydrometer.
    b. Speedometer.
    c. Pedometer.
    d. Odometer.
    e. Anemometer.

2. Why is the velocimeter popular for determining air velocities?
    a. It does not need the 16 positions.
    b. It can be mounted in any position.
    c. It is more accurate than the pitot tube.
    d. It is excellent for very low velocities.
    e. The velocities can be read directly.

3. Can the velocimeter be used to obtain velocities inside a duct?
    a. No.
    b. Yes.
    c. Yes, if the instrument can be put inside.
    d. Yes, if the duct is large enough for the person to get inside.
    e. Yes, but only if rough readings are desired.

4. Does the velocimeter operate on the principle of velocity pressure?
    a. Yes.
    b. No.
    c. Only at high velocities.
    d. Only at outlet grilles.
    e. Only at inlet grilles.

5. If a 12 in. X 12 in. grille has 40 metal strips 1/32 in. thick mounted lengthwise, what is its net opening?
    a. 144 sq. in.
    b. 156 sq. in.
    c. 129 sq. in.
    d. 142 3/4 sq. in.
    e. 141 1/4 sq. in.

MEASURE AIR VELOCITY AND AN AIRFLOW PATTERN IN AN OPEN ROOM USING A SMOKE DRAFT INDICATOR

OBJECTIVE: Given an air conditioning duct and fan system and open room, measure the air velocity and airflow pattern in the room using a smoke draft indicator.

REFERENCES: Required - Para. 18-18, 18-23, 18-52, 22-15, 22-16, 22-19, 22-40, 24-48, 24-49 and 24-50.
   Supplementary - Para. 22-17 and 22-18.

EQUIPMENT: A domestic air conditioning duct and fan system.

PREPARATION PROCEDURE:
1. Study methods of generating "smoke" and how smoke movement may be used to measure air movement. Study the reference paragraphs.   TEST√_____
2. Obtain: Tools - 1 pr. safety goggles.
3. Obtain: Instruments - 1 smoke generator, 1 stop watch, 1 50-ft. tape.
4. Obtain: Supplies - 1 pt. of aqua ammonia, 1 pt. of dilute hydrochloric acid.

TASK PROCEDURE (WEAR GOGGLES):
1. Prepare the smoke generator by first cleaning the unit. Next, fill the smoke generator bottles with the correct liquid. Do not contact the skin or clothing with the liquid.
2. Measure the drafts. Measure the air approximately ten feet away from the exhaust opening. Determine the direction of the draft. Measure twenty feet along this direction. Aspirate smoke into the air and time its travel for the 20 feet. Take five readings and calculate the average.   1-2√_____
3. Repeat Step #2 at another spot. Record readings on data sheet.   3√_____

CLOSING THE STATION:
   Clean up the work station, and return all materials to the tool crib.

DATA:
FIRST TEST: Place _____

	1	2	3	4	5	
Feet						
Time						
Feet/Min.						Average Feet/Min.

Comments:

SECOND TEST: Place _____

	1	2	3	4	5	
Feet						
Time						
Feet/Min.						Average Feet/Min.

Comments:

MEASURE AIR VELOCITY AND AN AIRFLOW PATTERN IN AN
OPEN ROOM USING A SMOKE DRAFT INDICATOR.

Indicate the best answer for each question below by encircling its letter.

1. What is the chemical composition of the smoke from the generator?
   a. Ammonia.
   b. Hydrochloric acid.
   c. Muriatic acid.
   d. Ammonium chloride.
   e. Ammonium hydroxide.

2. What is the density of the generated smoke?
   a. Heavier than air.
   b. Lighter than air.
   c. The same density as air.
   d. Same density as the moisture in the air.
   e. The same density as dry air.

3. What is the color of the smoke?
   a. Gray.
   b. White.
   c. Blue.
   d. Black.
   e. Brown.

4. If the smoke travels 20 feet in 45 seconds, what is its velocity?
   a. 20 ft. per min.
   b. 45 ft. per min.
   c. 15 ft. per min.
   d. 26.66 ft. per min.
   e. 25.67 ft. per min.

5. What is considered a maximum comfortable draft?
   a. 5 ft. per min.
   b. 10 ft. per min.
   c. 15 ft. per min.
   d. 20 ft. per min.
   e. 25 ft. per min.

MEASURE AIR VELOCITY AND AN AIRFLOW PATTERN AT A GRILLE OPENING USING AN ANEMOMETER

OBJECTIVE: Given a conventional forced air system: using an anemometer, measure the airflow pattern and velocity from three exhaust grilles.

REFERENCES: Required – Para. 18-18, 18-19, 18-20, 18-52, 22-8, 22-11, 22-14, 22-15, 22-16, 22-19 and 22-40.

EQUIPMENT: A system which provides a main duct and serveral branch ducts.

PREPARATION PROCEDURE:
1. Study the fan and duct system assigned. Study the reference paragraphs.   TEST√_____
2. Obtain: Tools – 1 pr. safety goggles.
3. Obtain: Instruments – 1 stop watch, 1 anemometer.
4. Obtain: Supplies – 1 wiping cloth.

TASK PROCEDURE (WEAR GOGGLES):
1. Determine the grille sizes by measuring the width and length. Also measure the width of the grille bars and record.
2. Start the unit and measure the velocities. Sixteen to twenty readings at each grille must be taken at the correct positions and recorded.   1-2√_____

CLOSING THE STATION:
Clean up the work station and return all materials to the tool crib.

DATA READINGS:

Fresh Air Grille	Position																			
	1	2	3	4	5	6	7	8	9	10	11	12	13	14	15	16	17	18	19	20
Feet-Start																				
Feet-End																				
Difference																				
Time																				
Velocity																				

Return Air Grille																				
Feet-Start																				
Feet-End																				
Difference																				
Time																				
Velocity																				

Record data for each opening using a form similar to the one above.

Duct Dimensions:	Fresh Air	Return Air
Width		
Length		
Area		
Grille Bars Area		
Effective Areas = Area - Grille Bars Area		
Volume: Eff. Area x Velocity		

Is the fresh air MORE or LESS than the return air? _____

MEASURE AIR VELOCITY AND AN AIRFLOW PATTERN AT
A GRILLE OPENING USING AN ANEMOMETER.

Indicate the best answer for each question below by encircling its letter.

1. Do all the particles of air travel at the same speed in the duct?
    a. No.
    b. Yes.
    c. Only if they are the same size.
    d. Only in round ducts.
    e. Only if the velocity is low.

2. Are the pressures the same throughout the duct system?
    a. No.
    b. Yes.
    c. Only if a slow speed fan is used.
    d. The pressures are higher at the inlet.
    e. Only if there is no turbulence.

3. What effect does a damper have on air flow?
    a. Improves it.
    b. Retards it.
    c. Streamlines the air flow.
    d. Maintains equal pressures.
    e. Prevents overloading the fan.

4. If all the outlet openings are the same size, what is the result?
    a. Each opening will discharge an equal volume of air.
    b. Each outlet will discharge an equal weight of air.
    c. The farthest opening will discharge the least volume of air.
    d. The closest opening to the fan will discharge the least volume of air.
    e. The closest opening to the fan will discharge all the air.

5. What is a balanced duct system?
    a. All the outlets discharge an equal volume of air.
    b. The air volume "in" equals the air volume "out".
    c. Each outlet discharges the correct volume of air.
    d. The fan size is correct for the motor size.
    e. The fan size is correct for the air volume to be handled.

MEASURE PRESSURE DROP THROUGH A FILTER

OBJECTIVE: Given a standard forced convection system, determine the pressure drop caused by an air filter.

REFERENCES: Required - Para. 18-43, 18-52, 22-8, 22-9, 22-11, 22-14 through 22-18, 22-21, 22-22, 22-24 through 22-26, 22-29, 22-30, 22-31, 22-32 and 22-40.
Supplementary - Para. 22-10, 22-12, 22-13, 22-19, 22-20, 22-23, 23-33 and 23-39.

EQUIPMENT: A warm air heating system using forced convection fan and air filter.

PREPARATION PROCEDURE:
1. Study the fan and filter system assigned. Study the reference paragraphs. TEST√_____
2. Obtain: Tools - 1 6-in. reg. screwdriver, 1 6-in. slip joint pliers, 1 small flexible spout oil can, 1 pr. safety goggles.
3. Obtain: Instruments - 1 0 to 4.0-in. water differential manometer, 1 10-in. manometer with tubes and fittings.
4. Obtain: Supplies - 1 wiping cloth.

TASK PROCEDURE (WEAR GOGGLES):
1. Locate or make holes for manometer tubes and connect manometer. Record original setting or reading.
2. Record readings of manometer after the unit has started. Pressure drop is the distance between the two liquid levels. 1-2√_____
3. Install differential manometer across the filter.
4. Operate fan system. Measure the pressure drop across the filter. 3-4√_____ _____
5. Stop the system. Remove the filter. Operate the system and take the readings.
6. Stop the system. Install a new filter. Operate the system and take the readings.
7. Reduce the fan system intake opening to half size. Operate the system and take readings. 5-7√_____
8. Take manometer readings on both sides of the filter.
9. Plug instrument openings in duct. 8-9√_____

CLOSING THE STATION:
Clean the work station and return all materials to the tool crib.

DATA:
Fan Motor, Make _____ Model _____ Type _____ Size _____
Voltage _____ Phase _____ Operating Current _____
Fan, Make _____ Type _____ Size _____
Filter, Make _____ Type _____ Length _____ Width _____ Thickness _____ No. _____
Pressure Differential, Old Filter _____ New Filter _____ No Filter _____
With One-Half of Intake Opening Closed _____
Manometer Reading, Inlet _____ Downstream from Filter _____
Pressure Drop: Original Reading _____ Final Reading _____
Rise _____ Drop _____ Difference _____

Remarks:

MEASURE PRESSURE DROP THROUGH A FILTER.

Indicate the best answer for each question below by encircling its letter.

1. What type air pressure is measured by a differential manometer?
   a. Pressure drop.
   b. Total pressure.
   c. Static pressure.
   d. Velocity pressure.
   e. Partial vacuum.

2. What is the pressure difference across an adhesive filter which indicates when the filter should be changed?
   a. 0.10 in. of water.
   b. 0.20 in. of water.
   c. 0.30 in. of water.
   d. 0.40 in. of water.
   e. 0.50 in. of water.

3. If the filter is on the intake side of the fan, what is the pressure on both sides of the filter?
   a. Positive pressure.
   b. Negative pressure.
   c. Both positive and negative pressure.
   d. Either positive or negative pressure.
   e. Negative pressure on one side of filter only.

4. When the cubic feet per minute of air is reduced, what happens to the pressure drop across the filter?
   a. Stays the same.
   b. Increases.
   c. Decreases.
   d. May either increase or decrease.
   e. Reduces to zero.

5. What does one inch of water column equal in psi?
   a. 29.9 psi.
   b. 14.7 psi.
   c. 0.432 psi.
   d. 0.036 psi.
   e. 2.31 psi.

INSTALL AND OPERATE AIRFLOW CONTROLS

OBJECTIVE: Given a forced air furnace, determine if the airflow control devices used on the system are properly functioning, and balance the airflow.

REFERENCES: Required – Para. 18-20, 18-21, 18-22, 18-52, 22-17, 22-18, 22-24, 22-26, 22-40, 24-29, 24-30, 24-33, 24-34, 24-35, 24-49, 24-50 and 24-53.

EQUIPMENT: One forced air furnace equipped with comfort cooling and power operated dampers.

PREPARATION PROCEDURE:
1. Study the total system and determine the type and purpose of the airflow control. Read the reference paragraphs.   TEST√ _____
2. Obtain: Tools – 1 inspection mirror, 1 pr. safety goggles.
3. Obtain: Instruments – 1 pitot tube complete with fittings and manometer, 1 anemometer, 1 velocimeter, 1 6-ft. steel tape, 1 thermometer.
4. Obtain: Supplies – 1 wiping cloth.

TASK PROCEDURE (WEAR GOGGLES):
1. Measure the duct size.
2. Determine the type of airflow control, damper control, or fire damper used, and its size.
3. Operate the system and measure the air velocities and calculate the air volumes and temperatures.   1-3√ _____
4. Have the instructor assign the air volumes desired at each opening.
5. Operate the system and adjust the damper controls or airflow controls to the desired volumes.   4-5 √ _____

CLOSING THE STATION:
Clean the station and return all materials to the tool crib.

DATA:
Airflow Control:

Duct	Air Volume			Air Velocity			Standards		
	Original	Recommended	Final	Original	Recommended	Final	Size	Type	Temp.
Main Duct									
1									
2									
3									
4									

Damper Control:

Duct									
1									
2									
3									
4									

Fire Damper:

Duct									
1									
2									
3									
4									

INSTALL AND OPERATE AIRFLOW CONTROLS.

Indicate the best answer for each question below by encircling its letter.

1. Which of the following will cause an airflow control to react?
    a. If the air temperature in the recirculated air is too high or too low.
    b. If the air temperature to the room is too high or too low.
    c. If the temperature in the fresh air is too high or too low.
    d. If the temperature in the exhaust air is too high or too low.
    e. All of the above.

2. What classification indicates a fire damper that will hold back a fire indefinitely?
    a. Class O.
    b. Class A.
    c. Class B.
    d. Class C.
    e. Class D.

3. What usually causes a fire damper to close?
    a. The heating of a fusible link.
    b. The lack of airflow in the ducts.
    c. A pressurestat in the room indicating overheating.
    d. The recycling of the air conditioner.
    e. All of the above.

4. What is the air fed into a fan called?
    a. Forced draft.
    b. Induced draft.
    c. Inertia.
    d. Axial flow.
    e. Radial flow.

5. If the velocity pressure reading of water in a pitot tube reading is .25, what is its velocity?
    a. 0.25-ft./min.
    b. 2025-ft./min.
    c. 4050-ft./min.
    d. 1012-ft./min.
    e. 5000-ft./min.

INSTALL A WINDOW TYPE COMFORT COOLER

OBJECTIVE: Given a window type comfort cooler: install, properly seal, and provide for proper condensate drainage.

REFERENCES: Required – Para. 19-9, 19-25, 21-3, 21-6, 21-7, 21-8 and 21-18.

EQUIPMENT: 1 window frame, 1 window type comfort cooler complete with installation base and window seals.

PREPARATION PROCEDURE:
1. Study the window unit and window frame assigned. Study the reference paragraphs.

TEST√_____

2. Obtain: Tools – 1 6-in. screwdriver, 1/4-in. blade, 1 #2 Phillips screwdriver, 1 1/2-in. socket and ratchet handle, 1 1/8-in. twist drill, 1 10-in. straight tin snips, 1 marking pencil, 1 electric drill, 1 pr. safety goggles.
3. Obtain: Instruments – 1 spirit level, 1 measuring tape.
4. Obtain: Supplies – 1 lb. sealing compound, 1 wiping cloth.

TASK PROCEDURE (WEAR GOGGLES):
1. Uncrate window unit, check for damage. Check voltage.
2. Open window, locate center of window and position the base in place. Level base and mark screw holes. Drill screw marks. Install rubber gasket on window sill. Fasten mounting base to window sill. Rustproof screws should be used. Adjust leveling screws.

1-2√_____

3. Prepare comfort cooler for operation. Loosen hold down bolts. Inspect unit for condition.
4. Mount unit on base. Fasten unit to base, Install spacers between each side of unit and window frame. Use sealer to fill small cracks. Install rubber gasket along the unit top. Install gasket between inner and outer double hung window. Install double hung sash lock.
5. Inspect for openings in the installation's partitions. Seal small cracks with sealing compound.
6. Operate the unit. Check damper adjustments. Check for noise.   3-6√_____

CLOSING THE STATION:
Clean the work station and return all materials to the tool crib.

DATA:
Air Conditioner, Make_____ Model_____ Serial No._____ Type_____
          Voltage_____ Starting Current_____ Running Current_____
Fan Motor, Number_____ Type_____ Speed_____
How is the condensate removed?_____

Noise, Unit_____ Fan, Condenser_____ Evaporator_____
EER _____

Remarks:

INSTALL A WINDOW TYPE COMFORT COOLER.

Indicate the best answer for each question below by encircling its letter.

1. Why is it important to mount the unit slightly slanted to the outside?
   a. For lubrication.
   b. To allow good refrigerant flow.
   c. To minimize noise.
   d. To insure proper control of condensate.
   e. To make a neat installation.

2. Where does the condenser cooling air come from?
   a. Indoors.
   b. Outdoors.
   c. From the cooling unit.
   d. From outdoors only in cool weather.
   e. From indoors only in warm weather.

3. How is the space between the unit and the side of the window closed?
   a. It is filled by the unit.
   b. The window closes the opening.
   c. Sheet metal or plastic closures are used.
   d. Sealing compound is used.
   e. Install glass panes.

4. If the unit drips condensate into the room, what may be wrong?
   a. Nothing.
   b. The wall is not strong enough.
   c. The filters are clogged.
   d. The unit may be slanted the wrong way.
   e. The compressor shipping bolts are too loose.

5. How may small openings to the outdoors be sealed?
   a. They need not be sealed.
   b. Sponge rubber gaskets.
   c. Sealing compound.
   d. Tar.
   e. Putty.

INSTALL A SELF-CONTAINED COMFORT COOLER (CONSOLE).

OBJECTIVE: Given a self-contained comfort cooler console: install in conformance with local refrigeration, electrical, and plumbing codes.

REFERENCES: Required - Para. 14-7 through 14-11, 14-13, 14-30, 14-52, 14-109, 21-9, 21-10, 21-11 and 21-18.
Supplementary - Para. 11-38, 11-45, 11-82, 14-12 and 14-49.

EQUIPMENT: One self-contained air conditioner.

PREPARATION PROCEDURE:
1. Study the console air conditioner. Study the reference paragraphs.   TEST√_____
2. Obtain: Tools - 1 ratchet wrench, 1 8-in. adjustable open end wrench, 1 8-in. side cutting pliers, 1 tube cutter, 1 brazing outfit, 1 pr. safety goggles, 1 spark lighter.
3. Obtain: Instruments - 1 leak detector, 1 gauge manifold and lines, 1 6-ft. steel tape, 1 electrical combination voltmeter, ammeter and ohmmeter.
4. Obtain: Supplies - 2 lengths of copper pipe, 1 set pipe fittings, 1 roll 50-50 solder, 1 jar solder flux.

TASK PROCEDURE (WEAR GOGGLES):
1. Inspect the unit and determine the tools and supplies needed.
2. Check to make certain that the electrical power is correct. Position the unit in the proper place. Install in accordance with local electrical code.   1-2√_____
3. Check the amount of pipe necessary to connect the water-cooled condenser. Install piping in accordance with the manufacturer's recommendation and local plumbing code.
4. Install outside air in and out ducts if it is air-cooled unit.   3-4√_____
5. Install the gauge manifold and operate the unit for 10 to 20 minutes. Check pressures, temperatures, and test for leaks. Charge and adjust if needed.   5√_____

CLOSING THE STATION:
Clean the work station and return all materials to the tool crib.

DATA:

Console Unit, Make _____ Model _____ Serial No. _____ Type _____
Voltage _____ Hertz _____
Starting Current _____ Running Current _____
HP _____ Btu Rating _____ Condenser, Type _____
Refrigerant _____ Amount _____
Operating Conditions: Pressures, High _____ Low _____
Air Temperature: Intake Grille _____ Outlet Grille _____

Remarks:

INSTALL A SELF-CONTAINED COMFORT COOLER (CONSOLE).

Indicate the best answer for each question below by encircling its letter.

1. Which two of the motor terminals will have the largest voltage drop or lowest amperage flow?
   a. Starting to common.
   b. Starting to running.
   c. Running to common.
   d. They are all the same.
   e. Two circuits are equal.

2. How is a motor winding open circuit detected?
   a. Fuse will blow.
   b. Circuit breaker will open.
   c. The unit will indicate a short.
   d. Neither winding will allow current to pass.
   e. One winding will not allow current to pass.

3. Why must the electrical power source be checked?
   a. The wrong type wall socket may be used.
   b. The outlet may be too far away.
   c. The wiring may be too large.
   d. The wiring may be overloaded.
   e. The black and white wires may be interchanged.

4. Does the self-contained type comfort cooler dehumidify the air?
   a. Only if a humidistat is used.
   b. Only if the unit has filters.
   c. Only if the air is very warm.
   d. Yes.
   e. No.

5. What does the overload motor cut-out protect?
   a. The thermostat.
   b. The motor.
   c. The wiring.
   d. The compressor.
   e. The filter.

INSTALL A RESIDENTIAL CENTRAL COOLING SYSTEM

OBJECTIVE: Given a residential central cooling system: install in conformance with the local refrigeration and electrical code, and adjust to proper operating temperatures.

REFERENCES: Required – Para. 11-27, 11-28, 21-12, 21-18, 23-29 through 23-32 and 23-39.
    Supplementary – Para. 11-38, 11-45, 11-46, 11-47, 11-82 and 23-33.

EQUIPMENT: 1 forced warm air furnace, 1 residential system consisting of 1 outdoor condenser, 1 set of precharged liquid and suction lines with quick disconnects, and 1 evaporator.

PREPARATION PROCEDURE:
1.   Study residential comfort cooling system and furnace. Study the reference paragraphs.
                                                      TEST√_____
2.   Obtain: Tools – 1 ratchet wrench, 2 8-in. adjustable open end wrenches, 1 8-in. side cutting pliers, 1 set of open end wrenches, 1 6-in. screwdriver, 1/4-in. blade, 1 electric portable drill, 1 set of twist drills, 1 set of sockets and drives, 1 pr. safety goggles, 1 #2 Phillips screwdriver.
3.   Obtain: Instruments – 1 leak detector, 1 combination voltmeter, ammeter and ohmmeter (multimeter), 1 gauge manifold and lines.
4.   Obtain: Supplies – 1 box sheet metal screws, 1 length of drain tube or hose, 1 lb. of sealing compound.

TASK PROCEDURE (WEAR GOGGLES):
1.   Install condensing unit on support platform.   1√_____
2.   Install evaporator in furnace plenum chamber. New duct section may be needed. Install condensate drain or pump.   2√_____
3.   Install suction and liquid lines. A liquid line filter-drier and sight glass is recommended.   3√_____
4.   Install thermostat.   4√_____
5.   Install electrical wiring for motor compressor and duct fan in accordance with the local electrical code.   5√_____
6.   Install gauge manifold.
7.   Operate system. Check operating pressures, temperatures, and test for leaks.
                                                                  6-7√_____

CLOSING THE STATION:
    Clean up station and return all materials to the tool crib.

DATA:
System, Make_____ Model_____ Serial No._____ Type_____
Voltage_____ Hertz_____ HP_____ Starting Current_____ Running Current_____
Btu Rating_____ Refrigerant_____ Amount_____
Operating Conditions. Pressures: High_____ Low_____ Outlet Temp._____
Condensing Unit Connections, Liquid Line Size_____ _____
                            Suction Line Size_____
                            Type_____
Evaporator Connections, Liquid Line Size_____ Type_____
                       Suction Line Size_____ Type_____

EER _____

INSTALL A RESIDENTIAL CENTRAL COOLING SYSTEM.

Indicate the best answer for each question below by encircling its letter.

1. What is a squirrel cage fan?
   a. A propeller fan.
   b. An axial flow fan.
   c. A radial flow fan.
   d. A fan with a wire guard mounted around it.
   e. A revolving fan.

2. With what basic function of air conditioning are duct velocities most concerned?
   a. Air heating.
   b. Air cooling.
   c. Air humidifying.
   d. Air distribution.
   e. Air cleanliness.

3. What is meant by balancing a duct system?
   a. Make all the openings equal in area.
   b. Make all the ducts equal in length.
   c. Make all openings discharge the correct amount of air.
   d. Make the inlet air equal the outlet air.
   e. Adjust the duct dampers until all the air velocities are the same.

4. Why is a filter-drier often installed in the suction line of a residential central system?
   a. Because of ease of installation.
   b. To prevent motor compressor burnouts.
   c. Because there is greater moisture in the suction line.
   d. To prevent refrigerant from backing up the suction line.
   e. To prevent frost back.

5. If the condensing unit is above the evaporator, why is a U bend sometimes put in the suction line?
   a. To prevent frost back.
   b. To assist the oil return.
   c. To prevent back pressure in the evaporator.
   d. To prevent high low-side pressures.
   e. To act as a vibration control.

INSTALL A ROOFTOP COMFORT COOLING SYSTEM

OBJECTIVE: Given a rooftop comfort cooling system, install in accordance with local code.

REFERENCES: Required - Para. 21-12, 21-18, 23-26, 23-27 and 23-39.
    Supplementary - Para. 11-27, 11-28, 11-38, 11-45, 11-46, 11-47, 11-82 and 23-28.

EQUIPMENT: One rooftop unit consisting of an air-cooled condenser and a blower evaporator.

PREPARATION PROCEDURE:
1. Study the system and the manufacturer's manuals. Study the reference paragraphs.
    TEST√ _____
2. Obtain: Tools - 1 complete service kit, consisting of the necessary wrenches, pliers, screwdrivers, 1 rigging system to hoist the system into place, 1 pr. safety goggles.
3. Obtain: Instruments - 1 gauge manifold, complete with lines, 1 thermometer, 1 leak detector, 1 electrical combination voltmeter, ammeter and ohmmeter, 1 vacuum pump.
4. Obtain: Supplies - 1 wiping cloth, 1 5- to 10-lb. refrigerant service cylinder.

TASK PROCEDURE (WEAR GOGGLES):
1. Position the system on the roof rails.
2. Install the electrical power and control circuits according to code.
3. Test the following: electrical circuit, main power supply, capacitor, relay, overload protector, motor compressor, control circuits, filters, air flow, heating unit, condensate drain, fresh air supply, condenser, thermostat. Check dampers in ducts, filters.
4. Install gauges, check pressure, and test for leaks.
5. Operate the system. Run unit for at least 15 minutes. Check the TEV operation, condenser and evaporator conditions, fans and motor temperatures.   1-5√ _____
6. Repair or replace the necessary parts.   6√ _____

CLOSING THE STATION:
    Clean the work station and return all materials to the tool crib.

DATA:

	At the Beginning	After 15 Min.	After Repair
Low-Side Pressure			
High-Side Pressure			
Suction Line Temp., Approx.			
Liquid Line Temp., Approx.			
Evaporator Temperature			
Noise, Compressor			
Motor			

EER _____

Remarks:

INSTALL A ROOFTOP COMFORT COOLING SYSTEM.

Indicate the best answer for each question below by encircling its letter.

1. What type evaporator is commonly used on rooftop installations?
    a. "A" type.
    b. Slant type.
    c. Vertical type.
    d. None of above.
    e. Any of the above.

2. What may be a common service call?
    a. Too cold.
    b. No cooling or insufficient cooling.
    c. Humidity too high.
    d. Conditioned air has stale odor.
    e. Any or all of the above.

3. What is the chief advantage of a rooftop system?
    a. A small space is required.
    b. Has a high thermal efficiency.
    c. Very easy to install.
    d. Uses otherwise wasted space.
    e. Easy to dispose of condensate.

4. What are some of the disadvantages when servicing a rooftop system?
    a. Sometimes difficult to get on the roof.
    b. Difficult to service the unit under bad weather conditions.
    c. There is a danger of damaging the roof and causing leaks.
    d. When electrical circuits are involved, it is difficult to communicate with the worker handling the electrical circuit.
    e. All of the above.

5. Are rooftop systems gaining in popularity?
    a. In some areas.
    b. Only in big commercial establishments.
    c. Quite generally, on a national basis.
    d. Very definitely no.
    e. Very definitely yes.

INSTALL A HEAT PUMP

OBJECTIVE: Given a heat pump unit, install and operate.

REFERENCES: Required - Para. 19-17, 19-18, 19-19, 19-25, 23-1 through 23-17 and 23-39.
  Supplementary - Para. 11-27, 11-28, 11-38, 11-45, 11-46, 11-47, 11-82 and 23-18.

EQUIPMENT: One heat pump unit.

PREPARATION PROCEDURE:
1. Study complete heat pump system assigned and reference paragraphs.   TEST√ _____
2. Obtain: Tools - 1 service technician's tool kit, 1 pr. safety goggles.
3. Obtain: Instruments - 1 spirit level, 1 leak detector, 1 complete gauge manifold,
    1 thermometer, 1 sling psychrometer, 1 velocimeter, 1 steel tape.
4. Obtain: Supplies - 1 wiping cloth.

TASK PROCEDURE (WEAR GOGGLES):
1. Install the unit in accordance with local electrical code and manufacturer's recommendations.
2. Install the gauge manifold.
3. Operate the system.
4. Determine the air conditions, both volume and properties. Measure the air openings and the
    air velocities. Determine the db and wb values on the inlet and outlet of both the
    evaporator and condenser. Record.   1-4√ _____
5. Reverse the cycle and determine the new conditions after the unit has stabilized.
    Record the data.   5√ _____

CLOSING THE STATION:
    Clean the work station and return all materials to the tool crib.

DATA:
System, Make_____ Model_____ Serial No._____ Type_____ EER _____
First Cycle (Heating Cycle):
Condenser-Air Velocity, In_____   Grille Size_____ Air Volume_____
                    Out_____   Grille Size_____ Air Volume_____
    db Temp. In_____   db Temp. Out_____
    wb Temp. In_____   wb Temp. Out_____ Heat Loss_____
    th In_____   th Out_____

Evaporator
    Air Velocity, In_____   Grille Size_____ Air Volume_____
    Air Velocity, Out_____   Grille Size_____ Air Volume_____
    db Temp. In_____   db Temp. Out_____
    wb Temp. In_____   wb Temp. Out_____ Heat Gain_____
    th In_____   th Out_____

Second Cycle-Reverse the Refrigerant Flow (Cooling Cycle):
Condenser-Air Velocity, In_____   Grille Size_____ Air Volume In_____
    Air Velocity, Out_____   Grille Size_____ Air Volume Out_____
    db Temp. In_____   db Temp. Out_____
    wb Temp. In_____   wb Temp. Out_____ Heat Loss_____
    th In_____   th Out_____

Evaporator
    Air Velocity, In_____   Grille Size_____ Air Volume In_____
    Air Velocity, Out_____   Grille Size_____ Air Volume Out_____
    db Temp. In_____   db Temp. Out_____
    wb Temp. In_____   wb Temp. Out_____ Heat Gain_____
    th In_____   th Out_____

INSTALL A HEAT PUMP.

Indicate the best answer for each question below by encircling its letter.

1. What is COP in relation to a heat pump?
   a. Chemically pure.
   b. Compressor oil pump.
   c. Coefficient of performance.
   d. Condensing pressure.
   e. Cooling off pressure.

2. What is used as an auxiliary heat source if one is needed?
   a. Steam.
   b. Hot water.
   c. Electrical heating.
   d. Another heat pump.
   e. Nothing.

3. How does the efficiency of the heating cycle of the heat pump change as the evaporator temperature decreases?
   a. Decreases.
   b. Increases.
   c. It does not change.
   d. Decreases only if the evaporator frosts.
   e. Increases only if the head pressure rises.

4. What is a ground coil?
   a. A coil electrically grounded.
   b. A coil mounted on the ground.
   c. A coil buried in the ground.
   d. A smoothly finished coil.
   e. Ground coils are not used in heat pumps.

5. What type valve can be used to reverse the cycle of a heat pump?
   a. A one-way valve.
   b. A two-way valve.
   c. A three-way valve.
   d. A four-way valve.
   e. A five-way valve.

LOCATE TROUBLE IN A WINDOW TYPE COMFORT COOLER

OBJECTIVE: Given a window type comfort cooler, locate and repair any troubles and obtain the
proper operation.

REFERENCES: Required - Para. 11-12 through 11-21, 11-82, 19-9, 19-10, 19-25, 21-6, 21-8,
21-18, manufacturer's installation and service manual.
Supplementary - Para. 9-27 through 9-29, 9-36, 14-90 and 14-109.

EQUIPMENT: One window air conditioner.

PREPARATION PROCEDURE:
1. Study the window air conditioner assigned. Study the reference paragraphs. TEST√ _____
2. Obtain: Tools - 1 1/4-in. ratchet wrench, 1 set open end wrenches, 1 8-in. adjustable
open end wrench, 1 hermetic valve adaptor kit, 1 6-in. screwdriver, 1/4-in. blade,
1 #2 Phillips screwdriver, 1 pr. safety goggles.
3. Obtain: Instruments - 1 gauge manifold, complete with lines, 1 thermometer, 1 vacuum
pump, 1 leak detector, 1 electrical combination voltmeter, ammeter and ohmmeter.
4. Obtain: Supplies - 1 oiler SAE 30, 1 wiping cloth, 1 1- to 5-lb. refrigerant
service cylinder.

TASK PROCEDURE (WEAR GOGGLES):
1. Test the external circuit: Power in, thermostat, relay, capacitors, overload protectors,
motor compressor, filters, air flow, etc.   1√ _____
2. Install gauges and test for leaks.
3. Run the unit for at least fifteen minutes. Oil fan motors.
4. If the unit is frosting or sweating down the suction line, the system may be overcharged.
5. If the evaporator is starved, the screen or drier may be partially clogged with moisture or
dirt or the unit is undercharged.
6. Repair what is necessary as follows: Remove the refrigerant. BE CAREFUL! Replace the
worn part. Assemble the unit. Evacuate the air, charge, and test for leaks.
7. Remove the gauge manifold and valve adaptor.   2-7√ _____

CLOSING THE STATION:
Clean the work station and return all materials to the tool crib.

DATA:

	At the Beginning	After 15 Minutes	After Repair
Low-Side Pressure			
High-Side Pressure			
Suction Line Temp., Approx.			
Liquid Line Temp., Approx.			
Evaporator Air Temperature			
Noise: Compressor			
Motor			

EER _____

Remarks:

LOCATE TROUBLE IN A WINDOW TYPE COMFORT COOLER.

Indicate the best answer for each question below by encircling its letter.

1. In a window air conditioner using a capillary tube, how can one tell if the system is overcharged?
   a. High-side pressure will increase.
   b. High-side temperature will decrease.
   c. The suction line will sweat or frost.
   d. The compressor will knock.
   e. The low-side pressure increases slowly.

2. What size replacement capillary tube is usually recommended?
   a. The next largest size.
   b. The next smallest size.
   c. The same size.
   d. Up to 1/6 of a ton more.
   e. None of the above; it is adjustable.

3. At what spot would internal moisture freeze in a window unit using a capillary tube?
   a. In the capillary tube.
   b. On the screen.
   c. At no place.
   d. In the evaporator.
   e. At the condenser.

4. Where does the air go after it cools the condenser?
   a. Indoors.
   b. Outdoors.
   c. Into the evaporator.
   d. Into the fresh air intake.
   e. Through the filter.

5. Why must window air conditioner units be slanted to the outside?
   a. To provide proper air circulation.
   b. To provide for proper flow of the condensate.
   c. To prevent freeze up of the evaporator.
   d. To compensate for wind direction.
   e. To assure proper lubrication.

LOCATE TROUBLE IN A HEAT PUMP

OBJECTIVE: Given a residential heat pump system, locate trouble, repair and obtain the correct operating temperatures.

REFERENCES: Required - Para. 11-82, 19-17, 19-18, 19-19, 23-10, 23-18 and 23-20.
Supplementary - Para. 11-27, 11-28, 11-38, 11-45, 11-47 and 23-17.

EQUIPMENT: One residential heat pump comfort cooling and heating system.

PREPARATION PROCEDURE:
1. Study the heat pump system assigned, package unit or remote split unit system. Study the reference paragraphs and electrical diagrams.   TEST √ _____
2. Obtain: Tools - 1 1/4-in. ratchet wrench, 1 set open end wrenches, 1 8-in. adjustable wrench, 1 pr. safety goggles, 1 6-in. screwdriver, 1/4-in. blade, 1 #2 Phillips screwdriver, 1 service wrench.
3. Obtain: Instruments - 1 gauge manifold complete with hoses, 1 thermometer, 1 vacuum pump, 1 leak detector, 1 electrical combination voltmeter, ammeter and ohmmeter.
4. Obtain: Supplies - 1 wiping cloth, 1 set of tubing fittings, 1 spout can of oil, 1 1- to 5-lb. refrigerant service cylinder.

TASK PROCEDURE (WEAR GOGGLES):
1. Test external circuit first. Then check power in thermostat, compressor motor, auxiliary electric heaters, solenoid valve, and four-way valve. Also check for temperature difference across the coils and airflow through the coils.

    1 √ _____
2. Install gauges, check pressures, and test for leaks.
3. Run the unit for at least 20 minutes. Check the reversing valve and TEV operations. Check outdoor and indoor coil, fans, motors, and temperatures.
4. Check reversing valve to see if it is acting slowly or not at all.
5. Repair what is necessary by pumping all refrigerant into the liquid receiver. Replace all defective parts and assemble the unit. Evacuate the system, charge, and test for leaks.

    2-5 √ _____

CLOSING THE STATION:
Clean the work area and return all materials to the tool crib.

DATA:

	At the Beginning		After 20 Minutes		After Repair	
	Cooling	Heating	Cooling	Heating	Cooling	Heating
Low-Side Pressure						
High-Side Pressure						
Suction Line Temp., Approx.						
Liquid Line Temp., Approx.						
Evaporator Temperature						
Noise: Compressor						
Fan Motor, Condenser						
Fan Motor, Evaporator						

Remarks:

LOCATE TROUBLE IN A HEAT PUMP.

Indicate the best answer for each question below be encircling its letter.

1. Which of the following is the most popular heat pump coil installation?
    a. Water cooled above ground.
    b. Rooftop mounted coil.
    c. Submerged in a lake.
    d. In the ground coil.
    e. Outdoor coil.

2. What is the purpose of a suction line accumulator?
    a. To collect water.
    b. To collect particles of dirt.
    c. To collect oil and refrigerant.
    d. To collect air.
    e. None of the above.

3. How are the wires to the motor compressor terminals best identified?
    a. Numbers.
    b. Tape.
    c. Color.
    d. Continuity test.
    e. Size.

4. How is the flow of refrigerant changed from the heating cycle to the cooling cycle?
    a. Flow is the same.
    b. Flow is reversed, sending hot discharge vapor from the compressor to the outdoor coil.
    c. Flow is reversed, sending hot discharge vapor from compressor to the indoor coil.
    d. Flow is to the inside coil which is used as the evaporator.
    e. None of the above.

5. The heating cycle of a standard heat pump system would contain the following metering device(s):
    a. Three TEV's.
    b. Three capillary tubes.
    c. One TEV and one capillary tube.
    d. Two TEV's.
    e. One TEV.

LOCATE TROUBLE IN A RESIDENTIAL CENTRAL COMFORT COOLING SYSTEM

OBJECTIVE: Given a malfunctioning residential central comfort cooling system: diagnose, repair and operate.

REFERENCES: Required - Para. 11-14, 11-15, 11-18 through 11-21, 11-82, 23-29 through 23-33, 23-39, 24-37, 24-53, manufacturer's installation and service manual.
Supplementary - Para. 9-27 through 9-36, 11-12, 11-13, 11-16, 11-17, 14-7 through 14-13, 14-90 and 14-109.

EQUIPMENT: One residential air conditioner installed in furnace.

PREPARATION PROCEDURE:
1. Study the central comfort cooling system assigned. Study the reference paragraphs.
TEST √ _____
2. Obtain: Tools - 1 1/4-in. ratchet wrench, 1 set open end wrenches, 1 8-in. adjustable wrench, 1 pr. safety goggles, 1 6-in. screwdriver, 1/4-in. blade, 1 #2 Phillips screwdriver, 1 set of valve adaptors.
3. Obtain: Instruments - 1 gauge manifold, complete with lines, 1 thermometer, 1 vacuum pump, 1 leak detector, 1 electrical combination voltmeter, ammeter and ohmmeter.
4. Obtain: Supplies - 1 wiping cloth, 1 set of tubing fittings, 1 spout can of oil, 1 1- to 5-lb. refrigerant service cylinder.

TASK PROCEDURE (WEAR GOGGLES):
1. Test external circuit first: Power in, thermostat, relay, capacitor, overload protector, motor compressor, filter, air flow, condensate drain, fresh air supply, and condenser cooling medium.
1 √ _____
2. Install gauges, check pressures, and test for leaks. Oil fan motors.
3. Run the unit for at least 15 minutes. Check the TEV operation, condenser condition, fans and motors and temperatures.
4. If the evaporator is frosting, the TEV may be leaking, the thermostat is not shutting off, or the TEV bulb is loose.
5. If the evaporator is starved, the valve may be partially clogged with moisture, or dirt, or the screen may be partially clogged, or there may be a lack of refrigerant.
6. Repair what is necessary as follows: Remove the refrigerant from the part to be repaired. BE CAREFUL! Replace the worn part and assemble the unit. Evacuate the air, charge, and test for leaks.
7. Remove the gauge manifold.
2-7 √ _____

CLOSING THE STATION:
Clean the station and return all materials to the tool crib.

DATA:

	At the Beginning	After 15 Minutes	After Repair
Low-Side Pressure			
High-Side Pressure			
Suction Line Temp., Approx.			
Liquid Line Temp., Approx.			
Evaporator Temperature			
Noise: Compressor			
Motor Evaporator			
Motor Condenser			

EER _____

LOCATE TROUBLE IN A RESIDENTIAL CENTRAL COMFORT COOLING SYSTEM.

Indicate the best answer for each question below by encircling its letter.

1. What is the best way to clean a condenser in the home?
   a. Carbon tetrachloride.
   b. Kerosene.
   c. Brush.
   d. Vacuum cleaner.
   e. Cloth.

2. What is the best indication of a stuck closed TEV?
   a. No cooling.
   b. Too cold.
   c. A partially frosted evaporator.
   d. A sweating or frosted suction line.
   e. A hot liquid line.

3. How may one find out if the thermostat is faulty, when the unit will not start?
   a. Short the thermostat terminals.
   b. Connect the power directly to the motor.
   c. A bad thermostat always causes continuous running.
   d. Heat the thermostat bulb.
   e. Cool the thermostat bulb.

4. What is wrong if the unit has an excessive head pressure with a normal low-side pressure?
   a. Too much refrigerant.
   b. Stuck closed TEV.
   c. Air in the system.
   d. Room too cold.
   e. Wrong refrigerant.

5. What may be wrong when the unit runs all the time and does not cool?
   a. Too much refrigerant.
   b. A stuck open TEV.
   c. A bad thermostat.
   d. An inefficient compressor.
   e. Moisture in the system.

LOCATE TROUBLE IN A WATER CHILLER

OBJECTIVE: Given a water chiller: locate trouble, repair and operate.

REFERENCES: Required – Para. 14-49 through 14-53, 14-109, 23-36, 23-37, 23-39,
   manufacturer's installation and service manual.
   Supplementary – Para. 14-7 through 14-13 and 14-90.

EQUIPMENT: A commercial water chiller.

PREPARATION PROCEDURE:
   1.   Study the water chiller system assigned. Study the reference paragraphs.   TEST√_____
   2.   Obtain: Tools – 1 kit refrigeration tools, 1 pr. safety goggles.
   3.   Obtain: Instruments – 1 leak detector, 1 stem thermometer, 1 electrical combination
         voltmeter, ammeter and ohmmeter, 1 gauge manifold and lines, 1 vacuum pump.
   4.   Obtain: Supplies – 1 wiping cloth, 1 set of tubing fittings, 1 1- to 5-lb. refrigerant
         cylinder.

TASK PROCEDURE (WEAR GOGGLES):
   1.   Install the gauge manifold and run the system for approximately 15 minutes. Record
         the pressures and temperature readings.   1√_____
   2.   Check the inlet and outlet condenser water temperatures and volume. Inspect the
         water circulation pump.
   3.   Check the high-side pressure, low-side pressure and oil pressure. Add refrigerant or
         purge if necessary. Test for leaks.
   4.   Check the inlet and outlet temperature of the chill water.
   5.   Remove the gauge manifold.   2-5√_____

CLOSING THE STATION:
   Clean the station and return all materials to the tool crib.

DATA:
System, Make_____ Model_____ Serial No._____ Type_____
Refrigerant, Kind_____ Refrigerant, Pounds_____
Refrigerant Control, Make_____ Model_____ Type_____
Water Temperature at Condenser: In_____ Out_____
Water Temperature at Evaporator: In_____ Out_____
High-Side Pressure_____ Low-Side Pressure_____ Oil Pressure_____

EER _____

Remarks:

LOCATE TROUBLE IN A WATER CHILLER (AIR CONDITIONING).

Indicate the best answer for each question below by encircling its letter.

1. Does the heat loss from the condenser equal the heat gain to the evaporator?
   a. It is more.
   b. It is less.
   c. They are equal.
   d. They are equal only after running for a certain time.
   e. The heat gain is 5 times the heat loss.

2. Why is the condenser always purged after charging, if possible?
   a. To remove excess refrigerant.
   b. To help the unit pump down.
   c. To remove non-condensable gases.
   d. It is not necessary to purge it.
   e. To check the oil level.

3. What temperature should the head pressure of a water-cooled unit correspond to when the unit is running?
   a. 50-70° F above outlet water temperature.
   b. 25-30° F above outlet water temperature.
   c. 15-20° F above outlet water temperature.
   d. 15° F above room temperature.
   e. 25° F above room temperature.

4. What type compressors do large water chillers usually have?
   a. Centrifugal.
   b. Hermetic.
   c. Rotary.
   d. Reciprocating.
   e. Free piston.

5. What must one do to purge the condenser of a fuel gas operated water chiller?
   a. Attach gauges.
   b. Isolate the condenser.
   c. They have automatic purging devices.
   d. Crack the line at the condenser header.
   e. It is not necessary to purge.

CALCULATE THE COMFORT COOLING
HEAT LOAD FOR AN ASSIGNED SPACE

OBJECTIVE: Given an assigned space, determine the correct heat load.

REFERENCES: Required - Para. 15-1 through 15-13, 15-63, 25-1, 25-2 and 25-4
   through 25-23. Supplementary - Para. 28-53.

EQUIPMENT: One assigned space.

PREPARATION PROCEDURE:
1. Study the space assigned. Study the reference paragraphs.   TEST√ _____
2. Obtain: Instruments - 1 50-ft. steel tape.
3. Obtain: Supplies - 1 sheet of cross-sectioned paper for the floor plan, 1 survey chart.

TASK PROCEDURE:
1. Make a survey of the premises. Obtain all the dimensions and note the window, wall,
   ceiling and floor construction. Record. Make a floor plan on cross-sectioned graph
   paper.   1 / _____
2. Complete the calculations. The sensible load is to be totaled. The latent heat load
   varies between 30 percent and 35 percent of the sensible load except in unusual cases.
                                                                        2 / _____

DATA:
Use, Residence _____ Commercial _____ Type _____
No. of Permanent Residents _____ No. of Transients _____ Average Hrs. _____ Total Hrs. _____
Building Construction and U. Coefficient:
  Construction, Walls _____ Windows _____ Ceiling _____ __
            Roof _____ Interior Partitions _____ Floor _____
  U. Coefficient, Walls _____ Windows _____ Ceiling _____
            Roof _____ Interior Partitions _____ Floor _____
Sun Exposure, Hrs./day, East _____ South _____ West _____
         Awnings, East _____ South _____ West _____
Dimensions, Exterior, Length _____ Width _____ Height _____ Area _____ Sq. Ft.
         Windows, Height _____ Width _____ x No. _____ Area _____ Sq. Ft.
Total Exterior Wall Area _____ Less the Window Area _____ = _____
Total Interior Wall Area _____
Heat Load Design Conditions, Outdoor db _____ wb _____ Indoor db _____ wb _____
  Walls: Area _____ x td _____ x Coeff. _____ = _____
  Windows: Area _____ x td _____ x Coeff. _____ = _____
  Ceiling: Area _____ x td _____ x Coeff. _____ = _____
  Floor: Area _____ x td _____ x Coeff. _____ = _____
                                                        Total _____

Sun Load East Wall, Area _____ x Coeff. _____ = _____
         South Wall, Area _____ x Coeff. _____ = _____ ___
         West Wall, Area _____ x Coeff. _____ = _____
                                                        Total _____

Ventilation Load, Volume _____ x Coeff. _____ = Total _____
Occupancy Load, No. of People _____ x Coeff. _____ = Total _____
Miscellaneous Load, Electrical _____ Watts x Coeff. _____ = Total _____
Total Load: Total Load _____ + Total Load x .35 _____ =TOTAL _____

CALCULATE THE COMFORT COOLING HEAT LOAD FOR AN ASSIGNED SPACE.

Indicate the best answer for each question below by encircling its letter.

1. What does mean temperature indicate?
    a. The average temperature.
    b. The lowest temperature.
    c. The highest temperature.
    d. The design temperature.
    e. The dry bulb temperature.

2. What does ambient temperature mean?
    a. Evaporator temperature.
    b. Condenser temperature.
    c. Surrounding temperature.
    d. Desired temperature.
    e. Dew point.

3. Does infiltrated air have latent heat?
    a. No.
    b. Yes.
    c. Only when it is dry.
    d. Only in the winter.
    e. Only if a humidifier is used.

4. Why must the electrical load be known for the enclosure?
    a. All of the electrical energy is changed to heat energy.
    b. The electrical light energy only is turned into heat.
    c. All the electrical energy is turned into latent heat.
    d. Only those electrical appliances which do not have motors
        turn the electrical energy into heat.
    e. Only the resistance units produce heat.

5. How many heat sources must be considered when calculating the cooling heat load?
    a. One.
    b. Two.
    c. Three.
    d. Four.
    e. Five.

MODERN REFRIGERATION AND AIR CONDITIONING
MODULE 6 - CLIMATE CONTROL-HEATING LABORATORY TASKS

		TASK TEST GRADE	SIG.	TASK GRADE	SIG.	TASK DATE
6-1	Install and Operate an Atmospheric Gas Burner with Pilot Light					
6-2	Install and Operate a Blower Type Gas Burner with Electric Ignition					
6-3	Install and Operate a Gun Type Oil Burner					
6-4	Check and Connect a Heating Thermostat					
6-5	Check and Connect a Combination Thermostat					
6-6	Remove, Clean and Replace an Oil Burner Nozzle					
6-7	Remove, Test and Replace an Oil Burner Motor					
6-8	Remove, Test and Install an Oil Burner Primary Control					
6-9	Remove, Test and Install an Oil Burner Safety Control					
6-10	Install a Power Humidifier in a Duct System					
6-11	Balance Airflow in Forced Air System ...					
6-12	Replace a Pump on a Hydronic System ..					
6-13	Install and Operate an Electric Heating System					
6-14	Install and Operate a Rooftop Heating System					
6-15	Locate Trouble in a Gas Burner System .					
6-16	Locate Trouble in an Oil Burner System.					
6-17	Check, Operate and Adjust a Gas-Fired Warm Air Heating System					
6-18	Check, Operate and Adjust a Hydronic Heating System					
6-19	Make a Stack Flue Gas Analysis					
6-20	Operate and Test a Baseboard Electric Resistance Heating System					

SAFETY IN SERVICING CLIMATE CONTROL EQUIPMENT
(HEATING)

When wood, coal, gas or oil furnaces are used, it is absolutely essential that NONE of the fumes (products of combustion) enter the air in the building. All products of combustion must be conducted out the stack.

Safety controls for a heating system or a cooling system should never be removed and bypassed to keep a system operating, because dangerous conditions, or damage to the system, may result.

It is essential that a heating system have enough capacity to heat a structure without taxing or overheating the heating system. The heating system should be slightly oversize - never undersize.

Coal, oil, and fuel gas furnaces use fires in a confined area. The fuel must be stored safely and it must be fed in a safe manner to the firepot of the furnace. Also, means must be provided to shut down the unit: if the fuel flow ceases; if any part of the system over-heats; if all the products of combustion gases cannot exit from the building; or if combustion ceases.

Always remember that, if fuel is in the presence of air and an ignition source exists, a fire will result. All furnaces have a safety device to make sure that the firepot is free of fuel before the system starts.

The gas piping system must be leakproof. Always use soapsuds to check for leaks. NEVER USE AN OPEN FLAME SUCH AS A MATCH, or an explosion may occur. Use an explosion-proof flashlight or an explosion-proof extension lamp when inspecting a furnace.

Be careful when working with or handling metal duct material. Use gloves with metal inserts.

Keep fingers, hair and loose clothing away from moving fans, pulleys and belts.

INSTALL AND OPERATE AN ATMOSPHERIC GAS BURNER WITH PILOT LIGHT

OBJECTIVE: Given an atmospheric gas burner warm air furnace: start, operate and adjust.

REFERENCES: Required – Para. 19-1, 20-2, 20-15 through 20-23, 20-55, 24-3, 24-21, 24-44 and 24-53.
  Supplementary – Para. 19-25 and 20-24.

EQUIPMENT: One operating domestic type warm air gas fired furnace.

PREPARATION PROCEDURE:
1. Study the assigned gas burner installation. Study the reference paragraphs.   TEST√_____
2. Obtain: Tools – 1 6-in. screwdriver, 1 pr. safety goggles, 1 6-in. adjustable open end wrench.
3. Obtain: Instruments – 1 inspection mirror, 1 gas pressure manometer, 1 carbon dioxide analyzer, 1 oxygen analyzer, 1 draft gauge, 1 stack thermometer.
4. Obtain: Supplies – 1 wiping cloth.

TASK PROCEDURE (WEAR GOGGLES):
1. Clean the pilot light, open the main gas valve and light the pilot light.
2. Test for leaks with soap suds, and then operate the system. Set the thermostat to above ambient temperature.
3. Check the gas pressure and the stack draft and temperature.   1-3√_____
4. Check the gas flame for size and color. Adjust the primary air.   4√_____
5. Check the bonnet temperature controls.
6. Shut the main gas valve and shut down the furnace.   5-6√_____

CLOSING THE STATION:
  Clean the station and return all materials to the tool crib.

DATA:
Furnace, Make_____Model_____Type_____Capacity_____
Gas Line Control Valve, Make_____Model_____
Primary Control, Make_____Model_____
Pilot Light, Make_____Model_____Type_____
Gas Pressure_____Stack Temperature_____Draft_____

Remarks:

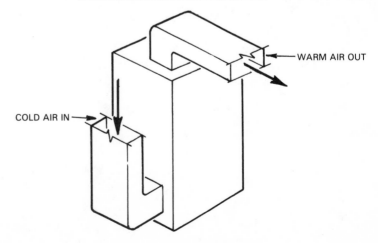

COLD AIR IN→

WARM AIR OUT

INSTALL AND OPERATE AN ATMOSPHERIC GAS BURNER WITH
PILOT LIGHT.

Indicate the best answer for each question below by encircling its letter.

1. What is the normal nozzle pressure in a natural gas domestic heating system?
   a. 1-in. water.
   b. 4-in. water.
   c. 27-in. water.
   d. 1 psi.
   e. 4 psi.

2. What type of valve automatically controls the flow of fuel gas to the burner?
   a. Diaphragm valve.
   b. Expansion valve.
   c. Pressure valve.
   d. Solenoid valve.
   e. Gate valve.

3. What is the heating value of natural gas per cubic foot?
   a. 500 Btu.
   b. 1,000 Btu.
   c. 2,000 Btu.
   d. 15,000 Btu.
   e. 24,000 Btu.

4. Why does a pilot light have a safety device?
   a. To relight the pilot light.
   b. To stop the pilot light gas flow if there is no pilot flame.
   c. To stop the main gas flow if there is no pilot flame.
   d. To shut off the furnace if the stack temperature is too high.
   e. To shut off the furnace if the furnace temperature is too high.

5. Where is the primary air adjustment?
   a. At the pilot light.
   b. At the gas spud.
   c. At the burner.
   d. At the pressure regulator outlet.
   e. At the entrance to the gas manifold.

INSTALL AND OPERATE A BLOWER TYPE
GAS BURNER WITH ELECTRIC IGNITION

OBJECTIVE: Given a blower type gas burner having electric ignition, operate the system and adjust the burner.

REFERENCES: Required - Para. 19-2, 19-25, 20-2, 20-15 through 20-23 and 20-55.
    Supplementary - Para. 20-24.

EQUIPMENT: One operating blower type gas burner with electric ignition.

PREPARATION PROCEDURE:
1. Study the assigned system. Study the reference paragraphs.   TEST√_____
2. Obtain: Tools - 1 6-in. screwdriver, 1 6-in. adjustable open end wrench, 1 pr. safety goggles.
3. Obtain: Instruments - 1 voltmeter, 1 gas pressure manometer, 1 carbon dioxide analyzer, 1 oxygen analyzer, 1 draft gauge, 1 stack thermometer.
4. Obtain: Supplies - 1 wiping cloth, 1 light weight bristle brush.

TASK PROCEDURE (WEAR GOGGLES):
1. Clean the pilot light, open the main gas line.
2. Test all lines for leaks with soapsuds.
3. Set thermostat to above ambient temperature.
4. Sketch the electric ignition circuit.
5. Check the gas pressure and the stack draft temperature.
6. Check the gas flame for height and color, and adjust the primary air.   1-6√_____
7. Check bonnet temperature controls.
8. Reset thermostat and repeat check procedures.
9. Shut off the main gas valve, thermostat, and shut down the furnace.   7-9√_____

CLOSING THE STATION:
    Clean the work station and return all materials to the tool crib.

DATA:

Furnace, Make_____ Model_____ Type_____ Capacity_____
Gas Line Control Valve, Make_____ Model_____ Type_____
Primary Control, Make_____ Model_____ Type_____
Thermostat, Make_____ Model_____ Type_____
Electric Pilot Light, Make_____ Model_____ Type_____
Gas Pressure_____ _____ Stack Temperature_____ Draft_____

Remarks:

INSTALL AND OPERATE A BLOWER TYPE GAS BURNER
WITH ELECTRIC IGNITION.

Indicate the best answer for each question below by encircling its letter.

1. What type of control is used on an electric ignition type oil burner?
   a. Thermocouple in series with a solenoid.
   b. A solenoid in parallel with a thermocouple.
   c. A gate valve.
   d. A solenoid valve.
   e. A pressure valve.

2. Why is a high-limit control used?
   a. To maintain the proper room temperature.
   b. To control the air flow through the cold air return.
   c. To control the temperature of the pilot light.
   d. To shut off the gas if the bonnet temperature exceeds the maximum temperature.
   e. To control the ventilating fan.

3. Why is a thermocouple and solenoid combination used?
   a. To maintain proper room temperature.
   b. To stop the gas flow if the electric spark does not light the furnace.
   c. To maintain proper stack temperature.
   d. To eliminate danger of a back draft in the chimney blowing out the pilot light.
   e. To make lighting the pilot light easy.

4. How is the operation of the burner automatically controlled?
   a. By the thermostat in series with a solenoid gas valve.
   b. By the gas pressure.
   c. By the stack pressure.
   d. By a bonnet thermostat.
   e. None of these.

5. What is the output voltage of an electronic spark igniter?
   a. 6,000V
   b. 10,000V
   c. 19,000V
   d. 28,000V
   e. 30,000V

INSTALL AND OPERATE A GUN TYPE OIL BURNER

OBJECTIVE: Given a furnance designed for use with an oil burner, install the oil burner and operate the furnance.

REFERENCES: Required – Para. 19-4, 19-25, 20-1, 20-2, 20-6 through 20-13, 20-55, 24-3, 24-9, 24-17, 24-20, 24-23, 24-31, 24-32, 24-44, 24-47, 24-48 and 24-53.
Supplementary – Para. 20-14, 24-4, 24-5, 24-6, 24-10, 24-14 and 24-33.

EQUIPMENT: One operating domestic type warm air oil fired furnace.

PREPARATION PROCEDURE:
1. Study the oil burner system assigned. Study the reference paragraphs.   TEST √_____
2. Obtain: Tools – 1 8-in. adjustable open end wrench, 1 6-in. screwdriver, 1 pr. safety goggles.
3. Obtain: Instruments – 1 oil pressure gauge, 1 stack thermometer, 1 draft gauge, 1 carbon dioxide analyzer, 1 a-c voltmeter, 1 inspection mirror.
4. Obtain: Supplies – 1 wiping cloth, 1 pt. cleaning fluid, 1 pt. clean fuel oil.

TASK PROCEDURE (WEAR GOGGLES):
1. Install oil burner per manufacturer's recommendations.
2. Install the oil pressure gauge on the fuel pump.
3. Install the stack thermometer.
4. Inspect the refractory firepot; if there is oil in the firepot, do NOT start the unit.
                                                                           1-4 √_____
5. Check to determine that the ignition system is operating.
6. Connect to the fuel tank, check for leaks, and start the unit.   5-6 √_____
7. Check the flame color, the stack temperature, and the firepot draft.
8. Make a carbon dixoide analysis.   7-8 √_____
9. Operate for five minutes and record pressures and temperatures.
10. Check the bonnet temperature controls.   9-10 √_____
11. Shut off the system.

CLOSING THE STATION:
        Clean the work station and return all materials to the tool crib.

DATA:

Oil Burner, Make _____ Model _____ Type _____ Capacity _____
Furnace, Make _____ Model _____ Type _____ Capacity _____
Limit Control, Make _____ Model _____ Type _____
Primary Control, Make _____ Model _____ Type _____
Thermostat, Make _____ Model _____ Type _____
Oil Pressure _____ Stack Temperature _____ Draft Pressure _____
Limit Control Cut-Out Temperature _____
Flame Color _____ Carbon Dioxide Stack Analysis _____

Remarks:

INSTALL AND OPERATE A GUN TYPE OIL BURNER.

Indicate the best answer for each question below by encircling its letter.

1. Which grades of fuel oil are most commonly used with domestic oil burners?
    a. 1 and 2
    b. 2 and 3
    c. 3 and 4
    d. 4 and 5
    e. 5 and 6

2. What is the heating value of domestic fuel oil?
    a. 1,400 Btu/lb.
    b. 14,000 Btu/lb.
    c. 140,000 Btu/lb.
    d. 100,000 Btu/lb.
    e. 50,000 Btu/lb.

3. How much air is required to burn one gallon of domestic fuel oil?
    a. 106 cu. ft.
    b. 1,000 cu. ft.
    c. 1,500 cu. ft.
    d. 140,000 cu. ft.
    e. 200,000 cu. ft.

4. What is the color of the correct combustion flame produced by a gun type domestic oil burner?
    a. Red.
    b. Green.
    c. Blue.
    d. Orange.
    e. Yellow.

5. How many oil filtering devices are usually installed in a domestic gun type oil burner oil circuit?
    a. One.
    b. Two.
    c. Three.
    d. Four.
    e. Five.

CHECK AND CONNECT A HEATING THERMOSTAT

OBJECTIVE: Given a mock-up panel board of a 24V control system, draw the wiring diagram, properly check and connect a heating thermostat, and be able to obtain desired heating temperature range.

REFERENCES: Required – Para. 6-8, 6-9, 6-79, 6-80, 8-1 through 8-6, 8-8, 8-43, 24-2, 24-9, 24-10, 24-13 and 24-53.
Supplementary – Para. 8-9 and 24-3.

EQUIPMENT: A panel board mock-up of a 24V heating control system.

PREPARATION PROCEDURE:
1. Study the low voltage panel board system assigned. Study the reference paragraphs.

    TEST √ _____
2. Obtain: Tools – 1 6-in. screwdriver, 1 4-in. screwdriver, 1 set Phillips screwdrivers, 1 6-in. combination pliers, 1 6-in. slim nose pliers.
3. Obtain: Instruments – 1 combination voltmeter, ammeter and ohmmeter (multimeter), 1 test light, 1 thermometer.
4. Obtain: Supplies – 1 wiping cloth, 1 roll 1/2-in. plastic tape.

TASK PROCEDURE:
1. Check the 24V circuit and test the parts using 24V. Make an electrical wiring diagram.

    1 √ _____
2. Remove all the wiring, remove the control devices, dismantle the control devices and study their design, construction and operation.

    2 √ _____
3. Reinstall the control devices, install the wiring and test the circuits.
4. Operate the system.

    3-4 √ _____

CLOSING THE STATION:
Clean the work station and return all materials to the tool crib.

DATA:

Thermostat, Make _____ Model _____ Type _____ Voltage _____
Transformer, Make _____ Model _____ Volts In _____ Volts Out _____ VA Rating _____
Relay Make _____ Model _____ Normally Open _____ Normally Closed _____
Limit Control, Make _____ Model _____ Settings, Open _____ Closed _____
Fan Control, Make _____ Model _____ Settings, Open _____ Closed _____
Solenoid Valve, Make _____ Model _____ Connections, Size-Fluid In _____ Fluid Out _____
Wire Sizes, 24V _____ 120V _____

Remarks:

CHECK AND CONNECT A HEATING THERMOSTAT.

Indicate the best answer for each question below by encircling its letter.

1. How can a low voltage thermostat operate from a 120V system?
    a. Use a solenoid valve.
    b. Use a transformer.
    c. Use a relay.
    d. Use a sequence control.
    e. Use a resistance.

2. How is a 24V circuit obtained?
    a. From the power company.
    b. Use a solenoid.
    c. Use a thermostat.
    d. Use a step-up transformer.
    e. Use a step-down transformer.

3. Where is a limit control located in the electrical circuits?
    a. In the 24V circuit.
    b. In the 120V circuit.
    c. In the 240V circuit.
    d. In both the 24V and 120V circuit.
    e. In either the 24V or 120V circuit.

4. What are the control devices which may be used on the 24V circuit in a domestic gas fueled heating hydronic system?
    a. Thermostat.
    b. Thermostat and relay, safety pilot.
    c. Thermostat, relay and circulation pump.
    d. Thermostat, relay, gas solenoid, limit control and safety pilot.
    e. Thermostat, relay, gas solenoid, limit control, safety pilot and circulation pump.

5. In a low voltage system, what voltage operates the heat anticipator?
    a. 24V
    b. 6V
    c. 120V
    d. 12V
    e. 240V

Task No. 6-5 Task Grade _____
Name _____
Date _____ Class _____

CHECK AND CONNECT A COMBINATION THERMOSTAT

OBJECTIVE: Given a mock-up panel board of a 24V to 30V combination heating and cooling thermostat, determine the type, the wiring, and the repair or replacement.

REFERENCES: Required - Para. 6-8, 6-9, 6-79, 6-80, 8-1, 8-2, 8-5, 8-6, 8-43, 24-13 through 24-17, 24-19 and 24-53.
Supplementary - Para. 24-18.

EQUIPMENT: A panel mock-up board of a 24V to 30V heating and cooling thermostat.

PREPARATION PROCEDURE:
1. Study the panel mock-up. Study the reference paragraphs.   TEST√_____
2. Obtain: Tools - 1 6-in. screwdriver, 1 4-in. screwdriver, 1 set Phillips screwdrivers, 1 6-in. slim nose pliers, 1 wire stripper, 1 6-in. adjustable pliers.
3. Obtain: Instruments - 1 combination voltmeter, ammeter and ohmmeter (multimeter), 1 test light, 1 thermometer.
4. Obtain: Supplies - 1 wiping cloth, 1 roll 1/2-in. plastic tape.

TASK PROCEDURE:
1. Check the 24V electrical circuit and test the parts; make an electrical wiring diagram.
                                                                            1√_____
2. Manually turn switch on and off and check system cycling.
3. Place thermometer next to thermostat, and observe cut-in and cut-out of thermostat; adjust range as needed.
4. Remove all the wiring, remove the control devices, dismantle the control devices and study their design, construction and operation.   2-4√_____
5. Reinstall the control devices, install the wiring, and test the circuits.
6. Operate the system.   5-6√_____

CLOSING THE STATION:
Clean the work station and return all materials to the tool crib.

DATA:

Thermostat, Make _____ Model ____ Type _____ Voltage _____
Transformer, Make _____ Model _____
        Volts In _____ Volts Out _____ VA Rating _____
Relay, Make _____ Model _____ Normally Open _____ Normally Closed _____
Limit Control, Make _____ Model _____ Settings, Open _____ Closed _____
Fan Control, Make _____ Model _____ Settings, Open _____ Closed _____
Solenoid Valve, Make _____ Model _____
        Connections Size, Fluid In _____ Fluid Out _____
Wire Sizes, 24V _____ 120V _____
Cooling System, Make _____ Model _____ Btu Rating _____
Refrigerant Type _____ Quantity _____
Refrigerant Control, Make _____ Type _____
Furnace, Make _____ Model _____ Type _____ Capacity _____

Remarks:

CHECK AND CONNECT A COMBINATION THERMOSTAT.

Indicate the best answer for each question below by encircling its letter.

1. How does a low voltage thermostat operate the heating and cooling fan?
   a. A direct line circuit.
   b. Relay.
   c. Stepdown transformer.
   d. Thermostat.
   e. Solenoid.

2. What is the voltage of a line voltage thermostat?
   a. 24V
   b. 120V
   c. 240V
   d. 30V
   e. 6 to 12V

3. What does the thermostat control?
   a. Heating.
   b. Cooling.
   c. Humidity and odor.
   d. Cooling and humidity.
   e. Heating and cooling.

4. In an electronic combination thermostat, what is the heating and cooling differential?
   a. 0.5° F.
   b. 1° F.
   c. 2° F.
   d. 3° F.
   e. 4° F.

5. What does the least complicated combination thermostat contain?
   a. Bimetal strip.
   b. Bimetal strip and heat anticipator.
   c. Bimetal strip, heat anticipator, and cold anticipator.
   d. Two separate circuits in sequence.
   e. Two separate mercury tube switches.

REMOVE, CLEAN AND REPLACE AN OIL BURNER NOZZLE

OBJECTIVE: Given a furnance with an oil burner: remove the burner nozzle, clean, replace, and operate the burner.

REFERENCES: Required - Para. 20-1, 20-2, 20-6 through 20-14, 20-55, manufacturer's service manual.

EQUIPMENT: A furnace equipped with an oil burner.

PREPARATION PROCEDURE:
1. Study the gun type oil burner assigned. Study the reference paragraphs.   TEST√_____
2. Obtain: Tools - 1 8-in. adjustable open end wrench, 1 6-in. screwdriver, 1 pr. safety goggles.
3. Obtain: Instruments - 1 0-150 psi pressure gauge with line and fittings, 1 6-in. rule, 1 flame mirror.
4. Obtain: Supplies - 1 wiping cloth, 1 pt. fuel oil, 1 bag asbestos cement.

TASK PROCEDURE (WEAR GOGGLES):
1. Open the electrical circuit and shut off the fuel oil line.
2. Remove the oil burner from the furnace; remove the nozzle using two wrenches. If the electrodes are moved, measure the electrode gap, the distance from the nozzle, and the distance above the nozzle orifice, before removing.   1-2√_____
3. Clean the nozzle and inspect the screen and orifice.
4. Replace the nozzle with a new or reconditioned one (same orifice size and pattern).
          3-4√_____
5. Position the electrode ends carefully.
6. Replace the gun burner in the furnace.
7. Install the pressure gauge in the gauge opening at the oil pump.   5-7√_____
8. Operate the burner for 10 to 15 minutes.
9. Adjust the oil pressure to the recommended pressure for the burner. Most burners operate at above 90 psi.
10. Adjust the air inlet to give the correct flame color.
11. Check the bonnet temperature controls.
12. Open the switch and shut down the burner.
13. Remove the pressure gauge and replace the plug in the gauge opening.   8-13√_____

CLOSING THE STATION:
Clean the work station and return all materials to the tool crib.

DATA:

Oil Burner, Make_____ Model_____ Type_____ Capacity_____
Furnace, Make_____ Model_____ Type_____ Capacity_____
Controls, Thermostat, Make_____ Model_____ Type_____
Primary Control, Make_____ Model_____ Type_____
Motor, Voltage_____ Phase_____ Hertz_____ Current Rating of Motor_____
Nozzle, Material_____ Screen Size_____ Orifice Size_____ Spray Angle_____
After 15 Minutes Operation: Stack Temp._____ Flame Color_____

Remarks:

REMOVE, CLEAN AND REPLACE AN OIL BURNER NOZZLE.

Indicate the best answer for each question below by encircling its letter.

1. What keeps the oil pressure constant at the nozzle?
   a. The oil level in the tank.
   b. The pressure relief valve.
   c. The oil pump.
   d. The size of the nozzle orifice.
   e. The pressure regulator.

2. What is the usual oil pressure at the nozzle in a high-pressure gun type oil burner?
   a. 15 psi.
   b. 30 psi.
   c. 50 psi.
   d. 100 psi.
   e. 200 psi.

3. To what temperature must the atomized oil be heated to start combustion?
   a. 72° F.
   b. 100° F.
   c. 212° F.
   d. 400° F.
   e. 700° F.

4. Why is it important to keep water out of the oil burner oil passages?
   a. It causes rust.
   b. It causes corrosion.
   c. It is heavier than oil.
   d. It will overload the motor.
   e. It may cause a "flame out."

5. Relative to the nozzle, how many electrode installation dimensions should be checked?
   a. One.
   b. Two.
   c. Three.
   d. Four.
   e. Five.

REMOVE, TEST AND REPLACE AN OIL BURNER MOTOR

OBJECTIVE: Given a warm air furnace, remove the oil burner motor, and check and install a
new replacement motor.

REFERENCES: Required – Para. 7-2 through 7-12, 7-24, 7-37 through 7-42, 7-50, 20-6 through 20-14,
20-55, 24-23, 24-46, 24-47, 24-53, manufacturer's service manual.
Supplementary – Para. 7-35 and 7-36.

EQUIPMENT: 1 domestic type warm air furnace, 1 gun type oil burner.

PREPARATION PROCEDURE:
1. Study the gun type oil burner assigned to you. Study the reference paragraphs.   TEST√ _____
2. Obtain: Tools – 1 set small sockets and socket drives, 1 set screwdrivers, 1 6-in. slip
joint pliers, 1 6-in. slim nose pliers, 1 set Allen screw wrenches, 1 pr. safety goggles.
3. Obtain: Instruments – 1 combination voltmeter, ammeter and ohmmeter (multimeter),
1 test light.
4. Obtain: Supplies – 1 wiping cloth, 1 roll 1/2-in. plastic tape, 1 roll 1/2-in. friction tape,
1 pt. fuel oil.

TASK PROCEDURE (WEAR GOGGLES):
1. Disconnect the electrical power and lock in "off" position.
2. Disconnect the motor leads in the terminal box.
3. Disconnect the conduit fitting at the terminal box and disconnect the motor wires.
4. Carefully remove the motor. Some models require removal of oil pump coupling and fan
before the motor can be completely removed.   1-4√ _____
5. Free run test the replacement motor. Check voltage current draw and direction of rotation.
6. Install the motor (on some units the fan and coupling are installed before motor can be
mounted). They must be carefully located on the motor shaft to allow end play of motor
rotor after complete installation. Tighten cap screws evenly.
7. Connect wiring; tighten connections. Use ohmmeter to check for continuity.
                                                                             5-7√ _____
8. Operate oil burner for 5 to 10 minutes.   8√ _____

CLOSING THE STATION:
Clean the work station and return all materials to the tool crib.

DATA:

Oil Burner, Make_____ Model_____ Type_____ Capacity_____
Motor, Make_____ Model_____ Voltage_____ Current Rating_____ rpm _____
Rotation_____ Shaft Diameter_____

Remarks:

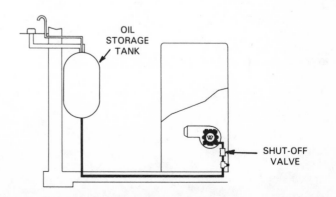

OIL
STORAGE
TANK

SHUT-OFF
VALVE

REMOVE, TEST AND REPLACE AN OIL BURNER MOTOR.

Indicate the best answer for each question below by encircling its letter.

1. How is the oil pump coupling usually attached to the motor shaft?
    a. A Woodruff key.
    b. A flat key.
    c. An Allen set screw.
    d. A cap screw.
    e. A machine screw.

2. How many controls does a gun type oil burner have when used on a warm air system?
    a. One.
    b. Two.
    c. Three.
    d. Four.
    e. Five.

3. What voltages are found in most domestic gun type oil burner systems?
    a. 24V and 120V
    b. 120V and 240V
    c. 24V and 230V
    d. 208V and 440V
    e. 24V and 220V

4. Where is the primary control mounted in a warm air system?
    a. The plenum chamber.
    b. The oil burner housing.
    c. The furnace stack.
    d. The cold air return.
    e. At the thermostat.

5. Where is the relay located in a gun type oil burner system?
    a. In the thermostat.
    b. In the limit control.
    c. In the primary control.
    d. In the motor terminal box.
    e. At the line switch.

REMOVE, TEST AND INSTALL AN OIL BURNER PRIMARY CONTROL

OBJECTIVE: Given a warm air oil furnace, replace the oil burner primary control by disconnecting the inoperative one, testing and installing the new one.

REFERENCES: Required – Para. 20-8, 24-20, 24-23, manufacturer's installation and service manual.

EQUIPMENT: One operating domestic type warm air oil fired furnace.

PREPARATION PROCEDURE:
1. Study the primary control of the heating system assigned. Study the reference paragraphs.

TEST √ _____

2. Obtain: Tools – 1 4-in. screwdriver, 1 6-in. screwdriver, 1 6-in. slim nose pliers, 1 pr. safety goggles.
3. Obtain: Instruments – 1 stack thermometer, 1 test light, 1 combination voltmeter, ammeter and ohmmeter (multimeter).
4. Obtain: Supplies – 1 wiping cloth, 1 pt. fuel oil, 1 small square of #000 sandpaper.

TASK PROCEDURE (WEAR GOGGLES):
1. Remove primary control cover.
2. Shut off electrical power, disconnect wires in primary control and remove primary control. Check color code of wires or use tape or tags to identify wires.
3. Install new primary control and connect wires.   1-3 √ _____
4. Check connections with ohmmeter.
5. Turn on electrical power, check power to primary control with test light.
6. Close fuel oil line, disconnect ignition transformer primary wire.
7. Close thermostat circuit and operate unit without ignition, check time required for unit to shut off.   4-7 √ _____
8. Install the stack thermometer.   8 √ _____
9. Remove any oil from firepot! Open fuel oil valve. Connect transformer wire. 9 √ _____
10. Turn on fuel and operate unit for 5 to 10 minutes.   10 √ _____

CLOSING THE STATION:
    Clean up work station and return all materials to the tool crib.

DATA:

Oil Burner, Make _____ Model _____ Serial No. _____ Type _____
Primary Control, Make _____ Model _____ Type _____
Primary Voltage _____ Thermostat Voltage _____ Stack Temperature _____
Time for Safety Control to Function _____ Seconds ___

Remarks:

REMOVE, TEST AND INSTALL AN OIL BURNER PRIMARY CONTROL.

Indicate the best answer for each question below by encircling its letter.

1. What is the purpose of the stack bimetal element?
   a. Turns system on when cold.
   b. Turns system off if it becomes too warm.
   c. Acts as a thermostat.
   d. Keeps contacts closed during heating part of cycle.
   e. Opens the circuit if not heated.

2. What circuit does the manual reset control?
   a. The 24V circuit.
   b. The 120V circuit.
   c. The limit switch circuit.
   d. The ignition circuit.
   e. The motor circuit.

3. How many sets of contact points are mounted in the intermittent ignition primary control?
   a. 3
   b. 5
   c. 7
   d. 9
   e. 11

4. In an intermittent ignition primary control, what circuits does the relay operate?
   a. The motor and the stack bimetal circuits.
   b. The ignition and the thermostat circuits.
   c. The ignition and the motor circuits.
   d. The transformer secondary circuits.
   e. The overload manual reset circuits.

5. Where is the step-down transformer located?
   a. In the limit switch.
   b. In the thermostat.
   c. In the primary control.
   d. In the ignition transformer.
   e. In the manual switch box.

Task No. 6-9 Task Grade _____
Name _____
Date _____ Class _____

REMOVE, TEST, AND INSTALL AN OIL BURNER SAFETY CONTROL

OBJECTIVE: Given a gun type oil furnace: check, repair and install the oil burner safety control.

REFERENCES: Required – Para. 8-4, 8-5, 8-43, 20-8, 20-10, 20-12, 20-13, 20-14, 20-55, 24-17, 24-23, 24-46, 24-47, 24-53, manufacturer's service manual.
 Supplementary – Para. 8-2, 8-3 and 24-48.

EQUIPMENT: One operating gun type oil fired furnace with burner safety control.

PREPARATION PROCEDURE:
1. Examine the unit. Study the reference paragraphs.   TEST √ _____
2. Obtain: Tools – 1 8-in. adjustable open end wrench, 1 6-in. screwdriver, 1 pr. safety goggles.
3. Obtain: Instruments – 1 combination voltmeter, ammeter and ohmmeter (multimeter), 1 oil pressure gauge, 1 inspection mirror, 1 carbon dioxide analyzer, 1 stack thermometer, 1 draft gauge.
4. Obtain: Supplies – 1 wiping cloth, 1 pt. clean fuel oil, 1 pt. safe cleaning fluid.

TASK PROCEDURE (WEAR GOGGLES):
1. Inspect the refractory oil pot; if there is oil in the fire pot, do not start the unit until all oil is removed.
2. Install the pressure gauge and stack thermometer.
3. Check ignition system to be certain it is operating.   1-3 √ _____
4. Connect a small fuel oil container to the pump, check for leaks, and start unit.
                                                                        4 √ _____
5. Check the flame color, stack temperature, and firepot draft.
6. Make carbon dioxide analysis.
7. Operate for five minutes and record pressures and temperatures.   5-7 √ _____
8. Open ignition control system. Connect test instrument to safety limit control.
9. Check circuit of control without presence of oil.   8-9 √ _____
10. Allow oil to spray into the combustion chamber. The safety limit control circuit must shut off the flow of oil after approximately 12 seconds. Remove oil.   10 √ _____
11. Draw schematic wiring diagram of safety limit control.   11 √ _____

CLOSING THE STATION:
 Clean up work station and return all materials to the tool crib.

DATA:

Oil Burner, Make _____ Model _____ Type _____ Capacity _____
Furnace, Make _____ Model _____ Type _____ Capacity _____
Primary Control, Make _____ Model _____
Oil Pressure _____ Stack Temperature _____ Draft Pressure _____
Bonnet Cut-Out Temperature _____
Flame Color _____ Carbon Dioxide Stack Analysis _____
Safety Limit Control, Make _____ Model _____
         Type _____ Electrical Rating _____

Remarks:

REMOVE, TEST, AND INSTALL AN OIL BURNER SAFETY CONTROL.

Indicate the best answer for each question below by encircling its letter.

1. What function does an oil burner safety control perform?
    a. Prevents continuing burning in cases of ignition failure.
    b. Prevents operation if the oil flame is extinguished.
    c. Will not allow ignition if the fire pot contains oil.
    d. None of the above.
    e. All of the above.

2. What causes the formation of sulphurous acid in the flue?
    a. The temperature of the flue gases too low.
    b. The temperature of the flue gases too high.
    c. Oil pressure too low.
    d. Flame sensor improperly placed.
    e. Blower speed too high.

3. What is probably the trouble if a flame burns only a few seconds and then goes out?
    a. Flame sensor not in correct position.
    b. Dirty chimney.
    c. Loose fan.
    d. Bonnet temperature set too high.
    e. Combustion chamber is dirty.

4. What flue gas temperature, minus furnace room temperature, will provide the greatest combustion efficiency?
    a. 1500° F (816° C).
    b. 1000° F (538° C).
    c.   800° F (427° C).
    d.   600° F (316° C).
    e.   400° F (204° C).

5. What will be the effect if there is oil in the fire box when system starts?
    a. A puff.
    b. Flame.
    c. Explosion.
    d. None of the above.
    e. Any or all of the above.

INSTALL A POWER HUMIDIFIER IN A DUCT SYSTEM

OBJECTIVE: Given a duct type warm air heating system: install a power humidifier, install a humidistat, and adjust the humidifier to give correct operation.

REFERENCES: Required - Para. 18-04 through 18-12, 18-32, 18-33, 18-52, 19-11, 19-25, 20-50 through 20-53, 20-55, 24-40, 24-41, 24-53, 28-33, manufacturer's service manual. Supplementary - Para. 18-13.

EQUIPMENT: A duct type warm air heating system and a power type humidifier.

PREPARATION PROCEDURE:
1. Study the power humidifier and the warm air system assigned. Study the reference paragraphs.
    TEST √_____
2. Obtain: Tools - 1 set screwdrivers, 1 set pliers, 1 1/4-in. twist drill, 1 1/8-in. twist drill, 1 portable electric drill, 1 pr. tin snips or sheet metal nibbler, 1 flaring tool, 1 set open end wrenches, 1 8-in. adjustable open end wrench, 1 soldering torch, 1 tube cutter, 1 file, 1 pr. safety goggles.
3. Obtain: Instruments - 1 spirit level, 1 steel tape.
4. Obtain: Supplies - 1 roll soft solder, 1 roll soft copper tubing, 1 set of internal and external cleaning brushes, 1 jar solder flux.

TASK PROCEDURE (WEAR GOGGLES):
1. Select the place on the duct for mounting the power humidifier.
2. Lay out the opening to be cut in the duct.
3. Drill and cut the duct opening. Remove sharp metal edges by filing.
4. Locate the mounting holes. Drill holes, remove chips.
5. Mount the humidifier and level it.   1-5 √_____
6. Install the water line. Carefully pierce the water supply line and test for leaks.
7. Install the drain line to the nearest drain. The line must slope down at all times.
8. Connect the solenoid valve to the furnace electrical supply. Mount the humidistat.
9. Open the water valve, adjust the humidistat to desired setting.
10. Operate system.
11. Check the unit for leaks.   6-11 √_____

CLOSING THE STATION:
    Clean the work station and return all materials to the tool crib.

DATA:

Humidifier: Make_____ Model_____ Type_____ Capacity_____
Water Line Size_____ Drain Line Size_____
Water Line Valve, Type_____ Humidifier Motor, Make_____
            Fittings_____ Type_____ Voltage_____
Humidistat, Model_____ Type_____ Voltage_____

Remarks:

INSTALL A POWER HUMIDIFIER IN A DUCT SYSTEM.

Indicate the best answer for each question below by encircling its letter.

1. How many grains of moisture will saturate one pound of dry air at $0°$ F?
    a. 5.5 grains.
    b. 10.5 grains.
    c. 15.5 grains.
    d. 20.5 grains.
    e. 25.5 grains.

2. How many grains of moisture will be added to one pound of dry air at $75°$ F to give 50 percent relative humidity?
    a. 5.5 grains.
    b. 36 grains.
    c. 50 grains.
    d. 60 grains.
    e. 132 grains.

3. Given a sample of air at $75°$ F db and $68°$ F wb, what is the relative humidity?
    a. 20 percent.
    b. 30 percent.
    c. 40 percent.
    d. 60 percent.
    e. 70 percent.

4. Why do power humidifiers have electric motors?
    a. To operate the valve.
    b. To stir the water.
    c. To expose more water surface to the air.
    d. To pump water into the humidifier.
    e. To scrape the scale out of the humidifier pan.

5. What type of material varies in size as the humidity changes?
    a. Ceramic.
    b. Metallic.
    c. Hygroscopic.
    d. Silicon.
    e. Hydraulic.

BALANCE THE AIRFLOW IN A FORCED AIR SYSTEM

OBJECTIVE: Given a forced warm air system, measure and balance the airflow until correct conditions are reached.

REFERENCES: Required – Para. 18-20, 18-21, 18-22, 18-43, 18-52, 22-1 through 22-4, 22-6 through 22-9, 22-24, 22-40, 24-50 and 24-53.
Supplementary – Para. 22-5, 22-10 through 22-23.

EQUIPMENT: A forced warm air system with duct work will be used for the task.

PREPARATION PROCEDURE:
1. Study the duct system assigned. Study the reference paragraphs.   TEST√_____
2. Obtain: Tools – 1 6-in. screwdriver, 1 pr. safety goggles.
3. Obtain: Instruments – 1 pitot tube complete with fittings and manometer, 1 6-ft. steel tape, 1 anemometer, 1 velocimeter, 6 thermometers.
4. Obtain: Supplies – 1 wiping cloth.

TASK PROCEDURE (WEAR GOGGLES)
1. Measure and calculate all duct cross-sectional areas.
2. Place a thermometer in each room.
3. Operate the system. Measure the air velocities and calculate the air volumes at each outlet grille. Record thermometer readings.   1-3 √_____
4. Have the instructor assign you the air volumes desired at each outlet grille and also the temperatures.
5. Operate the system and adjust the duct dampers until the desired outlet volumes and temperatures are obtained.   4-5 √_____

CLOSING THE STATION:
Clean the work station and return all materials to the tool crib.

DATA:

Outlet Grilles	Original Readings Cu.Ft./Min.	Temp.	Assigned Readings Cu.Ft./Min.	Temp.	Final Results Cu.Ft./Min.	Temp.
1						
2						
3						
4						
5						
6						

Remarks:

BALANCE THE AIRFLOW IN A FORCED AIR SYSTEM.

Indicate the best answer for each question below by encircling its letter.

1. How is velocity pressure measured with a pitot tube?
   a. Adding the static pressure and total pressure.
   b. Subtracting the static pressure from the total pressure.
   c. Adding the static pressure and atmospheric pressure.
   d. Subtracting the atmospheric pressure from the static pressure.
   e. Subtracting the total pressure from the static pressure.

2. What are the minimum number of pitot tube readings one should take in a rectangular duct?
   a. 4
   b. 8
   c. 10
   d. 12
   e. 16

3. Which instrument is used to measure outlet grille air velocities?
   a. Anemometer.
   b. Barometer.
   c. Manometer.
   d. Micrometer.
   e. Draft gauge.

4. What is the average effective area of an outlet grille?
   a. 50 percent.
   b. 60 percent.
   c. 70 percent.
   d. 80 percent.
   e. 90 percent.

5. Why must an air duct elbow be considered as having an equivalent length?
   a. The elbow is smaller.
   b. The air flow friction is lower.
   c. The air flow friction is higher.
   d. To know its curved length.
   e. Because all ducts have an equivalent length.

REPLACE A PUMP ON A HYDRONIC SYSTEM

OBJECTIVE: Given a forced circulation hydronic heating system: remove a faulty pump and install a replacement.

REFERENCES: Required – Para. 18-42, 18-52, 19-3, 19-25, 20-2, 20-3, 20-4, 20-26, 20-27, 20-28, 20-55 and 24-52.
Supplementary – Para. 24-3, 24-39 and 24-53.

EQUIPMENT: A forced circulation hydronic heating system, and a spare water pump.

PREPARATION PROCEDURE:
1. Study the forced circulation hydronic heating system. Study the reference paragraphs.
   TEST✓_____
2. Obtain: Tools – 1 set of sockets with handles, 1 pr. safety goggles, 1 6-in. screwdriver.
3. Obtain: Instruments – 1 test light, 1 combination voltmeter, ammeter and ohmmeter (multimeter).
4. Obtain: Supplies – 1 wiping cloth.

TASK PROCEDURE (WEAR GOGGLES):
1. Close the water shut-off valves on each side of the pump. Prepare a drain pan for the water in the pump part of the system.
2. Shut off the electrical power, and disconnect the power wires at the pump junction box.
   1-2 ✓_____
3. Loosen the flange bolts, carefully remove the bolts while supporting the motor and pump, and remove the motor-pump.
4. Clean the gasket surfaces, insert new gaskets, carefully install the replacement motor-pump.
5. Align the pump flanges, while inserting the assembly bolts. Tighten the flange bolts evenly.
6. Open hand shut-off valves, connect electrical leads and operate the system. (Check for water leaks at the joints and seals.)
   3-6 ✓_____

CLOSING THE STATION:
   Clean the work station and return all materials to the tool crib.

DATA:

Pump, Make_____	Model_____	Type_____	Capacity_____
Motor, Make_____	Model_____	Type_____	hp_____
Voltage_____	Hertz_____	Phase_____	Current Draw_____
Pipe Size, Inlet_____	Outlet_____	Flange Bolts, Size_____	

Remarks:

REPLACE A PUMP ON A HYDRONIC SYSTEM.

Indicate the best answer for each question below by encircling its letter.

1. How is the water circulated in a thermal convection hot water heating system?
    a. No pump.
    b. One pump.
    c. Two pumps.
    d. Three pumps.
    e. Four pumps.

2. What is the maximum number of pumps used in a three zone hydronic system?
    a. One.
    b. Two.
    c. Three.
    d. Four.
    e. Five.

3. How is a flow switch used in a hydronic system?
    a. It is used to start the pump motor.
    b. It is used to shut off the pump motor when the water is too cold.
    c. It is used to shut off the pump when the water is too hot.
    d. It is used to shut off the pump motor if the water stops flowing.
    e. It is used to shut off the pump motor if the water pressure is too low.

4. Why does a hydronic hot water system have an air compression tank?
    a. To create a pressure.
    b. To allow for expansion of the water.
    c. To fill the system when the water level is low.
    d. To collect the sediment in the system.
    e. To provide reserve heat.

5. What type of pump is used on a hydronic system?
    a. Centrifugal.
    b. Piston.
    c. Rotary.
    d. Diaphragm.
    e. Gear.

INSTALL AND OPERATE AN ELECTRIC HEATING SYSTEM

OBJECTIVE: Given a conventional forced warm air electric resistance heating system: check, adjust and
operate.

REFERENCES: Required - Para. 6-9, 6-15, 6-19, 6-20, 6-80, 19-6, 19-25, 20-34 through 20-37,
20-39, 20-41, 20-42, 20-55, 24-24, 24-53, manufacturer's service manual.
Supplementary - Para. 19-8, 20-38, 20-40 and 20-43.

EQUIPMENT: One forced warm air electrical resistance heating system furnace.

PREPARATION PROCEDURE:

1. Study the unit assigned. Study the reference paragraphs.   TEST √ _____
2. Obtain: Tools - 1 1/4-in. portable electric drill and bits, 1 installation technician's
   tool kit.
3. Obtain: Instruments - 1 test light, 1 combination voltmeter, ammeter and ohmmeter (multimeter),
   1 0 to 250° F thermometer, 1 anemometer.
4. Obtain: Supplies - 1 wiping cloth, 1 box electrical lead connectors, 1 1/2-in. roll plastic
   tape, 1 box sheet metal screws, 1 roll #12 two conductor cable with ground.

TASK PROCEDURE:

1. Install the unit, making certain it is level.
2. Install the power circuit in compliance with the electrical code.
3. Make the proper electrical connections per system wiring diagram.
4. Install the thermostat wiring.   1-4 √ _____
5. Test all the connections and circuits with an ohmmeter.
6. Test the power-in with the test light.
7. Install the duct connectors.   5-7 √ _____
8. Start the system, take the electrical readings, allow unit to operate at least one cycle.
9. Check the inlet air and outlet air temperatures. Check air flow.   8-9 √ _____

CLOSING THE STATION:
Clean the station and return all materials to the tool crib.

DATA:
Electrical Resistance Furnace, Make_____ Model_____

	Serial No._____	Type_____	Capacity_____

Voltage_____ Amperage_____ Connectors, Size_____
Thermostat, Make_____ Model_____ Type_____
Relay, Make_____ Model_____
Limit Control, Make_____ Model_____ Type_____
Blower, Make_____ Type_____
Motor, Make_____ Type_____

Remarks:

INSTALL AND OPERATE AN ELECTRIC HEATING SYSTEM

Indicate the best answer for each question below by encircling its letter.

1. What controls are used on a forced air resistance heating unit?
    a. A bonnet control.
    b. A high-limit control.
    c. A circuit breaker.
    d. A combination of all the above is used.
    e. None of the above is used.

2. What is probably the trouble if the blower runs but there is not enough heat?
    a. Dirty filters.
    b. Voltage too low.
    c. Only some of the heater elements are energized.
    d. Second stage of two-stage thermostat not operating.
    e. All of the above.

3. At what temperature are limit controls set to open?
    a. 0 to 10° F above the highest thermostat setting.
    b. 20 to 40° F above the highest thermostat setting.
    c. 0 to 10° F below the highest thermostat setting.
    d. 10 to 30° F below the highest thermostat setting.
    e. 20 to 40° F below the highest thermostat setting.

4. What is the advantage of an electric heating warm air furnace?
    a. Low fuel cost.
    b. Less danger of toxic conditions arising.
    c. Equipment normally requires less space.
    d. Provides low humidity.
    e. All of the above.

5. How many Btu's will be provided by 1000 watts of current?
    a. 746 Btu.
    b. 341.5 Btu.
    c. 408 Btu.
    d. 2546 Btu.
    e. 3600 Btu.

INSTALL AND OPERATE A ROOFTOP HEATING SYSTEM

OBJECTIVE: Given a rooftop fuel gas heating system, install and operate.

REFERENCES: Required - Para. 20-17, 20-18, 20-20, 20-21, 20-22, 20-55, 23-25 through 23-28
   and 23-39.
   Supplementary - Para. 20-19 and 20-23.

EQUIPMENT: One rooftop fuel gas heating system.

PREPARATION PROCEDURE:
1. Study the system assigned. Study the manufacturer's service manual. Study the reference paragraphs. TEST √ _____
2. Obtain: Tools - 1 service technician's tool kit, 1 level, 1 pr. safety goggles.
3. Obtain: Instruments - 1 combination voltmeter, ammeter and ohmmeter (multimeter), 1 room thermometer, 1 sling psychrometer, 1 draft gauge, 1 air velocity gauge, 1 water manometer.
4. Obtain: Supplies - 1 wiping cloth, 1 jar soap suds.

TASK PROCEDURE (WEAR GOGGLES):
1. Check rooftop unit to make certain it is level.
2. Install electrical connections, gas line, thermostat and wiring, and duct connections. Test electrical circuits. Test gas line for leaks. 1-2 √ _____
3. Operate the furnace and check the system after 10 minutes of operation.
4. Check the heating system for correct operation; determine the plenum chamber temperature.
5. Check the filter for cleanliness and pressure drop.
6. Check the fan and fan motor and belt condition. 3-6 √ _____
7. Measure air velocities and air temperatures at each outlet grille.
8. Check the plenum chamber limit control. 7-8 √ _____

CLOSING THE STATION:
   Clean the work station and return all materials to the tool crib.

DATA:
Furnace, Make _____ Model _____ Serial No. _____ Type _____ Capacity _____
Fan, Make _____ Type _____ Size _____ Shaft Size _____
Fan Motor, Make _____ Model _____ Type _____ hp _____ Shaft Size _____
Voltage _____ Hertz _____ Phase _____ Current _____
Belts, No. _____ Size _____ Length _____ Width _____
Filter, Make _____ Type _____ Condition _____
Bonnet Temperature _____

Room	Room Temp. High	Low	Velocity	Grille Size
1				
2				
3				

Room	Room Temp. High	Low	Velocity	Grille Size
4				
5				
6				

INSTALL AND OPERATE A ROOFTOP HEATING SYSTEM.

Indicate the best answer in each question below by encircling its letter.

1. How many Btu's will be provided by one watt of electrical energy in a resistance heater?
   a. 3.415 Btu.
   b. 8.415 Btu.
   c. 2.415 Btu.
   d. 34.15 Btu.
   e. 6.45 Btu.

2. What should be used to test for leaks in a gas-burning heater unit?
   a. A blow torch.
   b. A lighted match.
   c. An electronic leak detector.
   d. Soap suds.
   e. Any of the above.

3. What is the effect of altitude on the furnace capacity?
   a. Decreases 4 percent for each 1,000 ft. elevation above sea level.
   b. Decreases 6 percent for each 1,000 ft. elevation above sea level.
   c. Decreases 8 percent for each 1,000 ft. elevation above sea level.
   d. Decreases 10 percent for each 1,000 ft. elevation above sea level.
   e. Decreases 20 percent for each 1,000 ft. elevation above sea level.

4. What should be the size of the air supply opening to a furnace to provide proper combustion?
   a. 1 sq. in./1,000 Btu/hr. capacity of the furnace.
   b. 2 sq. in./1,000 Btu/hr. capacity of the furnace.
   c. 1 sq. in./2,000 Btu/hr. capacity of the furnace.
   d. 2 sq. in./2,000 Btu/hr. capacity of the furnace.
   e. 3 sq. in./1,000 Btu/hr. capacity of the furnace.

5. How are heating elements protected on electric furnaces?
   a. Rubber insulators.
   b. Metal insulators.
   c. Copper insulators.
   d. Ceramic insulators.
   e. Plastic insulators.

LOCATE TROUBLE IN A GAS BURNER SYSTEM

OBJECTIVE: Given a warm air furnace with gas burner, determine the location of trouble in the system.

REFERENCES: Required - Para. 20-2, 20-3, 20-4, 20-15 through 20-23, 20-55, 24-10, 24-21, 24-32, 24-44, 24-46, 24-47, 24-48 and 24-53.
Supplementary - Para. 18-43, 18-52 and 19-3.

EQUIPMENT: A warm air furnace - gas burner installation.

PREPARATION PROCEDURE: TEST √ _____
1. Study the gas burner system assigned. Study the reference paragraphs.
2. Obtain: Tools - 1 kit service technician's tools, 1 long-handled brush, 1 pr. safety goggles.
3. Obtain: Instruments - 1 water column manometer, 1 draft gauge, 1 stack thermometer, 1 electrical combination voltmeter, ammeter and ohmmeter (multimeter), 1 room thermometer, 1 CO_2 analyzer, 1 inspection mirror.
4. Obtain: Supplies - 1 wiping cloth, 1 roll plastic tape, 1 pt. colored water, 1 pt. soap suds and brush.

TASK PROCEDURE (WEAR GOGGLES):
1. Install the gas pressure manometer.
2. Turn on the gas supply, test for leaks with soap suds.
3. Inspect the pilot light, clean it, adjust safety device spacing and light the pilot.
    IF THERE IS A GAS ODOR, PURGE FURNACE BEFORE LIGHTING!   1-3 √ _____
4. Test the electrical parts and circuits.
5. Adjust the thermostat until the furnace starts, inspect the flame color and shape. Adjust
    the primary air to obtain correct flame color.
6. Check the stack temperature and the fire pot pressure.   4-6 √ _____
7. Repair or replace any faulty part.
8. Record the fuel consumption. Take at least three gas meter readings.
9. Shut down the furnace.   7-9 √ _____

CLOSING THE STATION:
Clean the work station and return all materials to the tool crib.

DATA:
Furnace, Make _____ Model _____ Type _____ Capacity _____
Burner, Make _____ Model _____ Type _____ Capacity _____
Controls: Thermostat, Make _____ Model _____ Type _____
          Limit, Make _____ Model _____ Type _____
          Pilot Light, Make _____ Model _____ Type _____
Gas Control, Make _____ Model _____ Type _____ Gas Line Size _____
Gas Pressure _____ Stack Temperature _____
Fire Pot Pressure _____ Gas Consumption Average _____

Remarks:

LOCATE TROUBLE IN A GAS BURNER SYSTEM.

Indicate the best answer in each question below by encircling its letter.

1. What is the color of a correctly adjusted natural gas flame?
   a. Orange.
   b. Red.
   c. Yellow.
   d. Blue.
   e. Green.

2. What may happen to the flame if too much primary air is used?
   a. It will not burn.
   b. The flame will be too short.
   c. The flame will be too hot.
   d. The flame will lift off the burner.
   e. The flame will be irregular.

3. Why must the stack temperature be above the condensation temperature of the flue gases?
   a. To obtain sufficient draft.
   b. To operate the limit controls.
   c. To keep corrosive liquids from forming.
   d. To keep dangerous gases out of the building.
   e. To keep condensate off the basement floor.

4. What three voltages may be used to operate domestic gas solenoid valves?
   a. 120, 240, and 440 V.
   b. 6, 24, and 110 V.
   c. 24, 120, and 240 V.
   d. 125 millivolts, 6 and 24 V.
   e. 125 millivolts, 24 and 120 V.

5. What percentage of the flue gas is CO_2 in order to have 70 percent efficiency at a 700° F stack temperature?
   a. 2 percent.
   b. 4 percent.
   c. 6 percent.
   d. 8 percent.
   e. 10 percent.

LOCATE TROUBLE IN AN OIL BURNER SYSTEM

OBJECTIVE: Given a warm air furnace with oil burner, find trouble in the system and correct it.

REFERENCES: Required – Para. 20-6 through 20-14, 20-49, 20-55, 24-23, 24-44 through 24-47, manufacturer's service manual.
Supplementary – Para. 20-43 and 20-48.

EQUIPMENT: A warm air furnace oil burner installation.

PREPARATION PROCEDURE:
1. Study the oil burner system assigned. Study the reference paragraphs.   TEST ✓ _____
2. Obtain: Tools – 1 service technician's tool kit, 1 pr. safety goggles.
3. Obtain: Instruments – 1 inspection mirror, 1 stack thermometer, 1 CO_2 analyzer, 1 oil pressure gauge, 1 draft gauge.
4. Obtain: Supplies – 1 wiping cloth, 1 pt. safe cleaning fluid, 1 pt. clean fuel oil.

TASK PROCEDURE (WEAR GOGGLES):
1. Inspect the system and fire pot.
2. Open the fuel supply and operate the system.
3. If the burner does not start when the thermostat calls for heat, list in order the things checked to locate the trouble:
   (1)_____   (3)_____
   (2)_____   (4)_____
4. Check the flame color.   1-4 ✓ _____
5. Obtain the combustion draft, the stack temperature, and the CO_2 analysis.
6. Make adjustments and/or replace parts to obtain normal values.   5-6 ✓ _____
7. Take new readings.
8. Shut down the system.   7-8 ✓ _____

CLOSING THE STATION:
   Clean the work station and return all materials to the tool crib.

DATA:
Furnace, Make _____ Model _____ Type _____ Serial No. _____
        Condition of _____ Capacity _____
Oil Burner, Make _____ Model _____ Type _____ Serial No. _____
        Condition of _____

Readings:

	CO_2	Stack Temp.	Draft
Before			
After			

Remarks:

LOCATE TROUBLE IN AN OIL BURNER SYSTEM.

Indicate the best answer for each question below by encircling its letter.

1. What is the efficiency of a gun type oil burner installation if the stack termperature is 700° F and the percent of CO_2 is 10 percent?
    a. 68.5 percent.
    b. 71.5 percent.
    c. 73 percent.
    d. 74 percent.
    e. 76.5 percent.

2. How much excess air is needed to produce 8 percent CO_2 in an oil burner system?
    a. 30 percent.
    b. 50 percent.
    c. 80 percent.
    d. 125 percent.
    e. 150 percent.

3. How is a smoke test made using the Ringelmann Scale?
    a. Binoculars are used to observe stack fumes.
    b. A sample is collected in distilled water.
    c. A sample is forced through a white filter.
    d. A filter is put in the stack for a definite time.
    e. The soot deposit on stack internal wall is inspected.

4. How can the amount of excess air be determined?
    a. By measuring the amount of air fed to the furnace.
    b. By using a draft gauge.
    c. By using a pitot tube.
    d. By using a stack indicator.
    e. By using combustion efficiency instruments.

5. What is the most probable cause of oil around the base of the gun type oil burner?
    a. Improper combustion.
    b. Loose filter cover.
    c. Excessive pressure.
    d. Leaking pump shaft seal.
    e. Dirty nozzle.

CHECK, OPERATE AND ADJUST A GAS-FIRED WARM AIR HEATING SYSTEM

OBJECTIVE: Given a gas-fired forced warm air heating system, adjust and operate.

REFERENCES: Required – Para. 20-2, 20-3, 20-4, 20-15, 20-16, 20-17, 20-20 through 20-25, 20-55, 24-31, 24-32, 24-44 through 24-48 and 24-53.
Supplementary – Para. 20-18, 20-19, 24-28, 24-29 and 24-30.

EQUIPMENT: A gas fuel forced warm air heating system.

PREPARATION PROCEDURE:
1. Study the warm air system assigned. Study the reference paragraphs.   TEST ✓ _____
2. Obtain: Tools – 1 service technician's tool kit, 1 pr. safety goggles.
3. Obtain: Instruments – 1 room thermometer, 1 sling psychrometer, 1 draft gauge, 1 air velocity gauge.
4. Obtain: Supplies – 1 wiping cloth.

TASK PROCEDURE (WEAR GOGGLES):
1. Operate the furnace and check the system after 10 minutes of operation.
2. If the burner does not start when the thermostat calls for heat, list in order the things checked to locate the trouble:
   (1)_____ (3)_____
   (2)_____ (4)_____
3. Check the heating system for correct operation; determine bonnet temperature.
4. Check the filter for cleanliness and pressure drop.
5. Check the fan and fan motor. Check belt condition, tightness and alignment if one is used. Oil the motor.
6. Measure air velocities and air temperatures at each outlet grille.
7. Check the bonnet limit control.   1-7 ✓ _____

CLOSING THE STATION:
   Clean the work station and return all materials to the tool crib.

DATA:
Furnace, Make_____ Model_____ Type_____ Capacity_____ Serial No._____
Fan, Make_____ Type_____ Size_____
Fan, Motor, Make_____ Model_____ Type_____ hp_____ Shaft Size_____
Voltage_____ Hertz_____ Phase_____ Current_____
Belts, Make_____ No._____ Length_____ Width_____
Filter, Make_____ Size_____ Type_____ Condition_____
Bonnet Temperature_____ Stack Temperature_____

Room	Room Temp. High	Low	Velocity	Grille Size
1				
2				
3				

Room	Room Temp. High	Low	Velocity	Grille Size
4				
5				
6				

CHECK, OPERATE AND ADJUST A GAS-FIRED WARM AIR HEATING SYSTEM.

Indicate the best answer for each question below by encircling its letter.

1. What is the sensible heat of dry air?
   a. 0.24 Btu per cu. ft.
   b. 0.24 Btu per lb.
   c. 0.32 Btu per cu. ft.
   d. 1.43 Btu per lb.
   e. 0.043 Btu per lb.

2. How much pressure drop is acceptable across a domestic filter?
   a. 0.5-in. of water.
   b. 1-in. of water.
   c. 2-in. of water.
   d. 3-in. of water.
   e. 6-in. of water.

3. What control is used to operate the fan motor?
   a. Room thermostat.
   b. Primary control.
   c. Stack thermostat.
   d. Bonnet thermostat.
   e. Outdoor thermostat.

4. What is the return air volume compared to the warm air volume?
   a. Less.
   b. More.
   c. Same.
   d. 10 percent more.
   e. 20 percent more.

5. What should be the average main duct temperature of a warm air system?
   a. 100° F.
   b. 120° F.
   c. 140° F.
   d. 160° F.
   e. 180° F.

CHECK, OPERATE AND ADJUST A HYDRONIC HEATING SYSTEM

OBJECTIVE: Given a faulty hydronic heating system: check and adjust to provide proper water circulation and water temperature.

REFERENCES: Required – Para. 20-1 through 20-5, 20-26, 20-27, 20-28, 20-55, 24-3, 24-9, 24-53, manufacturer's service manual.
Supplementary – Para. 19-3 and 24-10.

EQUIPMENT: A hydronic heating system equipped with a gas burner.

PREPARATION PROCEDURE:
1. Study the hydronic system assigned. Study the reference paragraphs.   TEST √ _____
2. Obtain: Tools – 1 service technician's tool kit, 1 pr. safety goggles.
3. Obtain: Instruments – 1 set of pipe thermometers, 1 stack thermometer, 1 draft gauge, 1 electrical combination voltmeter, ammeter and ohmmeter (multimeter).
4. Obtain: Supplies – 1 wiping cloth.

TASK PROCEDURE (WEAR GOGGLES):
1. Inspect the system.
2. Operate the system.
3. If the pump does not start when the thermostat calls for heat, list in order the things checked to locate the trouble:
    (1)_____   (3)_____
    (2)_____   (4)_____
4. After ten minutes operation, check the furnace and fuel system. Check the water supply, circulation and pressure. Check the water temperatures. Check the circulation pump and motor, and controls.
5. Repair or replace faulty parts.   1-5 √ _____

CLOSING THE STATION:
    Clean the work station and return all materials to the tool crib.

DATA:
Furnace, Make _____ Model _____ Serial No. _____ Type _____ Capacity _____
Pump, Make _____ Model _____ Serial No. _____ Type _____ Capacity _____
Pump Motor, Make _____ Model _____ Serial No. _____ Type _____ hp _____
Controls: Thermostat, Make _____ Type _____ Limit Control, Make _____ Type _____
Pipe Sizes, Feed _____ Return _____
Stack Temperature _____ Flame Color _____
Furnace Water Temp. _____ Feed Water Temp. _____
Return Water Temp. _____ Water Level _____

Remarks:

CHECK, OPERATE, AND ADJUST A HYDRONIC HEATING SYSTEM.

Indicate the best answer for each question below by encircling its letter.

1. How is hot water for domestic consumption often heated when a hydronic system is used?
    a. A separate hot water heater.
    b. A heat exchanger.
    c. The system water is used.
    d. The pipe within a pipe is used.
    e. The reserve water in the compression tank is used.

2. What type zone control valves are most used in domestic systems?
    a. Modular valves.
    b. Solenoid valves.
    c. Manual volves.
    d. Three-way valves.
    e. Four-way valves.

3. What type of safety device is used to indicate lack of water flow?
    a. A pressure switch.
    b. A vane type flow switch.
    c. An electrical control responsive to motor load.
    d. A thermostat.
    e. A bimetal limit control.

4. What device operates the pump motor?
    a. A relay.
    b. A thermostat.
    c. A pressure switch.
    d. A limit control.
    e. A flow switch.

5. How are the water temperatures in the pipes obtained?
    a. By bleeding some water from the pipe.
    b. By a clip-on thermometer.
    c. A thermometer well.
    d. A pyrometer is used.
    e. An anemometer is used.

MAKE A STACK FLUE GAS ANALYSIS

OBJECTIVE: Given an oil or gas furnace, determine the efficiency of the furnace through the
use of instruments.

REFERENCES: Required – Para. 18-23, 18-36, 18-52, 20-5, 20-6, 20-8, 20-20, 20-55, 24-46
through 24-49, 24-53, manufacturer's service manuals.
Supplementary – Para. 20-7, 20-9, 20-10, 20-13, 20-15, 20-17, 20-18, 20-19 and 20-23.

EQUIPMENT: One residential furnace fully installed.

PREPARATION PROCEDURE:
1. Study the system. Study the reference paragraphs.   TEST ✓ _____
2. Obtain: Tools – 1 service technician's tool kit, 1 inspection mirror, 1 pr. safety goggles.
3. Obtain: Instruments – 1 draft gauge, 1 stack thermometer, 1 CO_2 analyzer.
4. Obtain: Supplies – 1 wiping cloth.

TASK PROCEDURE (WEAR GOGGLES):
1. Turn on the gas or oil supply, test for leaks with soap suds.
2. Inspect pilot light system.
3. Inspect flue and stack.
4. Set thermostat, start the system and inspect the flame. Adjust primary air to obtain
correct flame color.
5. Install instruments and obtain the combustion draft, the stack temperature, and the
CO_2 analysis, and the smoke test.   1-5 ✓ _____
6. Make adjustments to obtain normal values.
7. Take new readings.
8. Shut down the system   6-8 ✓ _____

CLOSING THE STATION:
Clean the work station and return all materials to the tool crib.

DATA:
Furnace, Make _____ Model _____ Serial No. _____ Type _____ Capacity _____
          Condition of _____
Gas or Oil Burner, Make _____ Model _____ Serial No. _____ Type _____
          Condition of _____

Readings:

	CO_2	Stack Temp.	Combustion Efficiency	Smoke Test
Before				
After				

Remarks:

MAKE A STACK FLUE GAS ANALYSIS.

Indicate the best answer for each question below by encircling its letter.

1. What determines the rate of flue gas flow?
    a. Density of the flue gas.
    b. Density of the air.
    c. Pressure of air inside the building.
    d. Pressure of air outside the building.
    e. All of the above.

2. What is the range of allowable stack temperatures?
    a. $0-100^\circ$ F.
    b. $200-300^\circ$ F.
    c. $300-600^\circ$ F.
    d. $300-900^\circ$ F.
    e. $900-1500^\circ$ F.

3. When is it allowable to have some smoke appear at the chimney exit?
    a. Some smoke will appear at the chimney exit in very cold weather.
    b. Never.
    c. Only at the time the burner starts.
    d. After a long period of operation.
    e. Just before the burner shuts off.

4. What is the basis for the Ringelmann Scale?
    a. Percent of CO in the stack.
    b. Discoloration of filter paper.
    c. High draft gauge reading.
    d. Temperature of the stack gas.
    e. Amount of CO_2.

5. What is used to assure efficient and safe draft control in a gas furnace?
    a. A direct stack.
    b. A weighted butterfly valve.
    c. An air break system.
    d. A very large stack.
    e. No break in the stack.

OPERATE AND TEST A BASEBOARD ELECTRIC RESISTANCE HEATING SYSTEM

OBJECTIVE: Given a baseboard electric resistance heating system, test and operate.

REFERENCES: Required - Para. 20-34 through 20-37, 20-39, 20-40, 20-47, 20-48, 20-55, 24-11, 24-16, 24-17, 24-18 and 24-53.
Supplementary - Para. 19-8, 19-25 and 20-38.

EQUIPMENT: A residence having a complete electrical resistance heated system.

PREPARATION PROCEDURE:

1. Study the system assigned. Study the reference paragraphs.   TEST ✓_____
2. Obtain: Tools - 1 electrician's service kit.
3. Obtain: Instruments - 1 a-c ammeter, 1 a-c voltmeter, 1 ohmmeter, 1 room thermometer.
4. Obtain: Supplies - 1 wiping cloth, 1 roll plastic tape.

TASK PROCEDURE:

1. Turn on the thermostat on each heater equipped with a thermostat.
2. Determine the current required by each resistance unit.   1-2 ✓_____
3. Turn on the thermostat for areas controlled by a thermostatically operated relay.
4. Check the current flow.   3-4 ✓_____
5. Adjust the thermostat in one room to give the desired room temperature.
6. Record the current flow. Calculate the Btu's produced from the wattage.
7. Shut off the system.   5-7 ✓_____

CLOSING THE STATION:
Clean the work station and return all materials to the tool crib.

DATA:

Resistance Heater, Make_____ Model_____ Serial No._____
            Type_____ Capacity_____ Voltage_____
Thermostat, Make_____ Model_____ Type_____
Thermostat, Calibration_____

Remarks:

OPERATE AND TEST A BASEBOARD ELECTRIC RESISTANCE HEATING SYSTEM.

Indicate the best answer for each question below by encircling its letter.

1. What is the main disadvantage of the baseboard electric heating system?
   a. Clean heat.
   b. Very inexpensive to operate.
   c. Rather expensive to operate.
   d. Difficult to install.
   e. Unsightly.

2. How many Btu's will be provided by 200 watts of electricity used in a resistance heating unit?
   a. 212 Btu.
   b. 341 Btu.
   c. 683 Btu.
   d. 1364 Btu.
   e. 1500 Btu.

3. How does electric heat affect the humidity in the heated space?
   a. The humidity is slightly increased.
   b. The humidity is greatly increased.
   c. The humidity is not affected.
   d. The humidity is slightly reduced.
   e. The humidity is greatly reduced.

4. What is the most common voltage used on baseboard electric resistance heating?
   a. 24-V.
   b. 60-V.
   c. 120-V.
   d. 208-V.
   e. 240-V.

5. Compared to which other system is an electric resistance heating system easier to install?
   a. Compared to gravity warm air.
   b. Compared to warm air with forced convection.
   c. Compared to warm water gravity system.
   d. Compared to hydronic system with a pump.
   e. All of the above.